MATHEMATICAL TABLES

Compiled by

Charles D. Hodgman, M.S.,
Associate Professor of Physics at
Case School of Applied Science

Price $1.50

A reproduction in enlarged form of the mathematical section of the Handbook of Chemistry and Physics, a seventeen hundred page volume of chemical and physical data.

CHEMICAL RUBBER PUBLISHING CO.
1900 West 112th Street, CLEVELAND, OHIO

Preface

The collection of mathematical tables and formulae presented in this volume, although different in form, is identical in content with the mathematical section of the current edition of the Handbook of Chemistry and Physics.

Originally intended to provide adequate means for the ordinary computations of chemistry and physics the collection has been gradually enlarged and has for several years been published as a separate book. In response to the increasing demand for this volume the size and form is being changed to one better suited to constant use. Modified type and spacing made possible by the larger page, will very greatly increase legibility, and assist in avoiding fatigue.

Explanations of the nature and uses of the various tables have been considerably extended and collected at the end of the volume.

Every precaution has been used to insure accuracy in the numerical values, the proofs having been read against several sources. Notice of any errors which may be discovered will be sincerely appreciated.

CHEMICAL RUBBER PUBLISHING CO.

Cleveland, Ohio
April 3, 1931

Preface to the Second Edition

The material presented in the Mathematical Tables has been considerably increased and with particular reference to the needs of the student in calculus, the study of investments and the interpretation of statistical data.

The table of integrals has been very greatly extended in answer to requests from a large number of users of the book. It is believed that this section will be found more than adequate to meet the requirements of all undergraduate courses.

The interest tables have been increased to four times their previous extent to meet the needs of the student of investments.

The third important addition is a series of tables, of value in the application of statistical methods.

A list of the largely revised and new tables follows:

Integrals

Powers of Numbers

Factorials and their Logarithms

Factors for Computing Probable Errors

Probability of Occurrence of Deviations

Areas, Ordinates and Derivatives of the Normal Curve of Error

CHEMICAL RUBBER PUBLISHING CO.

Cleveland, Ohio
May 25, 1932

Preface to the Third Edition

The Mathematical Tables as presented in its third edition is not changed in general plan. All of the numerical tables have again been completely and carefully checked; the few minor errors found have been corrected and we have increased confidence in their accuracy.

One new table,—Factors and Primes,—has been added. This covers eight pages, giving the factors of factorable numbers and the logarithms of primes for all whole numbers up to 2000. It is believed that this table will be found an exceptionally useful addition.

The conversion table, Degrees to Radians, has been revised, now being extended to five decimal places throughout.

Several other lesser changes and additions have been made and the volume is offered with the hope that it may be increasingly valuable to its users.

CHEMICAL RUBBER PUBLISHING CO.

Cleveland, Ohio,
August 24, 1933.

CONTENTS

	Page
Algebraic Formulae	1
Mensuration Formulae	6
Trigonometrical Functions in a Right-angled Triangle	12
Signs and Limits of Value Assumed by the Functions	12
Value of the Functions of Various Angles	13
Relations of the Functions	13
Functions of Sums of Angles	13
Functions of Multiple Angles	14
Relations between Sides and Angles of Any Triangle	15
Differentials	16
Integrals	17
Analytical Geometry	33
Simpson's Rule	35
Four-place Logarithms	36
Four-place Antilogarithms	38
Five-place Logarithms	40
Logarithms of the Trigonometric Functions	62
Natural Trigonometrical Functions for Degrees and Minutes	109
Natural Trigonometrical Functions for Decimal Fractions of a Degree	133
Natural Logarithms	137
Exponentials	141
Hyperbolic Functions	143
Degrees, Minutes and Seconds to Radians	147
Degrees and Decimals to Radians	150
Radians to Degrees	150
Decimal Equivalents of Common Fractions	150
Minutes and Seconds to Decimal Parts of a Degree	151
Numerical Constants	152
Logarithmic Constants	152
Numerical Table	153
Powers of Numbers	173
Factorials and their Logarithms	175
Factors for Computing Probable Errors	176
Probability of Occurrence of Deviations	178
Areas, Ordinates and Derivatives of the Normal Curve of Error	179
Factors and Primes	184
Interest Tables	192
Use of Mathematical Tables	225

Explanations of the nature and use of the various tables have been collected at the end of the volume.

ALGEBRA

FACTORS AND EXPANSIONS

$$(a \pm b)^2 = a^2 \pm 2ab + b^2.$$
$$(a \pm b)^3 = a^3 \pm 3a^2b + 3ab^2 \pm b^3.$$
$$(a \pm b)^4 = a^4 \pm 4a^3b + 6a^2b^2 \pm 4ab^3 + b^4.$$
$$a^2 - b^2 = (a - b)(a + b).$$
$$a^2 + b^2 = (a + b\sqrt{-1})(a - b\sqrt{-1}).$$
$$a^3 - b^3 = (a - b)(a^2 + ab + b^2).$$
$$a^3 + b^3 = (a + b)(a^2 - ab + b^2).$$
$$a^4 + b^4 = (a^2 + ab\sqrt{2} + b^2)(a^2 - ab\sqrt{2} + b^2).$$
$$a^n - b^n = (a - b)(a^{n-1} + a^{n-2}b + \ldots + b^{n-1}).$$
$$a^n - b^n = (a + b)(a^{n-1} - a^{n-2}b + \ldots - b^{n-1}),$$
for even values of n.
$$a^n + b^n = (a + b)(a^{n-1} - a^{n-2}b + \ldots + b^{n-1}),$$
for odd values of n.
$$a^4 + a^2b^2 + b^4 = (a^2 + ab + b^2)(a^2 - ab + b^2).$$
$$(a + b + c)^2 = a^2 + b^2 + c^2 + 2ab + 2ac + 2bc.$$
$$(a + b + c)^3 = a^3 + b^3 + c^3 + 3a^2(b + c) + 3b^2(a + c) + 3c^2(a + b) + 6abc.$$
$$(a + b + c + d + \ldots)^2 = a^2 + b^2 + c^2 + d^2 + \ldots + 2a(b + c + d + \ldots) + 2b(c + d + \ldots) + 2c(d + \ldots) + \ldots$$

See also under Series.

POWERS AND ROOTS

$$a^x \times a^y = a^{(x+y)}. \qquad a^0 = 1. \qquad (ab)^x = a^x b^x.$$
$$\frac{a^x}{a^y} = a^{(x-y)}. \qquad a^{-x} = \frac{1}{a^x}. \qquad \left(\frac{a}{b}\right)^x = \frac{a^x}{b^x}.$$
$$(a^x)^y = a^{xy}. \qquad a^{\frac{1}{x}} = \sqrt[x]{a}. \qquad \sqrt[x]{ab} = \sqrt[x]{a}\,\sqrt[x]{b}.$$
$$\sqrt[x]{\sqrt[y]{a}} = \sqrt[xy]{a}. \qquad a^{\frac{x}{y}} = \sqrt[y]{a^x}. \qquad \sqrt[x]{\frac{a}{b}} = \frac{\sqrt[x]{a}}{\sqrt[x]{b}}.$$

PROPORTION

If $\dfrac{a}{b} = \dfrac{c}{d}$, then $\dfrac{a + b}{b} = \dfrac{c + d}{d}$,

$$\frac{a - b}{b} = \frac{c - d}{d}, \qquad \frac{a - b}{a + b} = \frac{c - d}{c + d}.$$

SUMS OF NUMBERS

The sum of the first n numbers, —

$$\Sigma(n) = 1 + 2 + 3 + 4 + 5 \ldots\ldots + n = \frac{n(n+1)}{2}$$

The sum of the squares of the first n numbers,

$$\Sigma(n^2) = 1^2 + 2^2 + 3^2 + 4^2 + 5^2 \ldots + n^2 = \frac{n(n+1)(2n+1)}{6}$$

The sum of the cubes of the first n numbers,

$$\Sigma(n^3) = 1^3 + 2^3 + 3^3 + 4^3 + 5^3 \ldots\ldots + n^3 = \frac{n^2(n+1)^2}{4}$$

ARITHMETICAL PROGRESSION

If a is the first term; l, the last term; d, the common difference; n, the number of terms and s, the sum of n terms, —

$$l = a + (n-1)d$$

$$s = \frac{n}{2}(a + l)$$

$$s = \frac{n}{2}\left\{2a + (n-1)d\right\}$$

GEOMETRICAL PROGRESSION

If a is the first term; l, the last term; r, the common ratio; n, the number of terms and s, the sum of n terms, —

$$l = ar^{n-1} \qquad s = a\frac{(1 - r^n)}{1 - r}$$

$$s = a\frac{(r^n - 1)}{r - 1} \qquad s = \frac{lr - a}{r - 1}$$

If n is infinity and r^2 less than unity, —

$$s = \frac{a}{1 - r}$$

PERMUTATIONS

If M denote the number of permutations of n things taken p at a time, —

$$M = n(n-1)(n-2) \ldots\ldots (n - p + 1)$$

COMBINATIONS

If M denote the number of combinations of n things taken p at a time, —

$$M = \frac{n(n-1)(n-2) \ldots\ldots (n - p + 1)}{p!}$$

$$M = \frac{n!}{p!(n-p)!}$$

QUADRATIC EQUATIONS

Any quadratic equation may be reduced to the form, —

$$ax^2 + bx + c = 0.$$

Then $$x = \frac{-b \pm \sqrt{b^2 - 4ac}}{2a}.$$

If $b^2 - 4ac$ is positive the roots are real and unequal.
If $b^2 - 4ac$ is zero the roots are real and equal.
If $b^2 - 4ac$ is negative the roots are imaginary and unequal.
If $b^2 - 4ac$ is a perfect square the roots are rational and unequal.

CUBIC EQUATIONS

A cubic equation, $y^3 + py^2 + qy + r = 0$ may be reduced to the form, —

$$x^3 + ax + b = 0$$

by substituting for y the value, $x - \frac{p}{3}$. Here

$$a = \tfrac{1}{3}(3q - p^2) \text{ and } b = \tfrac{1}{27}(2p^3 - 9pq + 27r).$$

For solution let, —

$$A = \sqrt[3]{-\frac{b}{2} + \sqrt{\frac{b^2}{4} + \frac{a^3}{27}}}, \qquad B = \sqrt[3]{-\frac{b}{2} - \sqrt{\frac{b^2}{4} + \frac{a^3}{27}}},$$

then the values of x will be given by,

$$x = A + B, \quad -\frac{A+B}{2} + \frac{A-B}{2}\sqrt{-3}, \quad -\frac{A+B}{2} - \frac{A-B}{2}\sqrt{-3}.$$

If $\frac{b^2}{4} + \frac{a^3}{27} > 0$, there will be one real root and two conjugate imaginary roots.

If $\frac{b^2}{4} + \frac{a^3}{27} = 0$, there will be three real roots of which at least two are equal.

If $\frac{b^2}{4} + \frac{a^3}{27} < 0$, there will be three real and unequal roots.

In the last case a trigonometric solution is useful. Compute the value of the angle ϕ in the expression, —

$$\cos\phi = \sqrt{\frac{b^2}{4} \div \left(-\frac{a^3}{27}\right)},$$

then x will have the following values:—

$$\mp 2\sqrt{-\frac{a}{3}}\cos\frac{\phi}{3}, \qquad \mp 2\sqrt{-\frac{a}{3}}\cos\left(\frac{\phi}{3} + 120^\circ\right),$$

$$\mp 2\sqrt{-\frac{a}{3}}\cos\left(\frac{\phi}{3} + 240^\circ\right).$$

APPROXIMATIONS

If a and b are small quantities, the following relations are approximately true,—

$$(1 \pm a)^m = 1 \pm ma,$$

$$(1 \pm a)^m (1 \pm b)^n = 1 \pm ma \pm nb.$$

If n is nearly equal to m,

$$\sqrt{mn} = \frac{n+m}{2}, \text{ approximately.}$$

If θ is a very small angle expressed in radians,—

$$\frac{\sin\theta}{\theta} = 1 \text{ and } \frac{\tan\theta}{\theta} = 1, \text{ approximately.}$$

SERIES

The expression in parentheses following certain of the series indicates the region of convergence. If not otherwise indicated it is to be understood that the series converges for all finite values of x.

BINOMIAL

$$(x+y)^n = x^n + nx^{n-1}y + \frac{n(n-1)}{2!}x^{n-2}y^2 + \dots$$

$$+\frac{n(n-1)(n-2)}{3!}x^{(n-3)}y^3 \dots + y^n \dots\dots \quad (y^2 < x^2)$$

$$(1 \pm x)^n = 1 \pm nx + \frac{n(n-1)x^2}{2!} \pm \frac{n(n-1)(n-2)x^3}{3!} + \dots \text{ etc.} \quad (x^2 < 1)$$

$$(1 \pm x)^{-n} = 1 \mp nx + \frac{n(n+1)x^2}{2!} \mp \frac{n(n+1)(n+2)x^3}{3!} + \dots \text{ etc.} \quad (x^2 < 1)$$

$$(1 \pm x)^{-1} = 1 \mp x + x^2 \mp x^3 + x^4 \mp x^5 + \dots \quad (x^2 < 1)$$

$$(1 \pm x)^{-2} = 1 \mp 2x + 3x^2 \mp 4x^3 + 5x^4 \mp 6x^5 + \dots \quad (x^2 < 1)$$

TAYLOR'S SERIES

$$f(x+h) = f(x) + hf'(x) + \frac{h^2}{2!}f''(x) + \frac{h^3}{3!}f'''(x) + \dots$$

$$= f(h) + xf'(h) + \frac{x^2}{2!}f''(h) + \frac{x^3}{3!}f'''(h) + \dots$$

MACLAURIN'S SERIES

$$f(x) = f(o) + xf'(o) + \frac{x^2}{2!}f''(o) + \frac{x^3}{3!}f'''(o) + \dots$$

EXPONENTIAL

$$e = 1 + \frac{1}{1} + \frac{1}{2!} + \frac{1}{3!} + \frac{1}{4!} + \dots$$

$$e^x = 1 + x + \frac{x^2}{2!} + \frac{x^3}{3!} + \frac{x^4}{4!} + \dots$$

$$a^x = 1 + x\log a + \frac{(x\log a)^2}{2!} + \frac{(x\log a)^3}{3!} + \dots$$

ALGEBRA

LOGARITHMIC

$$\log_e x = \frac{x-1}{x} + \frac{1}{2}\left(\frac{x-1}{x}\right)^2 + \frac{1}{3}\left(\frac{x-1}{x}\right)^3 + \ldots \qquad (x > \tfrac{1}{2})$$

$$\log_e x = (x-1) - \tfrac{1}{2}(x-1)^2 + \tfrac{1}{3}(x-1)^3 - \ldots \qquad (2 > x > 0)$$

$$\log_e x = 2\left[\frac{x-1}{x+1} + \frac{1}{3}\left(\frac{x-1}{x+1}\right)^3 + \frac{1}{5}\left(\frac{x-1}{x+1}\right)^5 + \ldots\right] \qquad (x > 0)$$

$$\log_e(1+x) = x - \tfrac{1}{2}x^2 + \tfrac{1}{3}x^3 - \tfrac{1}{4}x^4 + \ldots \qquad (-1 < x < 1)$$

$$\log_e(n+1) - \log_e(n-1) = 2\left[\frac{1}{n} + \frac{1}{3n^3} + \frac{1}{5n^5} + \ldots\right]$$

$$\log_e(a+x) = \log_e a + 2\left[\frac{x}{2a+x} + \frac{1}{3}\left(\frac{x}{2a+x}\right)^3 + \frac{1}{5}\left(\frac{x}{2a+x}\right)^5 + \ldots\right] \qquad (a > 0, -a < x < +\infty)$$

TRIGONOMETRIC

$$\sin x = x - \frac{x^3}{3!} + \frac{x^5}{5!} - \frac{x^7}{7!} + \ldots$$

$$\cos x = 1 - \frac{x^2}{2!} + \frac{x^4}{4!} - \frac{x^6}{6!} + \ldots$$

$$\tan x = x + \frac{x^3}{3} + \frac{2x^5}{15} + \frac{17x^7}{315} + \frac{62x^9}{2835} + \ldots \qquad \left(x^2 < \frac{\pi^2}{4}\right)$$

$$\sin^{-1} x = x + \frac{x^3}{6} + \frac{1}{2}\cdot\frac{3}{4}\cdot\frac{x^5}{5} + \frac{1}{2}\cdot\frac{3}{4}\cdot\frac{5}{6}\cdot\frac{x^7}{7} + \ldots \qquad (x^2 < 1)$$

$$\tan^{-1} x = x - \tfrac{1}{3}x^3 + \tfrac{1}{5}x^5 - \tfrac{1}{7}x^7 + \ldots \qquad (x^2 < 1)$$

$$= \frac{\pi}{2} - \frac{1}{x} + \frac{1}{3x^3} - \frac{1}{5x^5} + \ldots \qquad (x^2 > 1)$$

$$\log_e \sin x = \log_e x - \frac{x^2}{6} - \frac{x^4}{180} - \frac{x^6}{2835} - \ldots \qquad (x^2 < \pi^2)$$

$$\log_e \cos x = -\frac{x^2}{2} - \frac{x^4}{12} - \frac{x^6}{45} - \frac{17x^8}{2520} - \ldots \qquad \left(x^2 < \frac{\pi^2}{4}\right)$$

$$\log_e \tan x = \log_e x + \frac{x^2}{3} + \frac{7x^4}{90} + \frac{62x^6}{2835} + \ldots \qquad \left(x^2 < \frac{\pi^2}{4}\right)$$

$$e^{\sin x} = 1 + x + \frac{x^2}{2!} - \frac{3x^4}{4!} - \frac{8x^5}{5!} + \frac{3x^6}{6!}$$

$$e^{\cos x} = e\left(1 - \frac{x^2}{2!} + \frac{4x^4}{4!} - \frac{31x^6}{6!} + \ldots\right)$$

$$e^{\tan x} = 1 + x + \frac{x^2}{2!} + \frac{3x^3}{3!} + \frac{9x^4}{4!} + \frac{37x^5}{5!} + \ldots \qquad \left(x^2 < \frac{\pi^2}{4}\right)$$

MENSURATION FORMULAE

PLANE FIGURES BOUNDED BY STRAIGHT LINES

The **area of a triangle** whose base is b and altitude h

$$=\frac{hb}{2}.$$

The area of a **triangle** with angles A, B, and C and sides opposite a, b, and c, respectively

$$=\tfrac{1}{2}ab \sin C.$$

or

$$=\sqrt{s(s-a)(s-b)(s-c)},$$

where $s = \frac{1}{2}(a + b + c)$.

A **rectangle** with sides a and b has an area $= ab$.

The area of a **parallelogram** with side b and the perpendicular distance to the parallel side h

$$= bh.$$

The area of a **parallelogram** with sides a and b and the included angle θ

$$= ab \sin \theta.$$

The area of a **rhombus** with diagonals c and d,

$$= \tfrac{1}{2}cd.$$

The area of a **trapezoid** whose parallel sides are a and b and altitude h

$$= \tfrac{1}{2}(a + b)h.$$

The area of any **quadrilateral** with diagonals a and b and the angle between them θ

$$= \tfrac{1}{2}ab \sin \theta.$$

The area of a **regular polygon** with n sides, each of length l,

$$= \tfrac{1}{4}nl^2 \cot \frac{180}{n}.$$

For a regular polygon of n sides, each side of length l, the radius of the **inscribed circle,**

$$= \frac{l}{2} \cot \frac{180}{n}.$$

The radius of the **circumscribed circle,**

$$= \frac{l}{2} \operatorname{cosec} \frac{180}{n}.$$

AREA, RADIUS OF INSCRIBED AND CIRCUMSCRIBED CIRCLES FOR REGULAR POLYGONS

l = length of one side

Name	Number of sides	Area	Radius of inscribed circle	Radius of circumscribed circle
Triangle, equilateral......	3	$0.43301l^2$	$0.28867l$	$0.57735l$
Square.................	4	$1.00000l^2$	$0.50000l$	$0.70710l$
Pentagon...............	5	$1.72048l^2$	$0.68819l$	$0.85065l$
Hexagon................	6	$2.59808l^2$	$0.86602l$	$1.0000l$
Heptagon...............	7	$3.63391l^2$	$1.0383l$	$1.1523l$
Octagon................	8	$4.82843l^2$	$1.2071l$	$1.3065l$
Nonagon................	9	$6.18182l^2$	$1.3737l$	$1.4619l$
Decagon................	10	$7.69421l^2$	$1.5388l$	$1.6180l$
Undecagon..............	11	$9.36564l^2$	$1.7028l$	$1.7747l$
Dodecagon..............	12	$11.19615l^2$	$1.8660l$	$1.9318l$

Radius of circle inscribed in any triangle, whose sides are a, b, and c, where $s = \frac{1}{2}(a + b + c)$

$$= \frac{\sqrt{s(s-a)(s-b)(s-c)}}{s}.$$

The radius of the **circumscribed** circle

$$= \frac{abc}{4\sqrt{s(s-a)(s-b)(s-c)}}.$$

The **perimeter of a polygon inscribed in a circle** of radius r, where n is the number of sides,

$$= 2nr \sin \frac{\pi}{n}. \qquad (\pi \text{ radians} = 180°)$$

The area of the **inscribed** polygon,

$$= \tfrac{1}{2}nr^2 \sin \frac{2\pi}{n}.$$

The perimeter of a polygon circumscribed about a circle of radius r, number of sides n

$$= 2nr \tan \frac{\pi}{n}.$$

The area of the **circumscribed** polygon

$$= nr^2 \tan \frac{\pi}{n}.$$

PLANE FIGURES BOUNDED BY CURVED LINES

The **circumference of a circle** whose radius is r and diameter $d (d = 2r)$

$$= 2\pi r = \pi d. \qquad (\pi = 3.14159)$$

The **area of a circle**

$$= \pi r^2 = \tfrac{1}{4}\pi d^2 = .7854d^2.$$

The **length of an arc** of a circle for an arc of θ degrees

$$= \frac{\pi r \theta}{180}.$$

NOTE—In this and following similar formulae r denotes the radius of the circle, (OC, Fig. 1).

For an arc of θ radians the length

$$= r\theta.$$

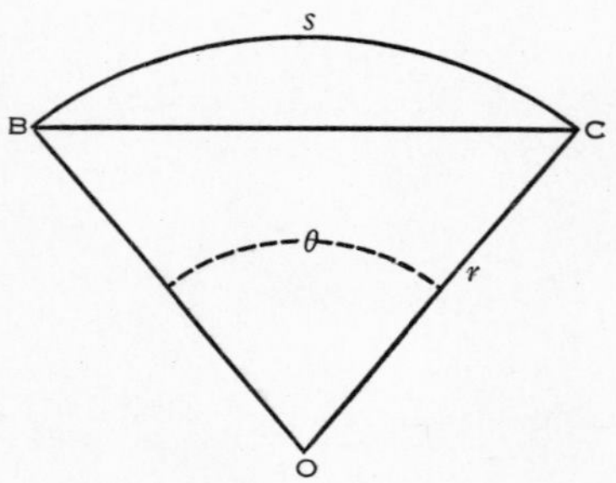

Fig. 1

The **length of a chord** subtending an angle θ

$$= 2r \sin \tfrac{1}{2}\theta.$$

The **area of a sector** where θ is the angle between the radii in degrees

$$= \frac{\pi r^2 \theta}{360}.$$

If s is the length of the arc, the area of the sector

$$= \frac{sr}{2}.$$

The **area of a segment** where θ is the angle between the two radii in degrees

$$= \frac{\pi r^2 \theta}{360} - \frac{r^2 \sin \theta}{2}. \qquad \left[\begin{array}{l}\theta^\circ = 180^\circ - [2x \sin^{-1}(x/r)] \\ x = \perp \text{ dist. center to chord}\end{array}\right]$$

If θ is in radians the area $= \frac{1}{2}r^2(\theta - \sin\theta)$.

The **area of the segment of a circle**

$$= \frac{\pi r^2}{2} - \left[x\sqrt{r^2 - x^2} + r^2 \sin^{-1}\left(\frac{x}{r}\right)\right]$$

where r is the radius of the circle and x the perpendicular distance of the chord from the center. The angle must be expressed in radians.

The **area of the ring** between two circles of radius r_1 and r_2, one of which encloses the other,

$$= \pi(r_1 + r_2)(r_1 - r_2).$$

The two circles are not necessarily concentric.

Area of the sector of an annulus. (Fig. 2.) — If angle $GOH = \theta$ and the lines GO and $JO = r_1$ and r_2 respectively, the area $GHIJ = \frac{1}{2}\theta(r_1 + r_2)(r_1 - r_2)$.

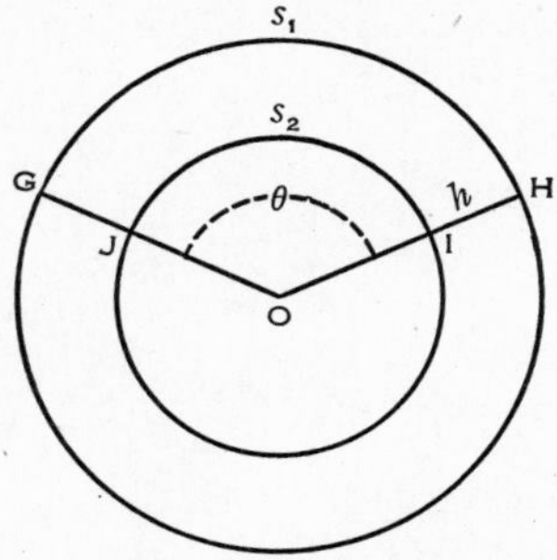

Fig. 2

If $s_1 =$ the length of the arc GH and $s_2 =$ the arc JI and $h = HI = r_1 - r_2$, the area $GHIJ = \frac{1}{2}h(s_1 + s_2)$.

The **circumference of an ellipse** whose semiaxes are a and b

$$= 2\pi\sqrt{\frac{a^2 + b^2}{2}}, \text{ approximately.}$$

The **area of an ellipse** $= \pi ab$.

The length of the **arc of a parabola,** as arc SPQ in Fig. 3, where $x = PR$, and $y = QR$

$$= 2\sqrt{y^2 + \frac{4x^2}{3}}.$$

The **area of the section of the parabola** $PQRS$, $= \frac{4}{3}xy$.

SOLIDS BOUNDED BY PLANES

The **lateral area of a regular prism** = perimeter of a right section × the length.

The **volume of a regular prism** = area of base × the altitude.

The **lateral area of a regular pyramid,** slant height l, length of one side of base a, and a number of sides n,

$$= \tfrac{1}{2}nal.$$

The **volume of a pyramid** = $\tfrac{1}{3}$ area of base × altitude.

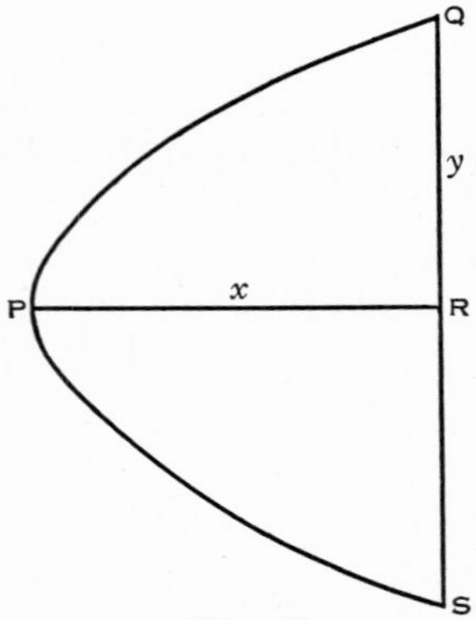

Fig. 3

SURFACE AND VOLUME OF REGULAR POLYHEDRA

Surface and volume of regular polyhedra in terms of the length of one edge l.

Name	Nature of Surface	Surface	Volume
Tetrahedron	4 equilateral triangles	$1.73205l^2$	$0.11785l^3$
Hexahedron or cube	6 squares	$6.00000l^2$	$1.00000l^3$
Octahedron	8 equilateral triangles	$3.46410l^2$	$0.47140l^3$
Dodecahedron	12 pentagons	$20.64578l^2$	$7.66312l^3$
Icosahedron	20 equilateral triangles	$8.66025l^2$	$2.18170l^3$

SOLIDS BOUNDED BY CURVED SURFACES

The **surface of a sphere** of radius r and diameter $d(= 2r)$

$$= 4\pi r^2 = \pi d^2 = 12.57 r^2.$$

The **volume of a sphere**

$$= \tfrac{4}{3}\pi r^3 = \tfrac{1}{6}\pi d^3 = 4.189 r^3.$$

The **area of a lune** on the surface of a sphere of radius r, included between two great circles whose inclination is θ radians

$$= 2r^2\theta.$$

The **area of a spherical triangle** whose angles are A, B, and C (radians) on a sphere of radius r

$$= (A + B + C - \pi)r^2.$$

The **area of a spherical polygon** of n sides where θ is the sum of its angles in radians

$$= [\theta - (n - 2)\pi]r^2.$$

The area of the curved surface of a **spherical segment** of height h, radius of sphere r

$$= 2\pi rh.$$

The **volume of a spherical segment**, data as above

$$= \tfrac{1}{3}\pi h^2(3r - h).$$

If a = radius of the base of the segment, the volume

$$= \tfrac{1}{6}\pi h(h^2 + 3a^2).$$

The **curved surface of a right cylinder** where r = the radius of the base and h, the altitude,

$$= 2\pi rh.$$

The **volume of a cylinder,** data as above,

$$= \pi r^2h.$$

The **curved surface of a right cone** whose altitude is h and radius of base r

$$= \pi r\sqrt{r^2 + h^2}.$$

The **volume of a cone,** data as above,

$$= \frac{\pi}{3}r^2h = 1.047\,r^2h.$$

The **curved surface of the frustum of a right cone,** radius of base r_1, of top r_2 and altitude h,

$$= \pi(r_1 + r_2)\sqrt{h^2 + (r_1 - r_2)^2}.$$

The **volume of the frustum of a cone,** data as above,

$$= \pi\frac{h}{3}(r_1{}^2 + r_1r_2 + r_2{}^2).$$

The **oblate spheroid** is formed by the rotation of an ellipse about its minor axis. If a and b are the major and minor semi-axes respectively, and e the eccentricity, the surface

$$= 2\pi a^2 + \pi\frac{b^2}{e}\log_e\frac{1 + e}{1 - e},$$

and volume $= \tfrac{4}{3}\pi a^2b.$

The **prolate spheroid** is formed by the rotation of an ellipse about its major axis ($2a$), data as above.

Surface $= 2\pi b^2 + 2\pi \frac{ab}{e} \sin^{-1} e$,

volume $= \frac{4}{3}\pi a b^2$.

TRIGONOMETRY

TRIGONOMETRIC FUNCTIONS IN A RIGHT-ANGLED TRIANGLE

If A, B, and C are the vertices (C the right angle), and a, b, and h the sides opposite respectively,

$\sin A = \frac{a}{h}$, $\cos A = \frac{b}{h}$,

$\tan A = \frac{a}{b}$, $\cot A = \frac{b}{a}$,

$\text{secant } A = \frac{h}{b}$, $\text{cosec } A = \frac{h}{a}$.

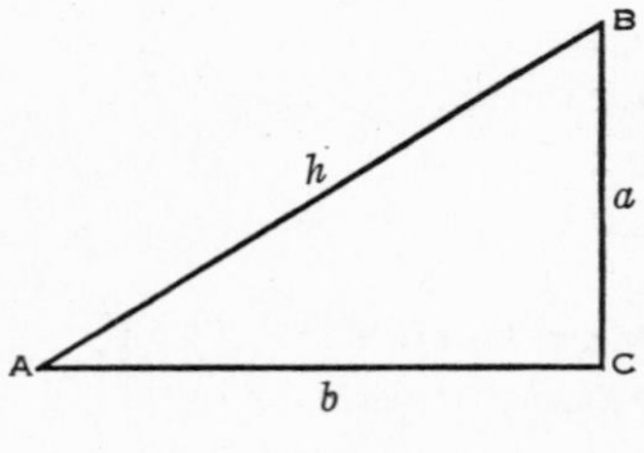

Fig. 4

SIGNS AND LIMITS OF VALUE ASSUMED BY THE FUNCTIONS

Function	Quadrant I		Quadrant II		Quadrant III		Quadrant IV	
	Sign	Value	Sign	Value	Sign	Value	Sign	Value
sin	+	0 to 1	+	1 to 0	—	0 to 1	—	1 to 0
cos	+	1 to 0	—	0 to 1	—	1 to 0	+	0 to 1
tan	+	0 to ∞	—	∞ to 0	+	0 to ∞	—	∞ to 0
cot	+	∞ to 0	—	0 to ∞	+	∞ to 0	—	0 to ∞
sec	+	1 to ∞	—	∞ to 1	—	1 to ∞	+	∞ to 1
cosec	+	∞ to 1	+	1 to ∞	—	∞ to 1	—	1 to ∞

VALUE OF THE FUNCTIONS OF VARIOUS ANGLES

	0°	30°	45°	60°	90°	180°	270°
sin........	0	$\frac{1}{2}$	$\frac{1}{2}\sqrt{2}$	$\frac{1}{2}\sqrt{3}$	1	0	– 1
cos........	1	$\frac{1}{2}\sqrt{3}$	$\frac{1}{2}\sqrt{2}$	$\frac{1}{2}$	0	– 1	0
tan........	0	$\frac{1}{3}\sqrt{3}$	1	$\sqrt{3}$	∞	0	∞
cot........	∞	$\sqrt{3}$	1	$\frac{1}{3}\sqrt{3}$	0	∞	0

RELATIONS OF THE FUNCTIONS

$$\sin x = \frac{1}{\operatorname{cosec} x}. \qquad \operatorname{cosec} x = \frac{1}{\sin x}.$$

$$\cos x = \frac{1}{\sec x}. \qquad \sec x = \frac{1}{\cos x}.$$

$$\tan x = \frac{1}{\cot x} = \frac{\sin x}{\cos x}. \qquad \sin^2 x + \cos^2 x = 1.$$

$$1 + \tan^2 x = \sec^2 x.$$

$$\cot x = \frac{1}{\tan x} = \frac{\cos x}{\sin x}. \qquad 1 + \cot^2 x = \operatorname{cosec}^2 x.$$

$$\sin x = \sqrt{1 - \cos^2 x}. \qquad \cos x = \sqrt{1 - \sin^2 x}.$$

$$\tan x = \sqrt{\sec^2 x - 1}. \qquad \sec x = \sqrt{\tan^2 x + 1}.$$

$$\cot x = \sqrt{\operatorname{cosec}^2 x - 1}. \qquad \operatorname{cosec} x = \sqrt{\cot^2 x + 1}.$$

$$\sin x = \cos (90 - x) = \sin (180 - x).$$

$$\cos x = \sin (90 - x) = -\cos (180 - x).$$

$$\tan x = \cot (90 - x) = -\tan (180 - x).$$

$$\cot x = \tan (90 - x) = -\cot (180 - x).$$

FUNCTIONS OF SUMS OF ANGLES

$$\sin (x + y) = \sin x \cos y + \cos x \sin y.$$

$$\sin (x - y) = \sin x \cos y - \cos x \sin y.$$

$$\cos (x + y) = \cos x \cos y - \sin x \sin y.$$

$$\cos (x - y) = \cos x \cos y + \sin x \sin y.$$

$$\tan (x + y) = \frac{\tan x + \tan y}{1 - \tan x \tan y}.$$

$$\tan (x - y) = \frac{\tan x - \tan y}{1 + \tan x \tan y}.$$

FUNCTIONS OF MULTIPLE ANGLES

$$\sin 2x = 2 \sin x \cos x.$$
$$\cos 2x = \cos^2 x - \sin^2 x = 2 \cos^2 x - 1 = 1 - 2 \sin^2 x.$$
$$\sin 3x = 3 \sin x - 4 \sin^3 x.$$
$$\cos 3x = 4 \cos^3 x - 3 \cos x.$$
$$\sin 4x = 8 \cos^3 x \sin x - 4 \cos x \sin x.$$
$$\cos 4x = 8 \cos^4 x - 8 \cos^2 x + 1.$$
$$\sin 5x = 5 \sin x - 20 \sin^3 x + 16 \sin^5 x.$$
$$\cos 5x = 16 \cos^5 x - 20 \cos^3 x + 5 \cos x.$$
$$\sin 6x = 32 \cos^5 x \sin x - 32 \cos^3 x \sin x + 6 \cos x \sin x.$$
$$\cos 6x = 32 \cos^6 x - 48 \cos^4 x + 18 \cos^2 x - 1.$$
$$\tan 2x = \frac{2 \tan x}{1 - \tan^2 x}.$$
$$\cot 2x = \frac{\cot^2 x - 1}{2 \cot x}.$$
$$\tan 3x = \frac{3 \tan x - \tan^3 x}{1 - 3 \tan^2 x}.$$
$$\sin \tfrac{1}{2}x = \pm \sqrt{\frac{1 - \cos x}{2}}$$
$$\cos \tfrac{1}{2}x = \pm \sqrt{\frac{1 + \cos x}{2}}.$$
$$\tan \tfrac{1}{2}x = \pm \sqrt{\frac{1 - \cos x}{1 + \cos x}} = \frac{1 - \cos x}{\sin x} = \frac{\sin x}{1 + \cos x}.$$

MISCELLANEOUS RELATIONS

$$\sin x \pm \sin y = 2 \sin \tfrac{1}{2} (x \pm y) \cdot \cos \tfrac{1}{2} (x \mp y).$$
$$\cos x + \cos y = 2 \cos \tfrac{1}{2} (x + y) \cdot \cos \tfrac{1}{2} (x - y).$$
$$\cos x - \cos y = -2 \sin \tfrac{1}{2} (x + y) \cdot \sin \tfrac{1}{2} (x - y).$$
$$\tan x \pm \tan y = \frac{\sin (x \pm y)}{\cos x \cdot \cos y}. \qquad \cot x \pm \cot y = \frac{\pm \sin (x \pm y)}{\sin x \cdot \sin y}.$$
$$\frac{1 + \tan x}{1 - \tan x} = \tan (45 + x). \qquad \frac{\cot x + 1}{\cot x - 1} = \cot (45 - x).$$
$$\frac{\sin x \pm \sin y}{\cos x + \cos y} = \tan \tfrac{1}{2} (x \pm y).$$
$$\frac{\sin x \pm \sin y}{\cos x - \cos y} = -\cot \tfrac{1}{2} (x \mp y).$$
$$\frac{\sin x + \sin y}{\sin x - \sin y} = \frac{\tan \tfrac{1}{2} (x + y)}{\tan \tfrac{1}{2} (x - y)}.$$
$$\sin^2 x - \sin^2 y = \sin (x + y) \cdot \sin (x - y).$$
$$\cos^2 x - \cos^2 y = -\sin (x + y) \sin (x - y).$$
$$\cos^2 x - \sin^2 y = \cos (x + y) \cos (x - y).$$

RELATIONS BETWEEN SIDES AND ANGLES OF ANY PLANE TRIANGLE

In a triangle with angles A, B, and C and sides opposite a, b, and c respectively,

$$\frac{\sin A}{a} = \frac{\sin B}{b} = \frac{\sin C}{c}.$$

$$a^2 = b^2 + c^2 - 2bc \cos A.$$

$$a = b \cos C + c \cos B.$$

$$\cos A = \frac{b^2 + c^2 - a^2}{2bc}.$$

$$\tan \frac{A - B}{2} = \frac{a - b}{a + b} \cot \frac{C}{2}.$$

$$\sin A = \frac{2}{bc} \sqrt{s(s - a)(s - b)(s - c)},$$

where $s = \frac{1}{2}(a + b + c)$ and $r = \sqrt{\frac{(s - a)(s - b)(s - c)}{s}}$

$$\sin \frac{A}{2} = \sqrt{\frac{(s - b)(s - c)}{bc}}.$$

$$\cos \frac{A}{2} = \sqrt{\frac{s(s - a)}{bc}}.$$

$$\tan \frac{A}{2} = \sqrt{\frac{(s - b)(s - c)}{s(s - a)}} = \frac{r}{s - a}.$$

$$\frac{a + b}{a - b} = \frac{\sin A + \sin B}{\sin A - \sin B} = \frac{\tan \frac{1}{2}(A + B)}{\tan \frac{1}{2}(A - B)} = \frac{\cot \frac{1}{2} C}{\tan \frac{1}{2}(A - B)}.$$

RELATIONS IN ANY SPHERICAL TRIANGLE

If A, B and C be the three angles and a, b, and c the opposite sides,

$$\frac{\sin A}{\sin a} = \frac{\sin B}{\sin b} = \frac{\sin C}{\sin c}.$$

$$\cos a = \cos b \cos c + \sin b \sin c \cos A = \frac{\cos b \cos(c \pm \theta)}{\cos \theta}$$

where $\tan \theta = \tan b \cos A.$

$$\cos A = -\cos B \cos C + \sin B \sin C \cos a.$$

$$\sin \tfrac{1}{2} A = \sqrt{\frac{\sin(s - b) \sin(s - c)}{\sin b \sin c}}$$

where $s = \frac{1}{2}(a + b + c).$

$$\cos \tfrac{1}{2} A = \sqrt{\frac{\sin s \sin(s - a)}{\sin b \sin c}}.$$

$$\tan \tfrac{1}{2} A = \frac{r}{\sin(s - a)}$$

where $r = \sqrt{\frac{\sin(s - a) \sin(s - b) \sin(s - c)}{\sin s}}$

$$\cos \tfrac{1}{2} a = \sqrt{\frac{\cos (S - B) \cos (S - C)}{\sin B \sin C}}$$

where $S = \tfrac{1}{2}(A + B + C).$

$$\sin \tfrac{1}{2} a = \sqrt{-\frac{\cos S \cos (S - A)}{\sin B \sin C}}.$$

$$\tan \tfrac{1}{2} a = R \cos (S - A)$$

where $R = \sqrt{\dfrac{-\cos S}{\cos (S - A) \cos (S - B) \cos (S - C)}}.$

$$\frac{\tan \frac{a+b}{2}}{\tan \frac{c}{2}} = \frac{\cos \frac{A-B}{2}}{\cos \frac{A+B}{2}}, \quad \frac{\tan \frac{A+B}{2}}{\cot \frac{C}{2}} = \frac{\cos \frac{a-b}{2}}{\cos \frac{a+b}{2}}.$$

$$\frac{\tan \frac{a-b}{2}}{\tan \frac{c}{2}} = \frac{\sin \frac{A-B}{2}}{\sin \frac{A+B}{2}}, \quad \frac{\tan \frac{A-B}{2}}{\cot \frac{C}{2}} = \frac{\sin \frac{a-b}{2}}{\sin \frac{a+b}{2}}.$$

CALCULUS

DIFFERENTIALS

$$d\, ax = a\,dx$$

$$d\, uv = u\,dv + v\,du$$

$$d\, \frac{u}{v} = \frac{v\,du - u\,dv}{v^2}$$

$$d\, x^n = n\, x^{n-1} dx$$

$$d\, e^x = e^x dx$$

$$d\, e^{ax} = a\, e^{ax} dx$$

$$d\, a^x = a^x \log_e a\, dx$$

$$d \log_e x = \frac{1}{x} dx$$

$$d \log_a x = \frac{1}{x} \log_a e\, dx$$

$$d\, x^x = x^x (1 + \log_e x)\, dx$$

$$d \sin x = \cos x\, dx$$

$$d \cos x = -\sin x\, dx$$

$$d \tan x = \sec^2 x\, dx$$

$$d \cot x = -\csc^2 x\, dx$$

$$d \sec x = \tan x \sec x\, dx$$

$$d \csc x = -\cot x \cdot \csc x\, dx$$

$$d \sin^{-1} x = (1 - x^2)^{-\frac{1}{2}} dx$$

$$d \cos^{-1} x = -(1 - x^2)^{-\frac{1}{2}} dx$$

$$d\ \tan^{-1}x = (1 + x^2)^{-1}dx$$
$$d\ \cot^{-1}x = -\ (1 + x^2)^{-1}dx$$
$$d\ \sec^{-1}x = x^{-1}\ (x^2 - 1)^{-\frac{1}{2}}dx$$
$$d\ \csc^{-1}x = -\ x^{-1}\ (x^2 - 1)^{-\frac{1}{2}}dx$$

INTEGRALS

Elementary Forms

1. $\int a\ dx = ax.$

2. $\int a \cdot f(x)dx = a \int f(x)dx.$

3. $\int \phi(y)dx = \int \frac{\phi(y)}{y'}\ dy,$ where $y' = dy/dx.$

4. $\int (u + v)\ dx = \int u\ dx + \int v\ dx,$ where u and v are any functions of x.

5. $\int u\ dv = uv - \int v\ du.$

6. $\int u\frac{dv}{dx}dx = uv - \int v\frac{du}{dx}dx.$

7. $\int x^n\ dx = \frac{x^{n+1}}{n+1},$ except $n = -1.$

8. $\int \frac{f'(x)\ dx}{f(x)} = \log f(x),$ $[d\ f(x) = f'(x)\ dx].$

9. $\int \frac{dx}{x} = \log x, \text{ or } \log(-x).$

10. $\int \frac{f'(x)\ dx}{2\sqrt{f(x)}} = \sqrt{f(x)},$ $[d\ f(x) = f'(x)\ dx].$

11. $\int e^x dx = e^x.$

12. $\int e^{ax}dx = e^{ax}/a.$

13. $\int b^{ax}dx = \frac{b^{ax}}{a \log b}.$

14. $\int \log x\ dx = x \log x - x.$

15. $$\int a^x \log a \, dx = a^x.$$

16. $$\int \frac{dx}{a^2 + x^2} = \frac{1}{a} \tan^{-1}\left(\frac{x}{a}\right), \text{ or } -\frac{1}{a} \cot^{-1}\left(\frac{x}{a}\right).$$

17. $$\int \frac{dx}{a^2 - x^2} = \frac{1}{a} \tanh^{-1}\left(\frac{x}{a}\right), \text{ or } \frac{1}{2a} \log \frac{a + x}{a - x}.$$

18. $$\int \frac{dx}{x^2 - a^2} = -\frac{1}{a} \coth^{-1}\left(\frac{x}{a}\right), \text{ or } \frac{1}{2a} \log \frac{x - a}{x + a}.$$

19. $$\int \frac{dx}{\sqrt{a^2 - x^2}} = \sin^{-1}\left(\frac{x}{a}\right), \text{ or } -\cos^{-1}\left(\frac{x}{a}\right).$$

20. $$\int \frac{dx}{\sqrt{x^2 \pm a^2}} = \log(x + \sqrt{x^2 \pm a^2}).$$

21. $$\int \frac{dx}{x\sqrt{x^2 - a^2}} = \frac{1}{a} \cos^{-1}\left(\frac{a}{x}\right).$$

22. $$\int \frac{dx}{x\sqrt{a^2 \pm x^2}} = -\frac{1}{a} \log\left(\frac{a + \sqrt{a^2 \pm x^2}}{x}\right).$$

23. $$\int \frac{dx}{x\sqrt{a + bx}} = \frac{2}{\sqrt{-a}} \tan^{-1} \sqrt{\frac{a + bx}{-a}}, \text{ or }$$

$$\frac{-2}{\sqrt{a}} \tanh^{-1} \sqrt{\frac{a + bx}{a}}.$$

Forms Containing $(a + bx)$

24. $$\int (a + bx)^n dx = \frac{(a + bx)^{n+1}}{(n + 1)b}, \qquad \text{except } n = -1.$$

25. $$\int \frac{dx}{a + bx} = \frac{1}{b} \log (a + bx).$$

26. $$\int \frac{dx}{(a + bx)^2} = -\frac{1}{b(a + bx)}.$$

27. $$\int \frac{dx}{(a + bx)^3} = -\frac{1}{2b(a + bx)^2}.$$

28. $$\int \frac{x\,dx}{a + bx} = \frac{1}{b^2} [a + bx - a \log (a + bx)].$$

29. $$\int \frac{x\,dx}{(a + bx)^2} = \frac{1}{b^2}\left[\log (a + bx) + \frac{a}{a + bx}\right].$$

30. $$\int \frac{x\,dx}{(a + bx)^3} = \frac{1}{b^2}\left[-\frac{1}{a + bx} + \frac{a}{2(a + bx)^2}\right].$$

31. $$\int \frac{x^2dx}{a + bx} = \frac{1}{b^3}\left[\frac{1}{2}(a + bx)^2 - 2a\,(a + bx) + a^2 \log\,(a+bx)\right].$$

32. $$\int \frac{x^2dx}{(a + bx)^2} = \frac{1}{b^3}\left[a + bx - 2a \log\,(a + bx) - \frac{a^2}{a + bx}\right].$$

33. $$\int \frac{dx}{x(a + bx)} = -\frac{1}{a} \log \frac{a + bx}{x}.$$

34. $$\int \frac{dx}{x(a + bx)^2} = \frac{1}{a(a + bx)} - \frac{1}{a^2} \log \frac{a + bx}{x}.$$

35. $$\int \frac{dx}{x^2(a + bx)} = -\frac{1}{ax} + \frac{b}{a^2} \log \frac{a + bx}{x}.$$

---

36. $$\int \frac{dx}{c^2 + x^2} = \frac{1}{c}\tan^{-1}\frac{x}{c},\ \text{or}\ \frac{1}{c}\sin^{-1}\frac{x}{\sqrt{c^2 + x^2}}.$$

37. $$\int \frac{dx}{c^2 - x^2} = \frac{1}{2c} \log \frac{c + x}{c - x},\ \text{or}\ \frac{1}{c}\tanh^{-1}\left(\frac{x}{c}\right).$$

38. $$\int \frac{dx}{x^2 - c^2} = \frac{1}{2c} \log \frac{x - c}{x + c},\ \text{or}\ -\frac{1}{c}\coth^{-1}\left(\frac{x}{c}\right).$$

Forms Containing $(a + bx^n)$

39. $$\int \frac{dx}{a + bx^2} = \frac{1}{\sqrt{ab}} \tan^{-1} \frac{x\sqrt{ab}}{a}.$$

40. $$\int \frac{dx}{a + bx^2} = \frac{1}{2\sqrt{-ab}} \log \frac{a + x\sqrt{-ab}}{a - x\sqrt{-ab}},\ \text{or}$$
$$\frac{1}{\sqrt{-ab}} \tanh^{-1} \frac{x\sqrt{-ab}}{a}.$$

41. $$\int \frac{xdx}{a + bx^2} = \frac{1}{2b} \log \left(x^2 + \frac{a}{b}\right).$$

42. $$\int \frac{x^2dx}{a + bx^2} = \frac{x}{b} - \frac{a}{b}\int \frac{dx}{a + bx^2}.$$

43. $$\int \frac{dx}{(a + bx^2)^2} = \frac{x}{2a(a + bx^2)} + \frac{1}{2a}\int \frac{dx}{a + bx^2}.$$

44. $$\int \frac{dx}{(a + bx^2)^{m+1}} = \frac{1}{2\,ma}\,\frac{x}{(a + bx^2)^m} + \frac{2m - 1}{2\,ma}\int \frac{dx}{(a + bx^2)^m}.$$

45. $$\int \frac{xdx}{(a + bx^2)^{m+1}} = \frac{1}{2}\int \frac{dz}{(a + bz)^{m+1}}, \qquad [z = x^2].$$

46. $$\int \frac{x^2dx}{(a+bx^2)^{m+1}} = \frac{-x}{2\,mb\,(a+bx^2)^m} + \frac{1}{2\,mb}\int \frac{dx}{(a+bx^2)^m}.$$

47. $$\int \frac{dx}{x^2(a+bx^2)^{m+1}} = \frac{1}{a}\int \frac{dx}{x^2(a+bx^2)^m} - \frac{b}{a}\int \frac{dx}{(a+bx^2)^{m+1}}.$$

48. $$\int \frac{dx}{x(a+bx^2)} = \frac{1}{2a}\log \frac{x^2}{a+bx^2}.$$

49. $$\int \frac{dx}{x^2(a+bx^2)} = -\frac{1}{ax} - \frac{b}{a}\int \frac{dx}{a+bx^2}.$$

50. $$\int \frac{dx}{a+bx^3} = \frac{k}{3a}\left[\frac{1}{2}\log \frac{(k+x)^2}{k^2-kx+x^2} + \sqrt{3}\tan^{-1}\frac{2x-k}{k\sqrt{3}}\right],$$
$$[bk^3 = a].$$

51. $$\int \frac{xdx}{a+bx^3} = \frac{1}{3bk}\left[\frac{1}{2}\log \frac{k^2-kx+x^2}{(k+x)^2} + \sqrt{3}\tan^{-1}\frac{2x-k}{k\sqrt{3}}\right],$$
$$[bk^3 = a].$$

52. $$\int \frac{dx}{x(a+bx^n)} = \frac{1}{an}\log \frac{x^n}{a+bx^n}.$$

53. $$\int \frac{dx}{(a+bx^n)^{m+1}} = \frac{1}{a}\int \frac{dx}{(a+bx^n)^m} - \frac{b}{a}\int \frac{x^n dx}{(a+bx^n)^{m+1}}.$$

54. $$\int \frac{x^m dx}{(a+bx^n)^{p+1}} = \frac{1}{b}\int \frac{x^{m-n}\,dx}{(a+bx^n)^p} - \frac{a}{b}\int \frac{x^{m-n}\,dx}{(a+bx^n)^{p+1}}.$$

55. $$\int \frac{dx}{x^m(a+bx^n)^{p+1}} = \frac{1}{a}\int \frac{dx}{x^m(a+bx^n)^p} - \frac{b}{a}\int \frac{dx}{x^{m-n}(a+bx^n)^{p+1}}.$$

56. $$\int x^m(a+bx^n)^p\,dx = \frac{x^{m-n+1}(a+bx^n)^{p+1}}{b(np+m+1)} - \frac{a\,(m-n+1)}{b\,(np+m+1)}\int x^{m-n}\,(a+bx^n)^p\,dx.$$

57. $$\int x^m(a+bx^n)^p\,dx = \frac{x^{m+1}\,(a+bx^n)^p}{np+m+1} + \frac{anp}{np+m+1}\int x^m(a+bx^n)^{p-1}\,dx.$$

58. $$\int x^{m-1}(a+bx^n)^p\,dx = \frac{1}{b(m+np)}\left[x^{m-n}(a+bx^n)^{p+1} - (m-n)a\int x^{m-n-1}(a+bx^n)^p\,dx\right].$$

59. $$\int x^{m-1}(a+bx^n)^p\,dx = \frac{1}{m+np}\left[x^m(a+bx^n)^p + npa\int x^{m-1}(a+bx^n)^{p-1}dx\right].$$

60. $$\int x^{m-1}(a+bx^n)^p\,dx = \frac{1}{ma}\left[x^m(a+bx^n)^{p+1} - (m+np+n)b\int x^{m+n-1}(a+bx^n)^p\,dx\right].$$

61. $$\int x^{m-1}(a+bx^n)^p\,dx = \frac{1}{an(p+1)}\left[-x^m(a+bx^n)^{p+1} + (m+np+n)\int x^{m-1}(a+bx^n)^{p+1}\,dx\right].$$

Forms Containing $(a + bx + cx^2)$

$X = a + bx + cx^2$ and $q = 4\,ac - b^2$

62. $$\int\frac{dx}{X} = \frac{2}{\sqrt{q}}\tan^{-1}\frac{2\,cx+b}{\sqrt{q}}.$$

63. $$\int\frac{dx}{X} = \frac{-2}{\sqrt{-q}}\tanh^{-1}\frac{2\,cx+b}{\sqrt{-q}}.$$

64. $$\int\frac{dx}{X} = \frac{1}{\sqrt{-q}}\log\frac{2\,cx+b-\sqrt{-q}}{2\,cx+b+\sqrt{-q}}.$$

65. $$\int\frac{dx}{X^2} = \frac{2\,cx+b}{qX} + \frac{2c}{q}\int\frac{dx}{X}.$$

66. $$\int\frac{dx}{X^3} = \frac{2\,cx+b}{q}\left(\frac{1}{2\,X^2} + \frac{3\,c}{qX}\right) + \frac{6\,c^2}{q^2}\int\frac{dx}{X}.$$

67. $$\int\frac{dx}{X^{n+1}} = \frac{2\,cx+b}{nqX^n} + \frac{2(2n-1)c}{qn}\int\frac{dx}{X^n}.$$

68. $$\int\frac{xdx}{X} = \frac{1}{2c}\log X - \frac{b}{2c}\int\frac{dx}{X}.$$

69. $$\int\frac{xdx}{X^2} = -\frac{bx+2\,a}{qX} - \frac{b}{q}\int\frac{dx}{X}.$$

70. $$\int\frac{xdx}{X^{n+1}} = -\frac{2\,a+bx}{nqX^n} - \frac{b(2n-1)}{nq}\int\frac{dx}{X^n}.$$

71. $$\int \frac{x^2}{X} dx = \frac{x}{c} - \frac{b}{2\,c^2} \log X + \frac{b^2 - 2\,ac}{2\,c^2} \int \frac{dx}{X}.$$

72. $$\int \frac{x^2}{X^2} dx = \frac{(b^2 - 2\,ac)\,x + ab}{cq\,X} + \frac{2a}{q} \int \frac{dx}{X}.$$

73. $$\int \frac{x^m dx}{X^{n+1}} = - \frac{x^{m-1}}{(2n - m + 1)c\,X^n} - \frac{n - m + 1}{2n - m + 1} \cdot \frac{b}{c} \int \frac{x^{m-1}\,dx}{X^{n+1}} + \frac{m - 1}{2n - m + 1} \cdot \frac{a}{c} \int \frac{x^{m-2}\,dx}{X^{n+1}}.$$

74. $$\int \frac{dx}{x\,X} = \frac{1}{2a} \log \frac{x^2}{X} - \frac{b}{2a} \int \frac{dx}{X}.$$

75. $$\int \frac{dx}{x^2\,X} = \frac{b}{2a^2} \log \frac{X}{x^2} - \frac{1}{ax} + \left(\frac{b^2}{2a^2} - \frac{c}{a}\right) \int \frac{dx}{X}.$$

76. $$\int \frac{dx}{x^m\,X^{n+1}} = - \frac{1}{(m - 1)\,ax^{m-1}\,X^n} - \frac{n + m - 1}{m - 1} \cdot \frac{b}{a} \int \frac{dx}{x^{m-1}\,X^{n+1}} - \frac{2n + m - 1}{m - 1} \cdot \frac{c}{a} \int \frac{dx}{x^{m-2}\,X^{n+1}}.$$

Forms Containing $\sqrt{a^2 + bx}$

77. $$\int \sqrt{a + bx}\,dx = \frac{2}{3\,b} \sqrt{(a + bx)^3}.$$

78. $$\int x \sqrt{a + bx}\,dx = - \frac{2\,(2a - 3\,bx)\,\sqrt{(a + bx)^3}}{15\,b^2}.$$

79. $$\int x^2 \sqrt{a + bx}\,dx = \frac{2\,(8\,a^2 - 12\,abx + 15\,b^2x^2)\,\sqrt{(a+bx)^3}}{105\,b^3}.$$

80. $$\int \frac{\sqrt{a + bx}}{x} dx = 2\sqrt{a + bx} + a \int \frac{dx}{x\sqrt{a + bx}}.$$

81. $$\int \frac{dx}{\sqrt{a + bx}} = \frac{2\sqrt{a + bx}}{b}.$$

82. $$\int \frac{xdx}{\sqrt{a + bx}} = - \frac{2\,(2a - bx)}{3\,b^2} \sqrt{a + bx}.$$

83. $$\int \frac{x^2dx}{\sqrt{a + bx}} = \frac{2\,(8\,a^2 - 4\,abx + 3\,b^2x^2)}{15\,b^3} \sqrt{a + bx}.$$

84. $$\int \frac{dx}{x\sqrt{a + bx}} = \frac{1}{\sqrt{a}} \log\left(\frac{\sqrt{a + bx} - \sqrt{a}}{\sqrt{a + bx} + \sqrt{a}}\right).$$

85. $$\int \frac{dx}{x\sqrt{a+bx}} = \frac{-2}{\sqrt{a}} \tanh^{-1}\sqrt{\frac{a+bx}{a}}.$$

86. $$\int \frac{dx}{x^2\sqrt{a+bx}} = -\frac{\sqrt{a+bx}}{ax} - \frac{b}{2a}\int \frac{dx}{x\sqrt{a+bx}}.$$

FORMS CONTAINING $\sqrt{x^2 \pm a^2}$

87. $$\int \sqrt{x^2 \pm a^2}\,dx = \tfrac{1}{2}\left[x\sqrt{x^2 \pm a^2} \pm a^2 \log\left(x + \sqrt{x^2 \pm a^2}\right)\right].$$

88. $$\int \frac{dx}{\sqrt{x^2 \pm a^2}} = \log\left(x + \sqrt{x^2 \pm a^2}\right).$$

89. $$\int \frac{dx}{x\sqrt{x^2 - a^2}} = \frac{1}{a}\cos^{-1}\left(\frac{a}{x}\right), \text{ or } \frac{1}{a}\sec^{-1}\left(\frac{x}{a}\right).$$

90. $$\int \frac{dx}{x\sqrt{x^2 + a^2}} = -\frac{1}{a}\log\left(\frac{a + \sqrt{x^2 + a^2}}{x}\right).$$

91. $$\int \frac{\sqrt{x^2 + a^2}}{x}dx = \sqrt{x^2 + a^2} - a\log\left(\frac{a + \sqrt{x^2 + a^2}}{x}\right).$$

92. $$\int \frac{\sqrt{x^2 - a^2}}{x}dx = \sqrt{x^2 - a^2} - a\cos^{-1}\frac{a}{x}.$$

93. $$\int \frac{x\,dx}{\sqrt{x^2 \pm a^2}} = \sqrt{x^2 \pm a^2}.$$

94. $$\int x\sqrt{x^2 \pm a^2}\,dx = \tfrac{1}{3}\sqrt{(x^2 \pm a^2)^3}.$$

95. $$\int \sqrt{(x^2 \pm a^2)^3}\,dx = \frac{1}{4}\left[x\sqrt{(x^2 \pm a^2)^3} \pm \frac{3a^2x}{2}\sqrt{x^2 \pm a^2} + \frac{3a^4}{2}\log\left(x + \sqrt{x^2 \pm a^2}\right)\right].$$

96. $$\int \frac{dx}{\sqrt{(x^2 \pm a^2)^3}} = \frac{\pm x}{a^2\sqrt{x^2 \pm a^2}}.$$

97. $$\int \frac{x\,dx}{\sqrt{(x^2 \pm a^2)^3}} = \frac{-1}{\sqrt{x^2 \pm a^2}}.$$

98. $$\int x\sqrt{(x^2 \pm a^2)^3}\,dx = \tfrac{1}{5}\sqrt{(x^2 \pm a^2)^5}.$$

99. $$\int x^2\sqrt{x^2 \pm a^2}dx = \frac{x}{4}\sqrt{(x^2 \pm a^2)^3} \mp \frac{a^2}{8}x\sqrt{x^2 \pm a^2} - \frac{a^4}{8}\log(x + \sqrt{x^2 \pm a^2}).$$

100. $$\int \frac{x^2dx}{\sqrt{x^2 \pm a^2}} = \frac{x}{2}\sqrt{x^2 \pm a^2} \mp \frac{a^2}{2}\log(x + \sqrt{x^2 \pm a^2}).$$

101. $$\int \frac{dx}{x^2\sqrt{x^2 \pm a^2}} = \mp \frac{\sqrt{x^2 \pm a^2}}{a^2x}.$$

102. $$\int \frac{\sqrt{x^2 \pm a^2}dx}{x^2} = -\frac{\sqrt{x^2 \pm a^2}}{x} + \log(x + \sqrt{x^2 \pm a^2}).$$

103. $$\int \frac{x^2dx}{\sqrt{(x^2 \pm a^2)^3}} = \frac{-x}{\sqrt{x^2 \pm a^2}} + \log(x + \sqrt{x^2 \pm a^2}).$$

Forms Containing $\sqrt{a^2 - x^2}$

104. $$\int \sqrt{a^2 - x^2}dx = \frac{1}{2}\left[x\sqrt{a^2 - x^2} + a^2\sin^{-1}\left(\frac{x}{a}\right)\right].$$

105. $$\int \frac{dx}{\sqrt{a^2 - x^2}} = \sin^{-1}\left(\frac{x}{a}\right), \quad \text{or } -\cos^{-1}\left(\frac{x}{a}\right).$$

106. $$\int \frac{dx}{x\sqrt{a^2 - x^2}} = -\frac{1}{a}\log\left(\frac{a + \sqrt{a^2 - x^2}}{x}\right).$$

107. $$\int \frac{\sqrt{a^2 - x^2}}{x}dx = \sqrt{a^2 - x^2} - a\log\left(\frac{a + \sqrt{a^2 - x^2}}{x}\right).$$

108. $$\int \frac{x\,dx}{\sqrt{a^2 - x^2}} = -\sqrt{a^2 - x^2}.$$

109. $$\int x\sqrt{a^2 - x^2}dx = -\tfrac{1}{3}\sqrt{(a^2 - x^2)^3}.$$

110. $$\int \sqrt{(a^2 - x^2)^3}dx = \frac{1}{4}\left[x\sqrt{(a^2 - x^2)^3} + \frac{3a^2x}{2}\sqrt{a^2 - x^2} + \frac{3a^4}{2}\sin^{-1}\frac{x}{a}\right].$$

111. $$\int \frac{dx}{\sqrt{(a^2 - x^2)^3}} = \frac{x}{a^2\sqrt{a^2 - x^2}}.$$

112. $$\int \frac{x\,dx}{\sqrt{(a^2 - x^2)^3}} = \frac{1}{\sqrt{a^2 - x^2}}.$$

113. $\int x\sqrt{(a^2 - x^2)^3}dx = -\tfrac{1}{5}\sqrt{(a^2 - x^2)^5}.$

114. $\int x^2\sqrt{a^2 - x^2}dx = -\frac{x}{4}\sqrt{(a^2 - x^2)^3} + \frac{a^2}{8}\left(x\sqrt{a^2 - x^2} + a^2\sin^{-1}\frac{x}{a}\right).$

115. $\int \frac{x^2\,dx}{\sqrt{a^2 - x^2}} = -\frac{x}{2}\sqrt{a^2 - x^2} + \frac{a^2}{2}\sin^{-1}\frac{x}{a}.$

116. $\int \frac{dx}{x^2\sqrt{a^2 - x^2}} = -\frac{\sqrt{a^2 - x^2}}{a^2x}.$

117. $\int \frac{\sqrt{a^2 - x^2}}{x^2}dx = -\frac{\sqrt{a^2 - x^2}}{x} - \sin^{-1}\frac{x}{a}.$

118. $\int \frac{x^2\,dx}{\sqrt{(a^2 - x^2)^3}} = \frac{x}{\sqrt{a^2 - x^2}} - \sin^{-1}\frac{x}{a}.$

Forms Containing $\sqrt{a + bx + cx^2}$

$X = a + bx + cx^2,\ q = 4\,ac - b^2,$ and $k = \frac{4\,c}{q}.$

119. $\int \frac{dx}{\sqrt{X}} = \frac{1}{\sqrt{c}}\log\left(\sqrt{X} + x\sqrt{c} + \frac{b}{2\sqrt{c}}\right).$

120. $\int \frac{dx}{\sqrt{X}} = \frac{1}{\sqrt{c}}\sinh^{-1}\left(\frac{2\,cx + b}{\sqrt{4\,ac - b^2}}\right),$ if $c > 0.$

121. $\int \frac{dx}{\sqrt{X}} = \frac{1}{\sqrt{-c}}\sin^{-1}\left(\frac{-2\,cx - b}{\sqrt{b^2 - 4\,ac}}\right),$ if $c < 0.$

122. $\int \frac{dx}{X\sqrt{X}} = \frac{2\,(2\,cx + b)}{q\sqrt{X}}.$

123. $\int \frac{dx}{X^2\sqrt{X}} = \frac{2\,(2\,cx + b)}{3q\sqrt{X}}\left(\frac{1}{X} + 2\,k\right).$

124. $\int \frac{dx}{X^n\sqrt{X}} = \frac{2\,(2\,cx + b)\sqrt{X}}{(2\,n - 1)qX^n} + \frac{2\,k\,(n - 1)}{2\,n - 1}\int \frac{dx}{X^{n-1}\sqrt{X}}.$

125. $\int \sqrt{X}\,dx = \frac{(2\,cx + b)\sqrt{X}}{4\,c} + \frac{1}{2\,k}\int \frac{dx}{\sqrt{X}}.$

126. $\int X\sqrt{X}\,dx = \frac{(2\,cx + b)\sqrt{X}}{8\,c}\left(X + \frac{3}{2\,k}\right) + \frac{3}{8\,k^2}\int \frac{dx}{\sqrt{X}}.$

127. $$\int X^2\sqrt{X}dx = \frac{(2cx+b)\sqrt{X}}{12c}\left(X^2+\frac{5X}{4k}+\frac{15}{8k^2}\right)+\frac{5}{16k^3}\int\frac{dx}{\sqrt{X}}.$$

128. $$\int X^n\sqrt{X}dx = \frac{(2cx+b)X^n\sqrt{X}}{4(n+1)c}+\frac{2n+1}{2(n+1)k}\int\frac{X^n dx}{\sqrt{X}}.$$

129. $$\int\frac{xdx}{\sqrt{X}} = \frac{\sqrt{X}}{c}-\frac{b}{2c}\int\frac{dx}{\sqrt{X}}.$$

130. $$\int\frac{xdx}{X\sqrt{X}} = -\frac{2(bx+2a)}{q\sqrt{X}}.$$

131. $$\int\frac{xdx}{X^n\sqrt{X}} = -\frac{\sqrt{X}}{(2n-1)cX^n}-\frac{b}{2c}\int\frac{dx}{X^n\sqrt{X}}.$$

132. $$\int\frac{x^2dx}{\sqrt{X}} = \left(\frac{x}{2c}-\frac{3b}{4c^2}\right)\sqrt{X}+\frac{3b^2-4ac}{8c^2}\int\frac{dx}{\sqrt{X}}.$$

133. $$\int\frac{x^2dx}{X\sqrt{X}} = \frac{(2b^2-4ac)x+2ab}{cq\sqrt{X}}+\frac{1}{c}\int\frac{dx}{\sqrt{X}}.$$

134. $$\int\frac{x^2dx}{X^n\sqrt{X}} = \frac{(2b^2-4ac)x+2ab}{(2n-1)cqX^{n-1}\sqrt{X}}+\frac{4ac+(2n-3)b^2}{(2n-1)cq}\int\frac{dx}{X^{n-1}\sqrt{X}}.$$

135. $$\int\frac{x^3dx}{\sqrt{X}} = \left(\frac{x^2}{3c}-\frac{5bx}{12c^2}+\frac{5b^2}{8c^3}-\frac{2a}{3c^2}\right)\sqrt{X}+\left(\frac{3ab}{4c^2}-\frac{5b^3}{16c^3}\right)\int\frac{dx}{\sqrt{X}}.$$

136. $$\int x\sqrt{X}\,dx = \frac{X\sqrt{X}}{3c}-\frac{b}{2c}\int\sqrt{X}\,dx.$$

137. $$\int xX\sqrt{X}\,dx = \frac{X^2\sqrt{X}}{5c}-\frac{b}{2c}\int X\sqrt{X}\,dx.$$

138. $$\int\frac{xX^n dx}{\sqrt{X}} = \frac{X^n\sqrt{X}}{(2n+1)c}-\frac{b}{2c}\int\frac{X^n dx}{\sqrt{X}}.$$

139. $$\int x^2\sqrt{X}\,dx = \left(x-\frac{5b}{6c}\right)\frac{X\sqrt{X}}{4c}+\frac{5b^2-4ac}{16c^2}\int\sqrt{X}dx.$$

140. $$\int \frac{dx}{x\sqrt{X}} = -\frac{1}{\sqrt{a}} \log\left(\frac{\sqrt{X}+\sqrt{a}}{x} + \frac{b}{2\sqrt{a}}\right), \text{ if } a > 0.$$

141. $$\int \frac{dx}{x\sqrt{X}} = \frac{1}{\sqrt{-a}} \sin^{-1}\left(\frac{bx+2a}{x\sqrt{b^2-4ac}}\right), \qquad \text{if } a < 0.$$

142. $$\int \frac{dx}{x\sqrt{X}} = -\frac{2\sqrt{X}}{bx}, \qquad \text{if } a = 0.$$

143. $$\int \frac{dx}{x^2\sqrt{X}} = -\frac{\sqrt{X}}{ax} - \frac{b}{2a}\int \frac{dx}{x\sqrt{X}}.$$

144. $$\int \frac{\sqrt{X}dx}{x} = \sqrt{X} + \frac{b}{2}\int \frac{dx}{\sqrt{X}} + a\int \frac{dx}{x\sqrt{X}}.$$

145. $$\int \frac{\sqrt{X}dx}{x^2} = -\frac{\sqrt{X}}{x} + \frac{b}{2}\int \frac{dx}{x\sqrt{X}} + c\int \frac{dx}{\sqrt{X}}.$$

Miscellaneous Algebraic Forms

146. $$\int \sqrt{2ax-x^2}\; dx = \tfrac{1}{2}\left[(x-a)\sqrt{2ax-x^2}+a^2 \sin^{-1}(x-a)/a\right].$$

147. $$\int \frac{dx}{\sqrt{2ax-x^2}} = \cos^{-1}\left(\frac{a-x}{a}\right).$$

148. $$\int \frac{dx}{\sqrt{a+bx}\cdot\sqrt{a'+b'x}} = \frac{2}{\sqrt{-bb'}} \tan^{-1}\sqrt{\frac{-b'(a+bx)}{b(a'+b'x)}}.$$

149. $$\int \sqrt{\frac{1+x}{1-x}}\, dx = \sin^{-1} x - \sqrt{1-x^2}.$$

150. $$\int \frac{dx}{\sqrt{a \pm 2bx + cx^2}} = \frac{1}{\sqrt{c}} \log\left(\pm b + cx + \sqrt{c}\sqrt{a \pm 2bx + cx^2}\right).$$

151. $$\int \frac{dx}{\sqrt{a \pm 2bx - cx^2}} = \frac{1}{\sqrt{c}} \sin^{-1} \frac{cx \mp b}{\sqrt{b^2+ac}}.$$

152. $$\int \frac{xdx}{\sqrt{a \pm 2bx + cx^2}} = \frac{1}{c}\sqrt{a \pm 2bx + cx^2} - \frac{b}{\sqrt{c^3}}\log\left(\pm b + cx + \sqrt{c}\sqrt{a \pm 2bx + cx^2}\right).$$

153. $$\int \frac{xdx}{\sqrt{a \pm 2bx - cx^2}} = \frac{1}{c}\sqrt{a \pm 2\,bx - cx^2} + \frac{b}{\sqrt{c^3}} \sin^{-1} \frac{cx \mp b}{\sqrt{b^2 + ac}}.$$

Trigonometric and Exponential Forms

154. $$\int \sin x \; dx = -\cos x, \text{ or versin } x.$$

155. $$\int \cos x \; dx = \sin x, \text{ or } - \text{coversin } x.$$

156. $$\int \tan x \; dx = -\log \cos x.$$

157. $$\int \cot x \; dx = \log \sin x.$$

158. $$\int \sec x \; dx = \log \tan\left(\frac{\pi}{4} + \frac{x}{2}\right).$$

159. $$\int \csc x \; dx = \log \tan \tfrac{1}{2}\, x.$$

160. $$\int \sin^2 x \; dx = -\tfrac{1}{2} \cos x \sin x + \tfrac{1}{2}\, x = \tfrac{1}{2}\, x - \tfrac{1}{4} \sin 2\, x.$$

161. $$\int \sin^3 x \; dx = -\tfrac{1}{3} \cos x \,(\sin^2 x + 2).$$

162. $$\int \sin^n x \; dx = -\frac{\sin^{n-1} x \cos x}{n} + \frac{n-1}{n}\int \sin^{n-2} x dx.$$

163. $$\int \cos^2 x \; dx = \tfrac{1}{2} \sin x \cos x + \tfrac{1}{2}\, x = \tfrac{1}{2}\, x + \tfrac{1}{4} \sin 2\, x.$$

164. $$\int \cos^3 x \; dx = \tfrac{1}{3} \sin x \,(\cos^2 x + 2).$$

165. $$\int \cos^n x \; dx = \frac{1}{n} \cos^{n-1} x \sin x + \frac{n-1}{n} \int \cos^{n-2} x \, dx.$$

166. $$\int \sin x \cos x \; dx = \tfrac{1}{2} \sin^2 x.$$

167. $$\int \sin^2 x \cos^2 x \; dx = -\tfrac{1}{8}\left(\tfrac{1}{4} \sin 4\, x - x\right).$$

168. $\int \sin x \cos^m x \, dx = -\frac{\cos^{m+1} x}{m+1}.$

169. $\int \sin^m x \cos x \, dx = \frac{\sin^{m+1} x}{m+1}.$

170. $\int \cos^m x \sin^n x \, dx = \frac{\cos^{m-1} x \sin^{n+1} x}{m+n} + \frac{m-1}{m+n}\int \cos^{m-2} x \sin^n x \, dx.$

171. $\int \cos^m x \sin^n x \, dx = -\frac{\sin^{n-1} x \cos^{m+1} x}{m+n} + \frac{n-1}{m+n}\int \cos^m x \sin^{n-2} x \, dx.$

172. $\int \frac{\cos^m x \, dx}{\sin^n x} = -\frac{\cos^{m+1} x}{(n-1)\sin^{n-1} x} - \frac{m-n+2}{n-1}\int \frac{\cos^m x \, dx}{\sin^{n-2} x}.$

173. $\int \frac{\cos^m x \, dx}{\sin^n x} = \frac{\cos^{m-1} x}{(m-n)\sin^{n-1} x} + \frac{m-1}{m-n}\int \frac{\cos^{m-2} x \, dx}{\sin^n x}.$

174. $\int \frac{\sin^m x \, dx}{\cos^n x} = -\int \frac{\cos^m\left(\frac{\pi}{2}-x\right) d\left(\frac{\pi}{2}-x\right)}{\sin^n\left(\frac{\pi}{2}-x\right)}.$

175. $\int \frac{\sin x \, dx}{\cos^2 x} = \frac{1}{\cos x} = \sec x.$

176. $\int \frac{\cos x \, dx}{\sin^2 x} = \frac{-1}{\sin x} = -\operatorname{cosec} x.$

177. $\int \frac{dx}{\sin x \cos x} = \log \tan x.$

178. $\int \frac{dx}{\sin^m x \cos^n x} = -\frac{1}{m-1} \cdot \frac{1}{\sin^{m-1} x \cdot \cos^{n-1} x} + \frac{m+n-2}{m-1}\int \frac{dx}{\sin^{m-2} x \cdot \cos^n x}.$

179. $\int \frac{dx}{\sin^m x} = -\frac{1}{m-1} \cdot \frac{\cos x}{\sin^{m-1} x} + \frac{m-2}{m-1}\int \frac{dx}{\sin^{m-2} x}.$

180. $\int \frac{dx}{\sin^2 x} = -\cot x.$

181. $\int \frac{dx}{\cos^n x} = \frac{1}{n-1} \cdot \frac{\sin x}{\cos^{n-1} x} + \frac{n-2}{n-1} \int \frac{dx}{\cos^{n-2} x}.$

182. $\int \frac{dx}{\cos^2 x} = \tan x$

---

183. $\int \tan^2 x \, dx = \tan x - x.$

184. $\int \tan^n x \, dx = \frac{\tan^{n-1} x}{n-1} - \int \tan^{n-2} x \, dx.$

185. $\int \cot^2 x \, dx = -\cot x - x.$

186. $\int \cot^n x \, dx = -\frac{\cot^{n-1} x}{n-1} - \int \cot^{n-2} x \, dx.$

187. $\int \sec^2 x \, dx = \tan x.$

188. $\int \sec^n x \, dx = \int \frac{dx}{\cos^n x}.$

189. $\int \csc^2 x \, dx = -\cot x.$

190. $\int \csc^n x \, dx = \int \frac{dx}{\sin^n x}.$

---

191. $\int x \sin x \, dx = \sin x - x \cos x.$

192. $\int x^2 \sin x \, dx = 2x \sin x - (x^2 - 2) \cos x.$

193. $\int x^3 \sin x \, dx = (3x^2 - 6) \sin x - (x^3 - 6x) \cos x.$

194. $\int x^m \sin x \, dx = -x^m \cos x + m \int x^{m-1} \cos x \, dx.$

195. $\int x \cos x \, dx = \cos x + x \sin x.$

196. $\int x^2 \cos x \, dx = 2x \cos x + (x^2 - 2) \sin x.$

197. $\int x^3 \cos x \, dx = (3\,x^2 - 6) \cos x + (x^3 - 6x) \sin x.$

198. $\int x^m \cos x \, dx = x^m \sin x - m \int x^{m-1} \sin x \, dx.$

199. $\int \frac{\sin x}{x} dx = x - \frac{x^3}{3\,.\,3!} + \frac{x^5}{5\,.\,5!} - \frac{x^7}{7\,.\,7!} + \frac{x^9}{9\,.\,9!} \cdots$

200. $\int \frac{\cos x}{x} dx = \log x - \frac{x^2}{2\,.\,2\,!} + \frac{x^4}{4\,.\,4\,!} - \frac{x^6}{6\,.\,6\,!} + \frac{x^8}{8\,.\,8\,!} \cdots$

---

201. $\int \sin^{-1}x \, dx = x \sin^{-1}x + \sqrt{1 - x^2}.$

202. $\int \cos^{-1}x \, dx = x \cos^{-1}x - \sqrt{1 - x^2}.$

203. $\int \tan^{-1}x \, dx = x \tan^{-1}x - \frac{1}{2} \log (1 + x^2).$

204. $\int \cot^{-1}x \, dx = x \cot^{-1}x + \frac{1}{2} \log (1 + x^2).$

205. $\int x \,.\, \sin^{-1}x \, dx = \frac{1}{4} \left[(2\,x^2 - 1) \sin^{-1}x + x \sqrt{1 - x^2}\right].$

206. $\int x^n \sin^{-1}x \, dx = \frac{x^{n+1} \sin^{-1}x}{n+1} - \frac{1}{n+1} \int \frac{x^{n+1}\, dx}{\sqrt{1 - x^2}}.$

207. $\int x^n \cos^{-1}x \, dx = \frac{x^{n+1} \cos^{-1}x}{n+1} + \frac{1}{n+1} \int \frac{x^{n+1}\, dx}{\sqrt{1 - x^2}}.$

208. $\int x^n \tan^{-1}x \, dx = \frac{x^{n+1} \tan^{-1}x}{n+1} - \frac{1}{n+1} \int \frac{x^{n+1}\, dx}{1 + x^2}.$

---

209. $\int \log x \, dx = x \log x - x.$

210. $\int \frac{(\log x)^n}{x} dx = \frac{1}{n+1} (\log x)^{n+1}.$

211. $\int \frac{dx}{x \log x} = \log (\log x).$

212. $\int \frac{dx}{x\,(\log x)^n} = - \frac{1}{(n-1)\,(\log x)^{n-1}}.$

213. $$\int x^m \log x \, dx = x^{m+1}\left[\frac{\log x}{m+1} - \frac{1}{(m+1)^2}\right].$$

---

214. $$\int e^{ax} dx = \frac{e^{ax}}{a}.$$

215. $$\int x\, e^{ax} dx = \frac{e^{ax}}{a^2}(ax - 1).$$

216. $$\int x^m e^{ax}\, dx = \frac{x^m e^{ax}}{a} - \frac{m}{a}\int x^{m-1} e^{ax}\, dx.$$

217. $$\int \frac{e^{ax}}{x^m}\, dx = -\frac{1}{m-1}\frac{e^{ax}}{x^{m-1}} + \frac{a}{m-1}\int \frac{e^{ax}}{x^{m-1}}\, dx.$$

218. $$\int e^{ax} \log x \, dx = \frac{e^{ax}\log x}{a} - \frac{1}{a}\int \frac{e^{ax}}{x} dx.$$

219. $$\int e^{ax} \cdot \sin px \, dx = \frac{e^{ax}(a \sin px - p \cos px)}{a^2 + p^2}.$$

220. $$\int e^{ax} \cdot \cos px \, dx = \frac{e^{ax}(a \cos px + p \sin px)}{a^2 + p^2}.$$

221. $$\int \sinh x \, dx = \cosh x.$$

222. $$\int \cosh x \, dx = \sinh x.$$

223. $$\int \tanh x \, dx = \log \cosh x.$$

224. $$\int \coth x \, dx = \log \sinh x.$$

225. $$\int \operatorname{sech} x \, dx = 2 \tan^{-1}(e^x).$$

226. $$\int \operatorname{csch} x \, dx = \log \tanh\left(\frac{x}{2}\right).$$

227. $$\int x \sinh x \, dx = x \cosh x - \sinh x.$$

228. $$\int x \cosh x \, dx = x \sinh x - \cosh x.$$

ANALYTICAL GEOMETRY

The distance between two points x_1, y_1, and x_2, y_2, — rectangular coördinates:

$$d = \pm \sqrt{(x_2 - x_1)^2 + (y_2 - y_1)^2}$$

For polar coördinates and points r_1, θ_1, and r_2, θ_2:

$$d = \pm \sqrt{r_1^2 + r_2^2 - 2r_1r_2 \cos (\theta_1 - \theta_2)}$$

The area of a triangle whose vertices are x_1, y_1; x_2, y_2, and x_3, y_3:

$$A = \tfrac{1}{2} (x_1y_2 - x_2y_1 + x_2y_3 - x_3y_2 + x_3y_1 - x_1y_3)$$

For polar coördinates and vertices, r_1, θ_1; r_2, θ_2, and r_3, θ_3:

$$A = \tfrac{1}{2}\{(r_1r_2 \sin (\theta_2 - \theta_1) + r_2r_3 \sin (\theta_3 - \theta_2) + r_3r_1 \sin (\theta_1 - \theta_3)\}$$

The equation of a straight line where m is the tangent of the angle of inclination and c, the distance of intersection with the Y axis from the origin:

$$y = mx + c$$

If a line of inclination m passes through the point x_1, y_1, its equation is:

$$y - y_1 = m(x - x_1)$$

The equation of a line through the points x_1, y_1, and x_2, y_2 is:

$$\frac{y - y_1}{y_2 - y_1} = \frac{x - x_1}{x_2 - x_1}$$

If the intercepts on the X and Y axes are a and b respectively, the equation is:

$$\frac{x}{a} + \frac{y}{b} = 1$$

If the length of the perpendicular from the origin is p and its angle of inclination θ the equation is:

$$x \cos \theta + y \sin \theta = p$$

General equation of the straight line:

$$Ax + By + C = 0$$

The equation of a circle whose center is at a, b, and whose radius is c:

$$(x - a)^2 + (y - b)^2 = c^2$$

If the origin is at the center:

$$x^2 + y^2 = c^2$$

The polar equation of a circle with the origin on the circumference and its center at point c, α:

$$r = 2c \cos (\theta - \alpha).$$

If the origin is not on the circumference, the radius a and the center at a point l, α, the equation becomes:

$$a^2 = r^2 + l^2 - 2rl \cos (\theta - \alpha)$$

The equation of a parabola with the origin at the vertex, where f is the distance from the focus to the vertex:

$$y^2 = 4fx$$

If p is the semi-latus rectum $(= 2f)$ the equation is:

$$y^2 = 2px$$

The polar equation, where the pole is at the focus and l the semi-latus rectum is:

$$\frac{l}{r} = 1 - \cos\theta$$

If the pole is at the vertex and p as above:

$$r = \frac{4p \cos\theta}{\sin^2\theta}$$

The equation of the ellipse with the origin at the center and semi-axes a and b:

$$\frac{x^2}{a^2} + \frac{y^2}{b^2} = 1$$

Polar equation where the pole is at the center:

$$r^2 = \frac{a^2b^2}{a^2\sin^2\theta + b^2\cos^2\theta}$$

The equation of the hyperbola with the origin at the center, semi-axes a and b:

$$\frac{x^2}{a^2} - \frac{y^2}{b^2} = 1$$

Polar equation, pole at center:

$$r^2 = \frac{a^2b^2}{a^2\sin^2\theta - b^2\cos^2\theta}$$

SIMPSON'S RULE FOR IRREGULAR AREAS

Divide the area into n panels (where n is some even number) by means of $n+1$ parallel lines, or ordinates, drawn at constant distance h apart; and denote the lengths of the ordinates by y_0, y_1, y_2, . . . y_n. The first and last ordinate may be zero. The area will then be:

$$A = \tfrac{1}{3} h\left[(y_0+y_n)+4(y_1+y_3+y_5 \ldots) + 2(y_2+y_4+y_6 \ldots)\right]$$

The greater the number of divisions, the more accurate the result. Simpson's rule may be applied to finding volumes if the ordinates y_0, y_1, y_2 be interpreted as the areas of plane sections, at constant distance h apart.

PRISMOIDAL FORMULA

The volume of a solid figure extending between two parallel planes in which the area of every cross-section parallel to those planes is a quadratic function of the distance of the section from a fixed plane parallel to them is given by the equation

$$V = \tfrac{1}{6} H(S_0+4S_1+S_2)$$

where H is the distance between the two limiting parallel planes; S_0 and S_2 the cross-sections in these planes (lower and upper bases) and S_1 the cross-section of the mid-section. The formula applies to such figures as the cone, sphere, ellipsoid and prismoid.

FOUR-PLACE

N	0	1	2	3	4	5	6	7	8	9	Proportional Parts 1	2	3	4	5
10	0000	0043	0086	0128	0170	0212	0253	0294	0334	0374	4	8	12	17	21
11	0414	0453	0492	0531	0569	0607	0645	0682	0719	0755	4	8	11	15	19
12	0792	0828	0864	0899	0934	0969	1004	1038	1072	1106	3	7	10	14	17
13	1139	1173	1206	1239	1271	1303	1335	1367	1399	1430	3	6	10	13	16
14	1461	1492	1523	1553	1584	1614	1644	1673	1703	1732	3	6	9	12	15
15	1761	1790	1818	1847	1875	1903	1931	1959	1987	2014	3	6	8	11	14
16	2041	2068	2095	2122	2148	2175	2201	2227	2253	2279	3	5	8	11	13
17	2304	2330	2355	2380	2405	2430	2455	2480	2504	2529	2	5	7	10	12
18	2553	2577	2601	2625	2648	2672	2695	2718	2742	2765	2	5	7	9	12
19	2788	2810	2833	2856	2878	2900	2923	2945	2967	2989	2	4	7	9	11
20	3010	3032	3054	3075	3096	3118	3139	3160	3181	3201	2	4	6	8	11
21	3222	3243	3263	3284	3304	3324	3345	3365	3385	3404	2	4	6	8	10
22	3424	3444	3464	3483	3502	3522	3541	3560	3579	3598	2	4	6	8	10
23	3617	3636	3655	3674	3692	3711	3729	3747	3766	3784	2	4	5	7	9
24	3802	3820	3838	3856	3874	3892	3909	3927	3945	3962	2	4	5	7	9
25	3979	3997	4014	4031	4048	4065	4082	4099	4116	4133	2	3	5	7	9
26	4150	4166	4183	4200	4216	4232	4249	4265	4281	4298	2	3	5	7	8
27	4314	4330	4346	4362	4378	4393	4409	4425	4440	4456	2	3	5	6	8
28	4472	4487	4502	4518	4533	4548	4564	4579	4594	4609	2	3	5	6	8
29	4624	4639	4654	4669	4683	4698	4713	4728	4742	4757	1	3	4	6	7
30	4771	4786	4800	4814	4829	4843	4857	4871	4886	4900	1	3	4	6	7
31	4914	4928	4942	4955	4969	4983	4997	5011	5024	5038	1	3	4	6	7
32	5051	5065	5079	5092	5105	5119	5132	5145	5159	5172	1	3	4	5	7
33	5185	5198	5211	5224	5237	5250	5263	5276	5289	5302	1	3	4	5	6
34	5315	5328	5340	5353	5366	5378	5391	5403	5416	5428	1	3	4	5	6
35	5441	5453	5465	5478	5490	5502	5514	5527	5539	5551	1	2	4	5	6
36	5563	5575	5587	5599	5611	5623	5635	5647	5658	5670	1	2	4	5	6
37	5682	5694	5705	5717	5729	5740	5752	5763	5775	5786	1	2	3	5	6
38	5798	5809	5821	5832	5843	5855	5866	5877	5888	5899	1	2	3	5	6
39	5911	5922	5933	5944	5955	5966	5977	5988	5999	6010	1	2	3	4	6
40	6021	6031	6042	6053	6064	6075	6085	6096	6107	6117	1	2	3	4	5
41	6128	6138	6149	6160	6170	6180	6191	6201	6212	6222	1	2	3	4	5
42	6232	6243	6253	6263	6274	6284	6294	6304	6314	6325	1	2	3	4	5
43	6335	6345	6355	6365	6375	6385	6395	6405	6415	6425	1	2	3	4	5
44	6435	6444	6454	6464	6474	6484	6493	6503	6513	6522	1	2	3	4	5
45	6532	6542	6551	6561	6571	6580	6590	6599	6609	6618	1	2	3	4	5
46	6628	6637	6646	6656	6665	6675	6684	6693	6702	6712	1	2	3	4	5
47	6721	6730	6739	6749	6758	6767	6776	6785	6794	6803	1	2	3	4	5
48	6812	6821	6830	6839	6848	6857	6866	6875	6884	6893	1	2	3	4	4
49	6902	6911	6920	6928	6937	6946	6955	6964	6972	6981	1	2	3	4	4
50	6990	6998	7007	7016	7024	7033	7042	7050	7059	7067	1	2	3	3	4
51	7076	7084	7093	7101	7110	7118	7126	7135	7143	7152	1	2	3	3	4
52	7160	7168	7177	7185	7193	7202	7210	7218	7226	7235	1	2	2	3	4
53	7243	7251	7259	7267	7275	7284	7292	7300	7308	7316	1	2	2	3	4
54	7324	7332	7340	7348	7356	7364	7372	7380	7388	7396	1	2	2	3	4
N	0	1	2	3	4	5	6	7	8	9	1	2	3	4	5

LOGARITHMS

N	0	1	2	3	4	5	6	7	8	9	Proportional Parts 1	2	3	4	5
55	7404	7412	7419	7427	7435	7443	7451	7459	7466	7474	1	2	2	3	4
56	7482	7490	7497	7505	7513	7520	7528	7536	7543	7551	1	2	2	3	4
57	7559	7566	7574	7582	7589	7597	7604	7612	7619	7627	1	2	2	3	4
58	7634	7642	7649	7657	7664	7672	7679	7686	7694	7701	1	1	2	3	4
59	7709	7716	7723	7731	7738	7745	7752	7760	7767	7774	1	1	2	3	4
60	7782	7789	7796	7803	7810	7818	7825	7832	7839	7846	1	1	2	3	4
61	7853	7860	7868	7875	7882	7889	7896	7903	7910	7917	1	1	2	3	4
62	7924	7931	7938	7945	7952	7959	7966	7973	7980	7987	1	1	2	3	3
63	7993	8000	8007	8014	8021	8028	8035	8041	8048	8055	1	1	2	3	3
64	8062	8069	8075	8082	8089	8096	8102	8109	8116	8122	1	1	2	3	3
65	8129	8136	8142	8149	8156	8162	8169	8176	8182	8189	1	1	2	3	3
66	8195	8202	8209	8215	8222	8228	8235	8241	8248	8254	1	1	2	3	3
67	8261	8267	8274	8280	8287	8293	8299	8306	8312	8319	1	1	2	3	3
68	8325	8331	8338	8344	8351	8357	8363	8370	8376	8382	1	1	2	3	3
69	8388	8395	8401	8407	8414	8420	8426	8432	8439	8445	1	1	2	3	3
70	8451	8457	8463	8470	8476	8482	8488	8494	8500	8506	1	1	2	2	3
71	8513	8519	8525	8531	8537	8543	8549	8555	8561	8567	1	1	2	2	3
72	8573	8579	8585	8591	8597	8603	8609	8615	8621	8627	1	1	2	2	3
73	8633	8639	8645	8651	8657	8663	8669	8675	8681	8686	1	1	2	2	3
74	8692	8698	8704	8710	8716	8722	8727	8733	8739	8745	1	1	2	2	3
75	8751	8756	8762	8768	8774	8779	8785	8791	8797	8802	1	1	2	2	3
76	8808	8814	8820	8825	8831	8837	8842	8848	8854	8859	1	1	2	2	3
77	8865	8871	8876	8882	8887	8893	8899	8904	8910	8915	1	1	2	2	3
78	8921	8927	8932	8938	8943	8949	8954	8960	8965	8971	1	1	2	2	3
79	8976	8982	8987	8993	8998	9004	9009	9015	9020	9025	1	1	2	2	3
80	9031	9036	9042	9047	9053	9058	9063	9069	9074	9079	1	1	2	2	3
81	9085	9090	9096	9101	9106	9112	9117	9122	9128	9133	1	1	2	2	3
82	9138	9143	9149	9154	9159	9165	9170	9175	9180	9186	1	1	2	2	3
83	9191	9196	9201	9206	9212	9217	9222	9227	9232	9238	1	1	2	2	3
84	9243	9248	9253	9258	9263	9269	9274	9279	9284	9289	1	1	2	2	3
85	9294	9299	9304	9309	9315	9320	9325	9330	9335	9340	1	1	2	2	3
86	9345	9350	9355	9360	9365	9370	9375	9380	9385	9390	1	1	2	2	3
87	9395	9400	9405	9410	9415	9420	9425	9430	9435	9440	0	1	1	2	2
88	9445	9450	9455	9460	9465	9469	9474	9479	9484	9489	0	1	1	2	2
89	9494	9499	9504	9509	9513	9518	9523	9528	9533	9538	0	1	1	2	2
90	9542	9547	9552	9557	9562	9566	9571	9576	9581	9586	0	1	1	2	2
91	9590	9595	9600	9605	9609	9614	9619	9624	9628	9633	0	1	1	2	2
92	9638	9643	9647	9652	9657	9661	9666	9671	9675	9680	0	1	1	2	2
93	9685	9689	9694	9699	9703	9708	9713	9717	9722	9727	0	1	1	2	2
94	9731	9736	9741	9745	9750	9754	9759	9763	9768	9773	0	1	1	2	2
95	9777	9782	9786	9791	9795	9800	9805	9809	9814	9818	0	1	1	2	2
96	9823	9827	9832	9836	9841	9845	9850	9854	9859	9863	0	1	1	2	2
97	9868	9872	9877	9881	9886	9890	9894	9899	9903	9908	0	1	1	2	2
98	9912	9917	9921	9926	9930	9934	9939	9943	9948	9952	0	1	1	2	2
99	9956	9961	9965	9969	9974	9978	9983	9987	9991	9996	0	1	1	2	2
N	0	1	2	3	4	5	6	7	8	9	1	2	3	4	5

ANTILOGARITHMS

	0	1	2	3	4	5	6	7	8	9	Proportional Parts 1	2	3	4	5
.00	1000	1002	1005	1007	1009	1012	1014	1016	1019	1021	0	0	1	1	1
.01	1023	1026	1028	1030	1033	1035	1038	1040	1042	1045	0	0	1	1	1
.02	1047	1050	1052	1054	1057	1059	1062	1064	1067	1069	0	0	1	1	1
.03	1072	1074	1076	1079	1081	1084	1086	1089	1091	1094	0	0	1	1	1
.04	1096	1099	1102	1104	1107	1109	1112	1114	1117	1119	0	1	1	1	1
.05	1122	1125	1127	1130	1132	1135	1138	1140	1143	1146	0	1	1	1	1
.06	1148	1151	1153	1156	1159	1161	1164	1167	1169	1172	0	1	1	1	1
.07	1175	1178	1180	1183	1186	1189	1191	1194	1197	1199	0	1	1	1	1
.08	1202	1205	1208	1211	1213	1216	1219	1222	1225	1227	0	1	1	1	1
.09	1230	1233	1236	1239	1242	1245	1247	1250	1253	1256	0	1	1	1	1
.10	1259	1262	1265	1268	1271	1274	1276	1279	1282	1285	0	1	1	1	1
.11	1288	1291	1294	1297	1300	1303	1306	1309	1312	1315	0	1	1	1	2
.12	1318	1321	1324	1327	1330	1334	1337	1340	1343	1346	0	1	1	1	2
.13	1349	1352	1355	1358	1361	1365	1368	1371	1374	1377	0	1	1	1	2
.14	1380	1384	1387	1390	1393	1396	1400	1403	1406	1409	0	1	1	1	2
.15	1413	1416	1419	1422	1426	1429	1432	1435	1439	1442	0	1	1	1	2
.16	1445	1449	1452	1455	1459	1462	1466	1469	1472	1476	0	1	1	1	2
.17	1479	1483	1486	1489	1493	1496	1500	1503	1507	1510	0	1	1	1	2
.18	1514	1517	1521	1524	1528	1531	1535	1538	1542	1545	0	1	1	1	2
.19	1549	1552	1556	1560	1563	1567	1570	1574	1578	1581	0	1	1	1	2
.20	1585	1589	1592	1596	1600	1603	1607	1611	1614	1618	0	1	1	1	2
.21	1622	1626	1629	1633	1637	1641	1644	1648	1652	1656	0	1	1	1	2
.22	1660	1663	1667	1671	1675	1679	1683	1687	1690	1694	0	1	1	2	2
.23	1698	1702	1706	1710	1714	1718	1722	1726	1730	1734	0	1	1	2	2
.24	1738	1742	1746	1750	1754	1758	1762	1766	1770	1774	0	1	1	2	2
.25	1778	1782	1786	1791	1795	1799	1803	1807	1811	1816	0	1	1	2	2
.26	1820	1824	1828	1832	1837	1841	1845	1849	1854	1858	0	1	1	2	2
.27	1862	1866	1871	1875	1879	1884	1888	1892	1897	1901	0	1	1	2	2
.28	1905	1910	1914	1919	1923	1928	1932	1936	1941	1945	0	1	1	2	2
.29	1950	1954	1959	1963	1968	1972	1977	1982	1986	1991	0	1	1	2	2
.30	1995	2000	2004	2009	2014	2018	2023	2028	2032	2037	0	1	1	2	2
.31	2042	2046	2051	2056	2061	2065	2070	2075	2080	2084	0	1	1	2	2
.32	2089	2094	2099	2104	2109	2113	2118	2123	2128	2133	0	1	1	2	2
.33	2138	2143	2148	2153	2158	2163	2168	2173	2178	2183	0	1	1	2	2
.34	2188	2193	2198	2203	2208	2213	2218	2223	2228	2234	1	1	2	2	3
.35	2239	2244	2249	2254	2259	2265	2270	2275	2280	2286	1	1	2	2	3
.36	2291	2296	2301	2307	2312	2317	2323	2328	2333	2339	1	1	2	2	3
.37	2344	2350	2355	2360	2366	2371	2377	2382	2388	2393	1	1	2	2	3
.38	2399	2404	2410	2415	2421	2427	2432	2438	2443	2449	1	1	2	2	3
.39	2455	2460	2466	2472	2477	2483	2489	2495	2500	2506	1	1	2	2	3
.40	2512	2518	2523	2529	2535	2541	2547	2553	2559	2564	1	1	2	2	3
.41	2570	2576	2582	2588	2594	2600	2606	2612	2618	2624	1	1	2	2	3
.42	2630	2636	2642	2649	2655	2661	2667	2673	2679	2685	1	1	2	2	3
.43	2692	2698	2704	2710	2716	2723	2729	2735	2742	2748	1	1	2	2	3
.44	2754	2761	2767	2773	2780	2786	2793	2799	2805	2812	1	1	2	3	3
.45	2818	2825	2831	2838	2844	2851	2858	2864	2871	2877	1	1	2	3	3
.46	2884	2891	2897	2904	2911	2917	2924	2931	2938	2944	1	1	2	3	3
.47	2951	2958	2965	2972	2979	2985	2992	2999	3006	3013	1	1	2	3	3
.48	3020	3027	3034	3041	3048	3055	3062	3069	3076	3083	1	1	2	3	3
.49	3090	3097	3105	3112	3119	3126	3133	3141	3148	3155	1	1	2	3	4
	0	1	2	3	4	5	6	7	8	9	1	2	3	4	5

ANTILOGARITHMS

	0	1	2	3	4	5	6	7	8	9	Proportional Parts 1	2	3	4	5
.50	3162	3170	3177	3184	3192	3199	3206	3214	3221	3228	1	1	2	3	4
.51	3236	3243	3251	3258	3266	3273	3281	3289	3296	3304	1	1	2	3	4
.52	3311	3319	3327	3334	3342	3350	3357	3365	3373	3381	1	1	2	3	4
.53	3388	3396	3404	3412	3420	3428	3436	3443	3451	3459	1	2	2	3	4
.54	3467	3475	3483	3491	3499	3508	3516	3524	3532	3540	1	2	2	3	4
.55	3548	3556	3565	3573	3581	3589	3597	3606	3614	3622	1	2	2	3	4
.56	3631	3639	3648	3656	3664	3673	3681	3690	3698	3707	1	2	2	3	4
.57	3715	3724	3733	3741	3750	3758	3767	3776	3784	3793	1	2	3	3	4
.58	3802	3811	3819	3828	3837	3846	3855	3864	3873	3882	1	2	3	3	4
.59	3890	3899	3908	3917	3926	3936	3945	3954	3963	3972	1	2	3	4	5
.60	3981	3990	3999	4009	4018	4027	4036	4046	4055	4064	1	2	3	4	5
.61	4074	4083	4093	4102	4111	4121	4130	4140	4150	4159	1	2	3	4	5
.62	4169	4178	4188	4198	4207	4217	4227	4236	4246	4256	1	2	3	4	5
.63	4266	4276	4285	4295	4305	4315	4325	4335	4345	4355	1	2	3	4	5
.64	4365	4375	4385	4395	4406	4416	4426	4436	4446	4457	1	2	3	4	5
.65	4467	4477	4487	4498	4508	4519	4529	4539	4550	4560	1	2	3	4	5
.66	4571	4581	4592	4603	4613	4624	4634	4645	4656	4667	1	2	3	4	5
.67	4677	4688	4699	4710	4721	4732	4742	4753	4764	4775	1	2	3	4	5
.68	4786	4797	4808	4819	4831	4842	4853	4864	4875	4887	1	2	3	5	6
.69	4898	4909	4920	4932	4943	4955	4966	4977	4989	5000	1	2	3	5	6
.70	5012	5023	5035	5047	5058	5070	5082	5093	5105	5117	1	2	3	5	6
.71	5129	5140	5152	5164	5176	5188	5200	5212	5224	5236	1	2	4	5	6
.72	5248	5260	5272	5284	5297	5309	5321	5333	5346	5358	1	2	4	5	6
.73	5370	5383	5395	5408	5420	5433	5445	5458	5470	5483	1	3	4	5	6
.74	5495	5508	5521	5534	5546	5559	5572	5585	5598	5610	1	3	4	5	6
.75	5623	5636	5649	5662	5675	5689	5702	5715	5728	5741	1	3	4	5	7
.76	5754	5768	5781	5794	5808	5821	5834	5848	5861	5875	1	3	4	5	7
.77	5888	5902	5916	5929	5943	5957	5970	5984	5998	6012	1	3	4	5	7
.78	6026	6039	6053	6067	6081	6095	6109	6124	6138	6152	1	3	4	6	7
.79	6166	6180	6194	6209	6223	6237	6252	6266	6281	6295	1	3	4	6	7
.80	6310	6324	6339	6353	6368	6383	6397	6412	6427	6442	1	3	4	6	7
.81	6457	6471	6486	6501	6516	6531	6546	6561	6577	6592	2	3	5	6	8
.82	6607	6622	6637	6653	6668	6683	6699	6714	6730	6745	2	3	5	6	8
.83	6761	6776	6792	6808	6823	6839	6855	6871	6887	6902	2	3	5	6	8
.84	6918	6934	6950	6966	6982	6998	7015	7031	7047	7063	2	3	5	7	8
.85	7079	7096	7112	7129	7145	7161	7178	7194	7211	7228	2	3	5	7	8
.86	7244	7261	7278	7295	7311	7328	7345	7362	7379	7396	2	3	5	7	8
.87	7413	7430	7447	7464	7482	7499	7516	7534	7551	7568	2	4	5	7	9
.88	7586	7603	7621	7638	7656	7674	7691	7709	7727	7745	2	4	5	7	9
.89	7762	7780	7798	7816	7834	7852	7870	7889	7907	7925	2	4	6	7	9
.90	7943	7962	7980	7998	8017	8035	8054	8072	8091	8110	2	4	6	7	9
.91	8128	8147	8166	8185	8204	8222	8241	8260	8279	8299	2	4	6	8	9
.92	8318	8337	8356	8375	8395	8414	8433	8453	8472	8492	2	4	6	8	10
.93	8511	8531	8551	8570	8590	8610	8630	8650	8670	8690	2	4	6	8	10
.94	8710	8730	8750	8770	8790	8810	8831	8851	8872	8892	2	4	6	8	10
.95	8913	8933	8954	8974	8995	9016	9036	9057	9078	9099	2	4	6	8	10
.96	9120	9141	9162	9183	9204	9226	9247	9268	9290	9311	2	4	6	9	11
.97	9333	9354	9376	9397	9419	9441	9462	9484	9506	9528	2	4	6	9	11
.98	9550	9572	9594	9616	9638	9661	9683	9705	9727	9750	2	4	7	9	11
.99	9772	9795	9817	9840	9863	9886	9908	9931	9954	9977	2	5	7	9	11
	0	1	2	3	4	5	6	7	8	9	1	2	3	4	5

N.	0	1	2	3	4	5	6	7	8	9
100	00 000	043	087	130	173	217	260	303	346	389
101	432	475	518	561	604	647	689	732	775	817
102	860	903	945	988	*030	*072	*115	*157	*199	*242
103	01 284	326	368	410	452	494	536	578	620	662
104	703	745	787	828	870	912	953	995	*036	*078
105	02 119	160	202	243	284	325	366	407	449	490
106	531	572	612	653	694	735	776	816	857	898
107	938	979	*019	*060	*100	*141	*181	*222	*262	*302
108	03 342	383	423	463	503	543	583	623	663	703
109	743	782	822	862	902	941	981	*021	*060	*100
110	04 139	179	218	258	297	336	376	415	454	493
111	532	571	610	650	689	727	766	805	844	883
112	922	961	999	*038	*077	*115	*154	*192	*231	*269
113	05 308	346	385	423	461	500	538	576	614	652
114	690	729	767	805	843	881	918	956	994	*032
115	06 070	108	145	183	221	258	296	333	371	408
116	446	483	521	558	595	633	670	707	744	781
117	819	856	893	930	967	*004	*041	*078	*115	*151
118	07 188	225	262	298	335	372	408	445	482	518
119	555	591	628	664	700	737	773	809	846	882
120	918	954	990	*027	*063	*099	*135	*171	*207	*243
121	08 279	314	350	386	422	458	493	529	565	600
122	636	672	707	743	778	814	849	884	920	955
123	991	*026	*061	*096	*132	*167	*202	*237	*272	*307
124	09 342	377	412	447	482	517	552	587	621	656
125	691	726	760	795	830	864	899	934	968	*003
126	10 037	072	106	140	175	209	243	278	312	346
127	380	415	449	483	517	551	585	619	653	687
128	721	755	789	823	857	890	924	958	992	*025
129	11 059	093	126	160	193	227	261	294	327	361
130	394	428	461	494	528	561	594	628	661	694
131	727	760	793	826	860	893	926	959	992	*024
132	12 057	090	123	156	189	222	254	287	320	352
133	385	418	450	483	516	548	581	613	646	678
134	710	743	775	808	840	872	905	937	969	*001
135	13 033	066	098	130	162	194	226	258	290	322
136	354	386	418	450	481	513	545	577	609	640
137	672	704	735	767	799	830	862	893	925	956
138	988	*019	*051	*082	*114	*145	*176	*208	*239	*270
139	14 301	333	364	395	426	457	489	520	551	582
140	613	644	675	706	737	768	799	829	860	891
141	922	953	983	*014	*045	*076	*106	*137	*168	*198
142	15 229	259	290	320	351	381	412	442	473	503
143	534	564	594	625	655	685	715	746	776	806
144	836	866	897	927	957	987	*017	*047	*077	*107
145	16 137	167	197	227	256	286	316	346	376	406
146	435	465	495	524	554	584	613	643	673	702
147	732	761	791	820	850	879	909	938	967	997
148	17 026	056	085	114	143	173	202	231	260	289
149	319	348	377	406	435	464	493	522	551	580
150	609	638	667	696	725	754	782	811	840	869
N.	0	1	2	3	4	5	6	7	8	9

Proportional Parts

	44	**43**	**42**
1	4.4	4.3	4.2
2	8.8	8.6	8.4
3	13.2	12.9	12.6
4	17.6	17.2	16.8
5	22.0	21.5	21.0
6	26.4	25.8	25.2
7	30.8	30.1	29.4
8	35.2	34.4	33.6
9	39.6	38.7	37.8
	41	**40**	**39**
1	4.1	4.0	3.9
2	8.2	8.0	7.8
3	12.3	12.0	11.7
4	16.4	16.0	15.6
5	20.5	20.0	19.5
6	24.6	24.0	23.4
7	28.7	28.0	27.3
8	32.8	32.0	31.2
9	36.9	36.0	35.1
	38	**37**	**36**
1	3.8	3.7	3.6
2	7.6	7.4	7.2
3	11.4	11.1	10.8
4	15.2	14.8	14.4
5	19.0	18.5	18.0
6	22.8	22.2	21.6
7	26.6	25.9	25.2
8	30.4	29.6	28.8
9	34.2	33.3	32.4
	35	**34**	**33**
1	3.5	3.4	3.3
2	7.0	6.8	6.6
3	10.5	10.2	9.9
4	14.0	13.6	13.2
5	17.5	17.0	16.5
6	21.0	20.4	19.8
7	24.5	23.8	23.1
8	28.0	27.2	26.4
9	31.5	30.6	29.7
	32	**31**	**30**
1	3.2	3.1	3.0
2	6.4	6.2	6.0
3	9.6	9.3	9.0
4	12.8	12.4	12.0
5	16.0	15.5	15.0
6	19.2	18.6	18.0
7	22.4	21.7	21.0
8	25.6	24.8	24.0
9	28.8	27.9	27.0

Proportional Parts

FIVE-PLACE LOGARITHMS

N.	0	1	2	3	4	5	6	7	8	9	Proportional parts		
150	17 609	638	667	696	725	754	782	811	840	869		**29**	**28**
151	898	926	955	984	*013	*041	*070	*099	*127	*156	1	2.9	2.8
152	18 184	213	241	270	298	327	355	384	412	441	2	5.8	5.6
153	469	498	526	554	583	611	639	667	696	724	3	8.7	8.4
154	752	780	808	837	865	893	921	949	977	*005	4	11.6	11.2
155	19 033	061	089	117	145	173	201	229	257	285	5	14.5	14.0
156	312	340	368	396	424	451	479	507	535	562	6	17.4	16.8
157	590	618	645	673	700	728	756	783	811	838	7	20.3	19.6
158	866	893	921	948	976	*003	*030	*058	*085	*112	8	23.2	22.4
159	20 140	167	194	222	249	276	303	330	358	385	9	26.1	25.2
160	412	439	466	493	520	548	575	602	629	656		**27**	**26**
161	683	710	737	763	790	817	844	871	898	925	1	2.7	2.6
162	952	978	*005	*032	*059	*085	*112	*139	*165	*192	2	5.4	5.2
163	21 219	245	272	299	325	352	378	405	431	458	3	8.1	7.8
164	484	511	537	564	590	617	643	669	696	722	4	10.8	10.4
165	748	775	801	827	854	880	906	932	958	985	5	13.5	13.0
166	22 011	037	063	089	115	141	167	194	220	246	6	16.2	15.6
167	272	298	324	350	376	401	427	453	479	505	7	18.9	18.2
168	531	557	583	608	634	660	686	712	737	763	8	21.6	20.8
169	789	814	840	866	891	917	943	968	994	*019	9	24.3	23.4
170	23 045	070	096	121	147	172	198	223	249	274		**25**	
171	300	325	350	376	401	426	452	477	502	528	1	2.5	
172	553	578	603	629	654	679	704	729	754	779	2	5.0	
173	805	830	855	880	905	930	955	980	*005	*030	3	7.5	
174	24 055	080	105	130	155	180	204	229	254	279	4	10.0	
175	304	329	353	378	403	428	452	477	502	527	5	12.5	
176	551	576	601	625	650	674	699	724	748	773	6	15.0	
177	797	822	846	871	895	920	944	969	993	*018	7	17.5	
178	25 042	066	091	115	139	164	188	212	237	261	8	20.0	
179	285	310	334	358	382	406	431	455	479	503	9	22.5	
180	527	551	575	600	624	648	672	696	720	744		**24**	**23**
181	768	792	816	840	864	888	912	935	959	983	1	2.4	2.3
182	26 007	031	055	079	102	126	150	174	198	221	2	4.8	4.6
183	245	269	293	316	340	364	387	411	435	458	3	7.2	6.9
184	482	505	529	553	576	600	623	647	670	694	4	9.6	9.2
185	717	741	764	788	811	834	858	881	905	928	5	12.0	11.5
186	951	975	998	*021	*045	*068	*091	*114	*138	*161	6	14.4	13.8
187	27 184	207	231	254	277	300	323	346	370	393	7	16.8	16.1
188	416	439	462	485	508	531	554	577	600	623	8	19.2	18.4
189	646	669	692	715	738	761	784	807	830	852	9	21.6	20.7
190	875	898	921	944	967	989	*012	*035	*058	*081		**22**	**21**
191	28 103	126	149	171	194	217	240	262	285	307	1	2.2	2.1
192	330	353	375	398	421	443	466	488	511	533	2	4.4	4.2
193	556	578	601	623	646	668	691	713	735	758	3	6.6	6.3
194	780	803	825	847	870	892	914	937	959	981	4	8.8	8.4
195	29 003	026	048	070	092	115	137	159	181	203	5	11.0	10.5
196	226	248	270	292	314	336	358	380	403	425	6	13.2	12.6
197	447	469	491	513	535	557	579	601	623	645	7	15.4	14.7
198	667	688	710	732	754	776	798	820	842	863	8	17.6	16.8
199	885	907	929	951	973	994	*016	*038	*060	*081	9	19.8	18.9
200	30 103	125	146	168	190	211	233	255	276	298			
N.	0	1	2	3	4	5	6	7	8	9	Proportional parts		

N.	0	1	2	3	4	5	6	7	8	9
200	30 103	125	146	168	190	211	233	255	276	298
201	320	341	363	384	406	428	449	471	492	514
202	535	557	578	600	621	643	664	685	707	728
203	750	771	792	814	835	856	878	899	920	942
204	963	984	*006	*027	*048	*069	*091	*112	*133	*154
205	31 175	197	218	239	260	281	302	323	345	366
206	387	408	429	450	471	492	513	534	555	576
207	597	618	639	660	681	702	723	744	765	785
208	806	827	848	869	890	911	931	952	973	994
209	32 015	035	056	077	098	118	139	160	181	201
210	222	243	263	284	305	325	346	366	387	408
211	428	449	469	490	510	531	552	572	593	613
212	634	654	675	695	715	736	756	777	797	818
213	838	858	879	899	919	940	960	980	*001	*021
214	33 041	062	082	102	122	143	163	183	203	224
215	244	264	284	304	325	345	365	385	405	425
216	445	465	486	506	526	546	566	586	606	626
217	646	666	686	706	726	746	766	786	806	826
218	846	866	885	905	925	945	965	985	*005	*025
219	34 044	064	084	104	124	143	163	183	203	223
220	242	262	282	301	321	341	361	380	400	420
221	439	459	479	498	518	537	557	577	596	616
222	635	655	674	694	713	733	753	772	792	811
223	830	850	869	889	908	928	947	967	986	*005
224	35 025	044	064	083	102	122	141	160	180	199
225	218	238	257	276	295	315	334	353	372	392
226	411	430	449	468	488	507	526	545	564	583
227	603	622	641	660	679	698	717	736	755	774
228	793	813	832	851	870	889	908	927	946	965
229	984	*003	*021	*040	*059	*078	*097	*116	*135	*154
230	36 173	192	211	229	248	267	286	305	324	342
231	361	380	399	418	436	455	474	493	511	530
232	549	568	586	605	624	642	661	680	698	717
233	736	754	773	791	810	829	847	866	884	903
234	922	940	959	977	996	*014	*033	*051	*070	*088
235	37 107	125	144	162	181	199	218	236	254	273
236	291	310	328	346	365	383	401	420	438	457
237	475	493	511	530	548	566	585	603	621	639
238	658	676	694	712	731	749	767	785	803	822
239	840	858	876	894	912	931	949	967	985	*003
240	38 021	039	057	075	093	112	130	148	166	184
241	202	220	238	256	274	292	310	328	346	364
242	382	399	417	435	453	471	489	507	525	543
243	561	578	596	614	632	650	668	686	703	721
244	739	757	775	792	810	828	846	863	881	899
245	917	934	952	970	987	*005	*023	*041	*058	*076
246	39 094	111	129	146	164	182	199	217	235	252
247	270	287	305	322	340	358	375	393	410	428
248	445	463	480	498	515	533	550	568	585	602
249	620	637	655	672	690	707	724	742	759	777
250	794	811	829	846	863	881	898	915	933	950
N.	0	1	2	3	4	5	6	7	8	9

Proportional parts

	22	**21**	**20**	**19**	**18**	**17**
1	2.2	2.1	2.0	1.9	1.8	1.7
2	4.4	4.2	4.0	3.8	3.6	3.4
3	6.6	6.3	6.0	5.7	5.4	5.1
4	8.8	8.4	8.0	7.6	7.2	6.8
5	11.0	10.5	10.0	9.5	9.0	8.5
6	13.2	12.6	12.0	11.4	10.8	10.2
7	15.4	14.7	14.0	13.3	12.6	11.9
8	17.6	16.8	16.0	15.2	14.4	13.6
9	19.8	18.9	18.0	17.1	16.2	15.3

N.	0	1	2	3	4	5	6	7	8	9	Proportional parts
250	39 794	811	829	846	863	881	898	915	933	950	**18**
251	967	985	*002	*019	*037	*054	*071	*088	*106	*123	1 | 1.8
252	40 140	157	175	192	209	226	243	261	278	295	2 | 3.6
253	312	329	346	364	381	398	415	432	449	466	3 | 5.4
254	483	500	518	535	552	569	586	603	620	637	4 | 7.2
255	654	671	688	705	722	739	756	773	790	807	5 | 9.0
256	824	841	858	875	892	909	926	943	960	976	6 | 10.8
257	993	*010	*027	*044	*061	*078	*095	*111	*128	*145	7 | 12.6
258	41 162	179	196	212	229	246	263	280	296	313	8 | 14.4
259	330	347	363	380	397	414	430	447	464	481	9 | 16.2
260	497	514	531	547	564	581	597	614	631	647	**17**
261	664	681	697	714	731	747	764	780	797	814	1 | 1.7
262	830	847	863	880	896	913	929	946	963	979	2 | 3.4
263	996	*012	*029	*045	*062	*078	*095	*111	*127	*144	3 | 5.1
264	42 160	177	193	210	226	243	259	275	292	308	4 | 6.8
265	325	341	357	374	390	406	423	439	455	472	5 | 8.5
266	488	504	521	537	553	570	586	602	619	635	6 | 10.2
267	651	667	684	700	716	732	749	765	781	797	7 | 11.9
268	813	830	846	862	878	894	911	927	943	959	8 | 13.6
269	975	991	*008	*024	*040	*056	*072	*088	*104	*120	9 | 15.3
270	43 136	152	169	185	201	217	233	249	265	281	**16**
271	297	313	329	345	361	377	393	409	425	441	1 | 1.6
272	457	473	489	505	521	537	553	569	584	600	2 | 3.2
273	616	632	648	664	680	696	712	727	743	759	3 | 4.8
274	775	791	807	823	838	854	870	886	902	917	4 | 6.4
275	933	949	965	981	996	*012	*028	*044	*059	*075	5 | 8.0
276	44 091	107	122	138	154	170	185	201	217	232	6 | 9.6
277	248	264	279	295	311	326	342	358	373	389	7 | 11.2
278	404	420	436	451	467	483	498	514	529	545	8 | 12.8
279	560	576	592	607	623	638	654	669	685	700	9 | 14.4
280	716	731	747	762	778	793	809	824	840	855	**15**
281	871	886	902	917	932	948	963	979	994	*010	1 | 1.5
282	45 025	040	056	071	086	102	117	133	148	163	2 | 3.0
283	179	194	209	225	240	255	271	286	301	317	3 | 4.5
284	332	347	362	378	393	408	423	439	454	469	4 | 6.0
285	484	500	515	530	545	561	576	591	606	621	5 | 7.5
286	637	652	667	682	697	712	728	743	758	773	6 | 9.0
287	788	803	818	834	849	864	879	894	909	924	7 | 10.5
288	939	954	969	984	*000	*015	*030	*045	*060	*075	8 | 12.0
289	46 090	105	120	135	150	165	180	195	210	225	9 | 13.5
290	240	255	270	285	300	315	330	345	359	374	**14**
291	389	404	419	434	449	464	479	494	509	523	1 | 1.4
292	538	553	568	583	598	613	627	642	657	672	2 | 2.8
293	687	702	716	731	746	761	776	790	805	820	3 | 4.2
294	835	850	864	879	894	909	923	938	953	967	4 | 5.6
295	982	997	*012	*026	*041	*056	*070	*085	*100	*114	5 | 7.0
296	47 129	144	159	173	188	202	217	232	246	261	6 | 8.4
297	276	290	305	319	334	349	363	378	392	407	7 | 9.8
298	422	436	451	465	480	494	509	524	538	553	8 | 11.2
299	567	582	596	611	625	640	654	669	683	698	9 | 12.6
300	712	727	741	756	770	784	799	813	828	842	
N.	0	1	2	3	4	5	6	7	8	9	Proportional parts

N.	0	1	2	3	4	5	6	7	8	9
300	47 712	727	741	756	770	784	799	813	828	842
301	857	871	885	900	914	929	943	958	972	986
302	48 001	015	029	044	058	073	087	101	116	130
303	144	159	173	187	202	216	230	244	259	273
304	287	302	316	330	344	359	373	387	401	416
305	430	444	458	473	487	501	515	530	544	558
306	572	586	601	615	629	643	657	671	686	700
307	714	728	742	756	770	785	799	813	827	841
308	855	869	883	897	911	926	940	954	968	982
309	996	*010	*024	*038	*052	*066	*080	*094	*108	*122
310	49 136	150	164	178	192	206	220	234	248	262
311	276	290	304	318	332	346	360	374	388	402
312	415	429	443	457	471	485	499	513	527	541
313	554	568	582	596	610	624	638	651	665	679
314	693	707	721	734	748	762	776	790	803	817
315	831	845	859	872	886	900	914	927	941	955
316	969	982	996	*010	*024	*037	*051	*065	*079	*092
317	50 106	120	133	147	161	174	188	202	215	229
318	243	256	270	284	297	311	325	338	352	365
319	379	393	406	420	433	447	461	474	488	501
320	515	529	542	556	569	583	596	610	623	637
321	651	664	678	691	705	718	732	745	759	772
322	786	799	813	826	840	853	866	880	893	907
323	920	934	947	961	974	987	*001	*014	*028	*041
324	51 055	068	081	095	108	121	135	148	162	175
325	188	202	215	228	242	255	268	282	295	308
326	322	335	348	362	375	388	402	415	428	441
327	455	468	481	495	508	521	534	548	561	574
328	587	601	614	627	640	654	667	680	693	706
329	720	733	746	759	772	786	799	812	825	838
330	851	865	878	891	904	917	930	943	957	970
331	983	996	*009	*022	*035	*048	*061	*075	*088	*101
332	52 114	127	140	153	166	179	192	205	218	231
333	244	257	270	284	297	310	323	336	349	362
334	375	388	401	414	427	440	453	466	479	492
335	504	517	530	543	556	569	582	595	608	621
336	634	647	660	673	686	699	711	724	737	750
337	763	776	789	802	815	827	840	853	866	879
338	892	905	917	930	943	956	969	982	994	*007
339	53 020	033	046	058	071	084	097	110	122	135
340	148	161	173	186	199	212	224	237	250	263
341	275	288	301	314	326	339	352	364	377	390
342	403	415	428	441	453	466	479	491	504	517
343	529	542	555	567	580	593	605	618	631	643
344	656	668	681	694	706	719	732	744	757	769
345	782	794	807	820	832	845	857	870	882	895
346	908	920	933	945	958	970	983	995	*008	*020
347	54 033	045	058	070	083	095	108	120	133	145
348	158	170	183	195	208	220	233	245	258	270
349	283	295	307	320	332	345	357	370	382	394
350	407	419	432	444	456	469	481	494	506	518
N.	0	1	2	3	4	5	6	7	8	9

Proportional parts

	15	**14**	**13**	**12**
1	1.5	1.4	1.3	1.2
2	3.0	2.8	2.6	2.4
3	4.5	4.2	3.9	3.6
4	6.0	5.6	5.2	4.8
5	7.5	7.0	6.5	6.0
6	9.0	8.4	7.8	7.2
7	10.5	9.8	9.1	8.4
8	12.0	11.2	10.4	9.6
9	13.5	12.6	11.7	10.8

N.	0	1	2	3	4	5	6	7	8	9
350	54 407	419	432	444	456	469	481	494	506	518
351	531	543	555	568	580	593	605	617	630	642
352	654	667	679	691	704	716	728	741	753	765
353	777	790	802	814	827	839	851	864	876	888
354	900	913	925	937	949	962	974	986	998	*011
355	55 023	035	047	060	072	084	096	108	121	133
356	145	157	169	182	194	206	218	230	242	255
357	267	279	291	303	315	328	340	352	364	376
358	388	400	413	425	437	449	461	473	485	497
359	509	522	534	546	558	570	582	594	606	618
360	630	642	654	666	678	691	703	715	727	739
361	751	763	775	787	799	811	823	835	847	859
362	871	883	895	907	919	931	943	955	967	979
363	991	*003	*015	*027	*038	*050	*062	*074	*086	*098
364	56 110	122	134	146	158	170	182	194	205	217
365	229	241	253	265	277	289	301	312	324	336
366	348	360	372	384	396	407	419	431	443	455
367	467	478	490	502	514	526	538	549	561	573
368	585	597	608	620	632	644	656	667	679	691
369	703	714	726	738	750	761	773	785	797	808
370	820	832	844	855	867	879	891	902	914	926
371	937	949	961	972	984	996	*008	*019	*031	*043
372	57 054	066	078	089	101	113	124	136	148	159
373	171	183	194	206	217	229	241	252	264	276
374	287	299	310	322	334	345	357	368	380	392
375	403	415	426	438	449	461	473	484	496	507
376	519	530	542	553	565	576	588	600	611	623
377	634	646	657	669	680	692	703	715	726	738
378	749	761	772	784	795	807	818	830	841	852
379	864	875	887	898	910	921	933	944	955	967
380	978	990	*001	*013	*024	*035	*047	*058	*070	*081
381	58 092	104	115	127	138	149	161	172	184	195
382	206	218	229	240	252	263	274	286	297	309
383	320	331	343	354	365	377	388	399	410	422
384	433	444	456	467	478	490	501	512	524	535
385	546	557	569	580	591	602	614	625	636	647
386	659	670	681	692	704	715	726	737	749	760
387	771	782	794	805	816	827	838	850	861	872
388	883	894	906	917	928	939	950	961	973	984
389	995	*006	*017	*028	*040	*051	*062	*073	*084	*095
390	59 106	118	129	140	151	162	173	184	195	207
391	218	229	240	251	262	273	284	295	306	318
392	329	340	351	362	373	384	395	406	417	428
393	439	450	461	472	483	494	506	517	528	539
394	550	561	572	583	594	605	616	627	638	649
395	660	671	682	693	704	715	726	737	748	759
396	770	780	791	802	813	824	835	846	857	868
397	879	890	901	912	923	934	945	956	966	977
398	988	999	*010	*021	*032	*043	*054	*065	*076	*086
399	60 097	108	119	130	141	152	163	173	184	195
400	206	217	228	239	249	260	271	282	293	304
N.	0	1	2	3	4	5	6	7	8	9

Proportional parts

	13	**12**	**11**	**10**
1	1.3	1.2	1.1	1.0
2	2.6	2.4	2.2	2.0
3	3.9	3.6	3.3	3.0
4	5.2	4.8	4.4	4.0
5	6.5	6.0	5.5	5.0
6	7.8	7.2	6.6	6.0
7	9.1	8.4	7.7	7.0
8	10.4	9.6	8.8	8.0
9	11.7	10.8	9.9	9.0

N.	0	1	2	3	4	5	6	7	8	9
400	60 206	217	228	239	249	260	271	282	293	304
401	314	325	336	347	358	369	379	390	401	412
402	423	433	444	455	466	477	487	498	509	520
403	531	541	552	563	574	584	595	606	617	627
404	638	649	660	670	681	692	703	713	724	735
405	746	756	767	778	788	799	810	821	831	842
406	853	863	874	885	895	906	917	927	938	949
407	959	970	981	991	*002	*013	*023	*034	*045	*055
408	61 066	077	087	098	109	119	130	140	151	162
409	172	183	194	204	215	225	236	247	257	268
410	278	289	300	310	321	331	342	352	363	374
411	384	395	405	416	426	437	448	458	469	479
412	490	500	511	521	532	542	553	563	574	584
413	595	606	616	627	637	648	658	669	679	690
414	700	711	721	731	742	752	763	773	784	794
415	805	815	826	836	847	857	868	878	888	899
416	909	920	930	941	951	962	972	982	993	*003
417	62 014	024	034	045	055	066	076	086	097	107
418	118	128	138	149	159	170	180	190	201	211
419	221	232	242	252	263	273	284	294	304	315
420	325	335	346	356	366	377	387	397	408	418
421	428	439	449	459	469	480	490	500	511	521
422	531	542	552	562	572	583	593	603	613	624
423	634	644	655	665	675	685	696	706	716	726
424	737	747	757	767	778	788	798	808	818	829
425	839	849	859	870	880	890	900	910	921	931
426	941	951	961	972	982	992	*002	*012	*022	*033
427	63 043	053	063	073	083	094	104	114	124	134
428	144	155	165	175	185	195	205	215	225	236
429	246	256	266	276	286	296	306	317	327	337
430	347	357	367	377	387	397	407	417	428	438
431	448	458	468	478	488	498	508	518	528	538
432	548	558	568	579	589	599	609	619	629	639
433	649	659	669	679	689	699	709	719	729	739
434	749	759	769	779	789	799	809	819	829	839
435	849	859	869	879	889	899	909	919	929	939
436	949	959	969	979	988	998	*008	*018	*028	*038
437	64 048	058	068	078	088	098	108	118	128	137
438	147	157	167	177	187	197	207	217	227	237
439	246	256	266	276	286	296	306	316	326	335
440	345	355	365	375	385	395	404	414	424	434
441	444	454	464	473	483	493	503	513	523	532
442	542	552	562	572	582	591	601	611	621	631
443	640	650	660	670	680	689	699	709	719	729
444	738	748	758	768	777	787	797	807	816	826
445	836	846	856	865	875	885	895	904	914	924
446	933	943	953	963	972	982	992	*002	*011	*021
447	65 031	040	050	060	070	079	089	099	108	118
448	128	137	147	157	167	176	186	196	205	215
449	225	234	244	254	263	273	283	292	302	312
450	321	331	341	350	360	369	379	389	398	408
N.	0	1	2	3	4	5	6	7	8	9

Proportional parts

	11
1	1.1
2	2.2
3	3.3
4	4.4
5	5.5
6	6.6
7	7.7
8	8.8
9	9.9

	10
1	1.0
2	2.0
3	3.0
4	4.0
5	5.0
6	6.0
7	7.0
8	8.0
9	9.0

	9
1	0.9
2	1.8
3	2.7
4	3.6
5	4.5
6	5.4
7	6.3
8	7.2
9	8.1

Proportional parts

N.	0	1	2	3	4	5	6	7	8	9
450	65 321	331	341	350	360	369	379	389	398	408
451	418	427	437	447	456	466	475	485	495	504
452	514	523	533	543	552	562	571	581	591	600
453	610	619	629	639	648	658	667	677	686	696
454	706	715	725	734	744	753	763	772	782	792
455	801	811	820	830	839	849	858	868	877	887
456	896	906	916	925	935	944	954	963	973	982
457	992	*001	*011	*020	*030	*039	*049	*058	*068	*077
458	66 087	096	106	115	124	134	143	153	162	172
459	181	191	200	210	219	229	238	247	257	266
460	276	285	295	304	314	323	332	342	351	361
461	370	380	389	398	408	417	427	436	445	455
462	464	474	483	492	502	511	521	530	539	549
463	558	567	577	586	596	605	614	624	633	642
464	652	661	671	680	689	699	708	717	727	736
465	745	755	764	773	783	792	801	811	820	829
466	839	848	857	867	876	885	894	904	913	922
467	932	941	950	960	969	978	987	997	*006	*015
468	67 025	034	043	052	062	071	080	089	099	108
469	117	127	136	145	154	164	173	182	191	201
470	210	219	228	237	247	256	265	274	284	293
471	302	311	321	330	339	348	357	367	376	385
472	394	403	413	422	431	440	449	459	468	477
473	486	495	504	514	523	532	541	550	560	569
474	578	587	596	605	614	624	633	642	651	660
475	669	679	688	697	706	715	724	733	742	752
476	761	770	779	788	797	806	815	825	834	843
477	852	861	870	879	888	897	906	916	925	934
478	943	952	961	970	979	988	997	*006	*015	*024
479	68 034	043	052	061	070	079	088	097	106	115
480	124	133	142	151	160	169	178	187	196	205
481	215	224	233	242	251	260	269	278	287	296
482	305	314	323	332	341	350	359	368	377	386
483	395	404	413	422	431	440	449	458	467	476
484	485	494	502	511	520	529	538	547	556	565
485	574	583	592	601	610	619	628	637	646	655
486	664	673	681	690	699	708	717	726	735	744
487	753	762	771	780	789	797	806	815	824	833
488	842	851	860	869	878	886	895	904	913	922
489	931	940	949	958	966	975	984	993	*002	*011
490	69 020	028	037	046	055	064	073	082	090	099
491	108	117	126	135	144	152	161	170	179	188
492	197	205	214	223	232	241	249	258	267	276
493	285	294	302	311	320	329	338	346	355	364
494	373	381	390	399	408	417	425	434	443	452
495	461	469	478	487	496	504	513	522	531	539
496	548	557	566	574	583	592	601	609	618	627
497	636	644	653	662	671	679	688	697	705	714
498	723	732	740	749	758	767	775	784	793	801
499	810	819	827	836	845	854	862	871	880	888
500	897	906	914	923	932	940	949	958	966	975
N.	0	1	2	3	4	5	6	7	8	9

Proportional parts

	10	**9**	**8**
1	1.0	0.9	0.8
2	2.0	1.8	1.6
3	3.0	2.7	2.4
4	4.0	3.6	3.2
5	5.0	4.5	4.0
6	6.0	5.4	4.8
7	7.0	6.3	5.6
8	8.0	7.2	6.4
9	9.0	8.1	7.2

N.	0	1	2	3	4	5	6	7	8	9
500	69 897	906	914	923	932	940	949	958	966	975
501	984	992	*001	*010	*018	*027	*036	*044	*053	*062
502	70 070	079	088	096	105	114	122	131	140	148
503	157	165	174	183	191	200	209	217	226	234
504	243	252	260	269	278	286	295	303	312	321
505	329	338	346	355	364	372	381	389	398	406
506	415	424	432	441	449	458	467	475	484	492
507	501	509	518	526	535	544	552	561	569	578
508	586	595	603	612	621	629	638	646	655	663
509	672	680	689	697	706	714	723	731	740	749
510	757	766	774	783	791	800	808	817	825	834
511	842	851	859	868	876	885	893	902	910	919
512	927	935	944	952	961	969	978	986	995	*003
513	71 012	020	029	037	046	054	063	071	079	088
514	096	105	113	122	130	139	147	155	164	172
515	181	189	198	206	214	223	231	240	248	257
516	265	273	282	290	299	307	315	324	332	341
517	349	357	366	374	383	391	399	408	416	425
518	433	441	450	458	466	475	483	492	500	508
519	517	525	533	542	550	559	567	575	584	592
520	600	609	617	625	634	642	650	659	667	675
521	684	692	700	709	717	725	734	742	750	759
522	767	775	784	792	800	809	817	825	834	842
523	850	858	867	875	883	892	900	908	917	925
524	933	941	950	958	966	975	983	991	999	*008
525	72 016	024	032	041	049	057	066	074	082	090
526	099	107	115	123	132	140	148	156	165	173
527	181	189	198	206	214	222	230	239	247	255
528	263	272	280	288	296	304	313	321	329	337
529	346	354	362	370	378	387	395	403	411	419
530	428	436	444	452	460	469	477	485	493	501
531	509	518	526	534	542	550	558	567	575	583
532	591	599	607	616	624	632	640	648	656	665
533	673	681	689	697	705	713	722	730	738	746
534	754	762	770	779	787	795	803	811	819	827
535	835	843	852	860	868	876	884	892	900	908
536	916	925	933	941	949	957	965	973	981	989
537	997	*006	*014	*022	*030	*038	*046	*054	*062	*070
538	73 078	086	094	102	111	119	127	135	143	151
539	159	167	175	183	191	199	207	215	223	231
540	239	247	255	263	272	280	288	296	304	312
541	320	328	336	344	352	360	368	376	384	392
542	400	408	416	424	432	440	448	456	464	472
543	480	488	496	504	512	520	528	536	544	552
544	560	568	576	584	592	600	608	616	624	632
545	640	648	656	664	672	679	687	695	703	711
546	719	727	735	743	751	759	767	775	783	791
547	799	807	815	823	830	838	846	854	862	870
548	878	886	894	902	910	918	926	933	941	949
549	957	965	973	981	989	997	*005	*013	*020	*028
550	74 036	044	052	060	068	076	084	092	099	107
N.	0	1	2	3	4	5	6	7	8	9

Proportional parts

	9
1	0.9
2	1.8
3	2.7
4	3.6
5	4.5
6	5.4
7	6.3
8	7.2
9	8.1

	8
1	0.8
2	1.6
3	2.4
4	3.2
5	4.0
6	4.8
7	5.6
8	6.4
9	7.2

	7
1	0.7
2	1.4
3	2.1
4	2.8
5	3.5
6	4.2
7	4.9
8	5.6
9	6.3

Proportional parts

N.	0	1	2	3	4	5	6	7	8	9	Proportional parts
550	74 036	044	052	060	068	076	084	092	099	107	
551	115	123	131	139	147	155	162	170	178	186	
552	194	202	210	218	225	233	241	249	257	265	
553	273	280	288	296	304	312	320	327	335	343	
554	351	359	367	374	382	390	398	406	414	421	
555	429	437	445	453	461	468	476	484	492	500	
556	507	515	523	531	539	547	554	562	570	578	
557	586	593	601	609	617	624	632	640	648	656	
558	663	671	679	687	695	702	710	718	726	733	
559	741	749	757	764	772	780	788	796	803	811	
560	819	827	834	842	850	858	865	873	881	889	**8**
561	896	904	912	920	927	935	943	950	958	966	1 **0.8**
562	974	981	989	997	*005	*012	*020	*028	*035	*043	2 **1.6**
563	75 051	059	066	074	082	089	097	105	113	120	3 **2.4**
564	128	136	143	151	159	166	174	182	189	197	4 **3.2**
565	205	213	220	228	236	243	251	259	266	274	5 **4.0**
566	282	289	297	305	312	320	328	335	343	351	6 **4.8**
567	358	366	374	381	389	397	404	412	420	427	7 **5.6**
568	435	442	450	458	465	473	481	488	496	504	8 **6.4**
569	511	519	526	534	542	549	557	565	572	580	9 **7.2**
570	587	595	603	610	618	626	633	641	648	656	
571	664	671	679	686	694	702	709	717	724	732	
572	740	747	755	762	770	778	785	793	800	808	
573	815	823	831	838	846	853	361	868	876	884	
574	891	899	906	914	921	929	937	944	952	959	
575	967	974	982	989	997	*005	*012	*020	*027	*035	
576	76 042	050	057	065	072	080	087	095	103	110	
577	118	125	133	140	148	155	163	170	178	185	
578	193	200	208	215	223	230	238	245	253	260	
579	268	275	283	290	298	305	313	320	328	335	
580	343	350	358	365	373	380	388	395	403	410	**7**
581	418	425	433	440	448	455	462	470	477	485	1 **0.7**
582	492	500	507	515	522	530	537	545	552	559	2 **1.4**
583	567	574	582	589	597	604	612	619	626	634	3 **2.1**
584	641	649	656	664	671	678	686	693	701	708	4 **2.8**
585	716	723	730	738	745	753	760	768	775	782	5 **3.5**
586	790	797	805	812	819	827	834	842	849	856	6 **4.2**
587	864	871	879	886	893	901	908	916	923	930	7 **4.9**
588	938	945	953	960	967	975	982	989	997	*004	8 **5.6**
589	77 012	019	026	034	041	048	056	063	070	078	9 **6.3**
590	085	093	100	107	115	122	129	137	144	151	
591	159	166	173	181	188	195	203	210	217	225	
592	232	240	247	254	262	269	276	283	291	298	
593	305	313	320	327	335	342	349	357	364	371	
594	379	386	393	401	408	415	422	430	437	444	
595	452	459	466	474	481	488	495	503	510	517	
596	525	532	539	546	554	561	568	576	583	590	
597	597	605	612	619	627	634	641	648	656	663	
598	670	677	685	692	699	706	714	721	728	735	
599	743	750	757	764	772	779	786	793	801	808	
600	815	822	830	837	844	851	859	866	873	880	
N.	0	1	2	3	4	5	6	7	8	9	Proportional parts

N.	0	1	2	3	4	5	6	7	8	9
600	77 815	822	830	837	844	851	859	866	873	880
601	887	895	902	909	916	924	931	938	945	952
602	960	967	974	981	988	996	*003	*010	*017	*025
603	78 032	039	046	053	061	068	075	082	089	097
604	104	111	118	125	132	140	147	154	161	168
605	176	183	190	197	204	211	219	226	233	240
606	247	254	262	269	276	283	290	297	305	312
607	319	326	333	340	347	355	362	369	376	383
608	390	398	405	412	419	426	433	440	447	455
609	462	469	476	483	490	497	504	512	519	526
610	533	540	547	554	561	569	576	583	590	597
611	604	611	618	625	633	640	647	654	661	668
612	675	682	689	696	704	711	718	725	732	739
613	746	753	760	767	774	781	789	796	803	810
614	817	824	831	838	845	852	859	866	873	880
615	888	895	902	909	916	923	930	937	944	951
616	958	965	972	979	986	993	*000	*007	*014	*021
617	79 029	036	043	050	057	064	071	078	085	092
618	099	106	113	120	127	134	141	148	155	162
619	169	176	183	190	197	204	211	218	225	232
620	239	246	253	260	267	274	281	288	295	302
621	309	316	323	330	337	344	351	358	365	372
622	379	386	393	400	407	414	421	428	435	442
623	449	456	463	470	477	484	491	498	505	511
624	518	525	532	539	546	553	560	567	574	581
625	588	595	602	609	616	623	630	637	644	650
626	657	664	671	678	685	692	699	706	713	720
627	727	734	741	748	754	761	768	775	782	789
628	796	803	810	817	824	831	837	844	851	858
629	865	872	879	886	893	900	906	913	920	927
630	934	941	948	955	962	969	975	982	989	996
631	80 003	010	017	024	030	037	044	051	058	065
632	072	079	085	092	099	106	113	120	127	134
633	140	147	154	161	168	175	182	188	195	202
634	209	216	223	229	236	243	250	257	264	271
635	277	284	291	298	305	312	318	325	332	339
636	346	353	359	366	373	380	387	393	400	407
637	414	421	428	434	441	448	455	462	468	475
638	482	489	496	502	509	516	523	530	536	543
639	550	557	564	570	577	584	591	598	604	611
640	618	625	632	638	645	652	659	665	672	679
641	686	693	699	706	713	720	726	733	740	747
642	754	760	767	774	781	787	794	801	808	814
643	821	828	835	841	848	855	862	868	875	882
644	889	895	902	909	916	922	929	936	943	949
645	956	963	969	976	983	990	996	*003	*010	*017
646	81 023	030	037	043	050	057	064	070	077	084
647	090	097	104	111	117	124	131	137	144	151
648	158	164	171	178	184	191	198	204	211	218
649	224	231	238	245	251	258	265	271	278	285
650	291	298	305	311	318	325	331	338	345	351
N.	0	1	2	3	4	5	6	7	8	9

Proportional parts

	8
1	0.8
2	1.6
3	2.4
4	3.2
5	4.0
6	4.8
7	5.6
8	6.4
9	7.2

	7
1	0.7
2	1.4
3	2.1
4	2.8
5	3.5
6	4.2
7	4.9
8	5.6
9	6.3

	6
1	0.6
2	1.2
3	1.8
4	2.4
5	3.0
6	3.6
7	4.2
8	4.8
9	5.4

N.	0	1	2	3	4	5	6	7	8	9
650	81 291	298	305	311	318	325	331	338	345	351
651	358	365	371	378	385	391	398	405	411	418
652	425	431	438	445	451	458	465	471	478	485
653	491	498	505	511	518	525	531	538	544	551
654	558	564	571	578	584	591	598	604	611	617
655	624	631	637	644	651	657	664	671	677	684
656	690	697	704	710	717	723	730	737	743	750
657	757	763	770	776	783	790	796	803	809	816
658	823	829	836	842	849	856	862	869	875	882
659	889	895	902	908	915	921	928	935	941	948
660	954	961	968	974	981	987	994	*000	*007	*014
661	82 020	027	033	040	046	053	060	066	073	079
662	086	092	099	105	112	119	125	132	138	145
663	151	158	164	171	178	184	191	197	204	210
664	217	223	230	236	243	249	256	263	269	276
665	282	289	295	302	308	315	321	328	334	341
666	347	354	360	367	373	380	387	393	400	406
667	413	419	426	432	439	445	452	458	465	471
668	478	484	491	497	504	510	517	523	530	536
669	543	549	556	562	569	575	582	588	595	601
670	607	614	620	627	633	640	646	653	659	666
671	672	679	685	692	698	705	711	718	724	730
672	737	743	750	756	763	769	776	782	789	795
673	802	808	814	821	827	834	840	847	853	860
674	866	872	879	885	892	898	905	911	918	924
675	930	937	943	950	956	963	969	975	982	988
676	995	*001	*008	*014	*020	*027	*033	*040	*046	*052
677	83 059	065	072	078	085	091	097	104	110	117
678	123	129	136	142	149	155	161	168	174	181
679	187	193	200	206	213	219	225	232	238	245
680	251	257	264	270	276	283	289	296	302	308
681	315	321	327	334	340	347	353	359	366	372
682	378	385	391	398	404	410	417	423	429	436
683	442	448	455	461	467	474	480	487	493	499
684	506	512	518	525	531	537	544	550	556	563
685	569	575	582	588	594	601	607	613	620	626
686	632	639	645	651	658	664	670	677	683	689
687	696	702	708	715	721	727	734	740	746	753
688	759	765	771	778	784	790	797	803	809	816
689	822	828	835	841	847	853	860	866	872	879
690	885	891	897	904	910	916	923	929	935	942
691	948	954	960	967	973	979	985	992	998	*004
692	84 011	017	023	029	036	042	048	055	061	067
693	073	080	086	092	098	105	111	117	123	130
694	136	142	148	155	161	167	173	180	186	192
695	198	205	211	217	223	230	236	242	248	255
696	261	267	273	280	286	292	298	305	311	317
697	323	330	336	342	348	354	361	367	373	379
698	386	392	398	404	410	417	423	429	435	442
699	448	454	460	466	473	479	485	491	497	504
700	510	516	522	528	535	541	547	553	559	566
N.	0	1	2	3	4	5	6	7	8	9

Proportional parts

	7
1	0.7
2	1.4
3	2.1
4	2.8
5	3.5
6	4.2
7	4.9
8	5.6
9	6.3

	6
1	0.6
2	1.2
3	1.8
4	2.4
5	3.0
6	3.6
7	4.2
8	4.8
9	5.4

N.	0	1	2	3	4	5	6	7	8	9
700	84 510	516	522	528	535	541	547	553	559	566
701	572	578	584	590	597	603	609	615	621	628
702	634	640	646	652	658	665	671	677	683	689
703	696	702	708	714	720	726	733	739	745	751
704	757	763	770	776	782	788	794	800	807	813
705	819	825	831	837	844	850	856	862	868	874
706	880	887	893	899	905	911	917	924	930	936
707	942	948	954	960	967	973	979	985	991	997
708	85 003	009	016	022	028	034	040	046	052	058
709	065	071	077	083	089	095	101	107	114	120
710	126	132	138	144	150	156	163	169	175	181
711	187	193	199	205	211	217	224	230	236	242
712	248	254	260	266	272	278	285	291	297	303
713	309	315	321	327	333	339	345	352	358	364
714	370	376	382	388	394	400	406	412	418	425
715	431	437	443	449	455	461	467	473	479	485
716	491	497	503	509	516	522	528	534	540	546
717	552	558	564	570	576	582	588	594	600	606
718	612	618	625	631	637	643	649	655	661	667
719	673	679	685	691	697	703	709	715	721	727
720	733	739	745	751	757	763	769	775	781	788
721	794	800	806	812	818	824	830	836	842	848
722	854	860	866	872	878	884	890	896	902	908
723	914	920	926	932	938	944	950	956	962	968
724	974	980	986	992	998	*004	*010	*016	*022	*028
725	86 034	040	046	052	058	064	070	076	082	088
726	094	100	106	112	118	124	130	136	141	147
727	153	159	165	171	177	183	189	195	201	207
728	213	219	225	231	237	243	249	255	261	267
729	273	279	285	291	297	303	308	314	320	326
730	332	338	344	350	356	362	368	374	380	386
731	392	398	404	410	415	421	427	433	439	445
732	451	457	463	469	475	481	487	493	499	504
733	510	516	522	528	534	540	546	552	558	564
734	570	576	581	587	593	599	605	611	617	623
735	629	635	641	646	652	658	664	670	676	682
736	688	694	700	705	711	717	723	729	735	741
737	747	753	759	764	770	776	782	788	794	800
738	806	812	817	823	829	835	841	847	853	859
739	864	870	876	882	888	894	900	906	911	917
740	923	929	935	941	947	953	958	964	970	976
741	982	988	994	999	*005	*011	*017	*023	*029	*035
742	87 040	046	052	058	064	070	075	081	087	093
743	099	105	111	116	122	128	134	140	146	151
744	157	163	169	175	181	186	192	198	204	210
745	216	221	227	233	239	245	251	256	262	268
746	274	280	286	291	297	303	309	315	320	326
747	332	338	344	349	355	361	367	373	379	384
748	390	396	402	408	413	419	425	431	437	442
749	448	454	460	466	471	477	483	489	495	500
750	506	512	518	523	529	535	541	547	552	558

N. 0 1 2 3 4 5 6 7 8 9

Proportional parts

	7
1	0.7
2	1.4
3	2.1
4	2.8
5	3.5
6	4.2
7	4.9
8	5.6
9	6.3

	6
1	0.6
2	1.2
3	1.8
4	2.4
5	3.0
6	3.6
7	4.2
8	4.8
9	5.4

	5
1	0.5
2	1.0
3	1.5
4	2.0
5	2.5
6	3.0
7	3.5
8	4.0
9	4.5

Proportional parts

N.	0	1	2	3	4	5	6	7	8	9
750	87 506	512	518	523	529	535	541	547	552	558
751	564	570	576	581	587	593	599	604	610	616
752	622	628	633	639	645	651	656	662	668	674
753	679	685	691	697	703	708	714	720	726	731
754	737	743	749	754	760	766	772	777	783	789
755	795	800	806	812	818	823	829	835	841	846
756	852	858	864	869	875	881	887	892	898	904
757	910	915	921	927	933	938	944	950	955	961
758	967	973	978	984	990	996	*001	*007	*013	*018
759	88 024	030	036	041	047	053	058	064	070	076
760	081	087	093	098	104	110	116	121	127	133
761	138	144	150	156	161	167	173	178	184	190
762	195	201	207	213	218	224	230	235	241	247
763	252	258	264	270	275	281	287	292	298	304
764	309	315	321	326	332	338	343	349	355	360
765	366	372	377	383	389	395	400	406	412	417
766	423	429	434	440	446	451	457	463	468	474
767	480	485	491	497	502	508	513	519	525	530
768	536	542	547	553	559	564	570	576	581	587
769	593	598	604	610	615	621	627	632	638	643
770	649	655	660	666	672	677	683	689	694	700
771	705	711	717	722	728	734	739	745	750	756
772	762	767	773	779	784	790	795	801	807	812
773	818	824	829	835	840	846	852	857	863	868
774	874	880	885	891	897	902	908	913	919	925
775	930	936	941	947	953	958	964	969	975	981
776	986	992	997	*003	*009	*014	*020	*025	*031	*037
777	89 042	048	053	059	064	070	076	081	087	092
778	098	104	109	115	120	126	131	137	143	148
779	154	159	165	170	176	182	187	193	198	204
780	209	215	221	226	232	237	243	248	254	260
781	265	271	276	282	287	293	298	304	310	315
782	321	326	332	337	343	348	354	360	365	371
783	376	382	387	393	398	404	409	415	421	426
784	432	437	443	448	454	459	465	470	476	481
785	487	492	498	504	509	515	520	526	531	537
786	542	548	553	559	564	570	575	581	586	592
787	597	603	609	614	620	625	631	636	642	647
788	653	658	664	669	675	680	686	691	697	702
789	708	713	719	724	730	735	741	746	752	757
790	763	768	774	779	785	790	796	801	807	812
791	818	823	829	834	840	845	851	856	862	867
792	873	878	883	889	894	900	905	911	916	922
793	927	933	938	944	949	955	960	966	971	977
794	982	988	993	998	*004	*009	*015	*020	*026	*031
795	90 037	042	048	053	059	064	069	075	080	086
796	091	097	102	108	113	119	124	129	135	140
797	146	151	157	162	168	173	179	184	189	195
798	200	206	211	217	222	227	233	238	244	249
799	255	260	266	271	276	282	287	293	298	304
800	309	314	320	325	331	336	342	347	352	358

| N. | 0 | 1 | 2 | 3 | 4 | 5 | 6 | 7 | 8 | 9 |

Proportional parts

	6
1	0.6
2	1.2
3	1.8
4	2.4
5	3.0
6	3.6
7	4.2
8	4.8
9	5.4

	5
1	0.5
2	1.0
3	1.5
4	2.0
5	2.5
6	3.0
7	3.5
8	4.0
9	4.5

N.	0	1	2	3	4	5	6	7	8	9	Proportional parts
800	90 309	314	320	325	331	336	342	347	352	358	
801	363	369	374	380	385	390	396	401	407	412	
802	417	423	428	434	439	445	450	455	461	466	
803	472	477	482	488	493	499	504	509	515	520	
804	526	531	536	542	547	553	558	563	569	574	
805	580	585	590	596	601	607	612	617	623	628	
806	634	639	644	650	655	660	666	671	677	682	
807	687	693	698	703	709	714	720	725	730	736	
808	741	747	752	757	763	768	773	779	784	789	
809	795	800	806	811	816	822	827	832	838	843	
810	849	854	859	865	870	875	881	886	891	897	**6**
811	902	907	913	918	924	929	934	940	945	950	1 | 0.6
812	956	961	966	972	977	982	988	993	998	*004	2 | 1.2
813	91 009	014	020	025	030	036	041	046	052	057	3 | 1.8
814	062	068	073	078	084	089	094	100	105	110	4 | 2.4
815	116	121	126	132	137	142	148	153	158	164	5 | 3.0
816	169	174	180	185	190	196	201	206	212	217	6 | 3.6
817	222	228	233	238	243	249	254	259	265	270	7 | 4.2
818	275	281	286	291	297	302	307	312	318	323	8 | 4.8
819	328	334	339	344	350	355	360	365	371	376	9 | 5.4
820	381	387	392	397	403	408	413	418	424	429	
821	434	440	445	450	455	461	466	471	477	482	
822	487	492	498	503	508	514	519	524	529	535	
823	540	545	551	556	561	566	572	577	582	587	
824	593	598	603	609	614	619	624	630	635	640	
825	645	651	656	661	666	672	677	682	687	693	
826	698	703	709	714	719	724	730	735	740	745	
827	751	756	761	766	772	777	782	787	793	798	
828	803	808	814	819	824	829	834	840	845	850	
829	855	861	866	871	876	882	887	892	897	903	
830	908	913	918	924	929	934	939	944	950	955	**5**
831	960	965	971	976	981	986	991	997	*002	*007	1 | 0.5
832	92 012	018	023	028	033	038	044	049	054	059	2 | 1.0
833	065	070	075	080	085	091	096	101	106	111	3 | 1.5
834	117	122	127	132	137	143	148	153	158	163	4 | 2.0
835	169	174	179	184	189	195	200	205	210	215	5 | 2.5
836	221	226	231	236	241	247	252	257	262	267	6 | 3.0
837	273	278	283	288	293	298	304	309	314	319	7 | 3.5
838	324	330	335	340	345	350	355	361	366	371	8 | 4.0
839	376	381	387	392	397	402	407	412	418	423	9 | 4.5
840	428	433	438	443	449	454	459	464	469	474	
841	480	485	490	495	500	505	511	516	521	526	
842	531	536	542	547	552	557	562	567	572	578	
843	583	588	593	598	603	609	614	619	624	629	
844	634	639	645	650	655	660	665	670	675	681	
845	686	691	696	701	706	711	716	722	727	732	
846	737	742	747	752	758	763	768	773	778	783	
847	788	793	799	804	809	814	819	824	829	834	
848	840	845	850	855	860	865	870	875	881	886	
849	891	896	901	906	911	916	921	927	932	937	
850	942	947	952	957	962	967	973	978	983	988	

N. 0 1 2 3 4 5 6 7 8 9 Proportional parts

N.	0	1	2	3	4	5	6	7	8	9
850	92 942	947	952	957	962	967	973	978	983	988
851	993	998	*003	*008	*013	*018	*024	*029	*034	*039
852	93 044	049	054	059	064	069	075	080	085	090
853	095	100	105	110	115	120	125	131	136	141
854	146	151	156	161	166	171	176	181	186	192
855	197	202	207	212	217	222	227	232	237	242
856	247	252	258	263	268	273	278	283	288	293
857	298	303	308	313	318	323	328	334	339	344
858	349	354	359	364	369	374	379	384	389	394
859	399	404	409	414	420	425	430	435	440	445
860	450	455	460	465	470	475	480	485	490	495
861	500	505	510	515	520	526	531	536	541	546
862	551	556	561	566	571	576	581	586	591	596
863	601	606	611	616	621	626	631	636	641	646
864	651	656	661	666	671	676	682	687	692	697
865	702	707	712	717	722	727	732	737	742	747
866	752	757	762	767	772	777	782	787	792	797
867	802	807	812	817	822	827	832	837	842	847
868	852	857	862	867	872	877	882	887	892	897
869	902	907	912	917	922	927	932	937	942	947
870	952	957	962	967	972	977	982	987	992	997
871	94 002	007	012	017	022	027	032	037	042	047
872	052	057	062	067	072	077	082	086	091	096
873	101	106	111	116	121	126	131	136	141	146
874	151	156	161	166	171	176	181	186	191	196
875	201	206	211	216	221	226	231	236	240	245
876	250	255	260	265	270	275	280	285	290	295
877	300	305	310	315	320	325	330	335	340	345
878	349	354	359	364	369	374	379	384	389	394
879	399	404	409	414	419	424	429	433	438	443
880	448	453	458	463	468	473	478	483	488	493
881	498	503	507	512	517	522	527	532	537	542
882	547	552	557	562	567	571	576	581	586	591
883	596	601	606	611	616	621	626	630	635	640
884	645	650	655	660	665	670	675	680	685	689
885	694	699	704	709	714	719	724	729	734	738
886	743	748	753	758	763	768	773	778	783	787
887	792	797	802	807	812	817	822	827	832	836
888	841	846	851	856	861	866	871	876	880	885
889	890	895	900	905	910	915	919	924	929	934
890	939	944	949	954	959	963	968	973	978	983
891	988	993	998	*002	*007	*012	*017	*022	*027	*032
892	95 036	041	046	051	056	061	066	071	075	080
893	085	090	095	100	105	109	114	119	124	129
894	134	139	143	148	153	158	163	168	173	177
895	182	187	192	197	202	207	211	216	221	226
896	231	236	240	245	250	255	260	265	270	274
897	279	284	289	294	299	303	308	313	318	323
898	328	332	337	342	347	352	357	361	366	371
899	376	381	386	390	395	400	405	410	415	419
900	424	429	434	439	444	448	453	458	463	468

N. 0 1 2 3 4 5 6 7 8 9

Proportional parts

	6
1	0.6
2	1.2
3	1.8
4	2.4
5	3.0
6	3.6
7	4.2
8	4.8
9	5.4

	5
1	0.5
2	1.0
3	1.5
4	2.0
5	2.5
6	3.0
7	3.5
8	4.0
9	4.5

	4
1	0.4
2	0.8
3	1.2
4	1.6
5	2.0
6	2.4
7	2.8
8	3.2
9	3.6

Proportional parts

N.	0	1	2	3	4	5	6	7	8	9
900	95 424	429	434	439	444	448	453	458	463	468
901	472	477	482	487	492	497	501	506	511	516
902	521	525	530	535	540	545	550	554	559	564
903	569	574	578	583	588	593	598	602	607	612
904	617	622	626	631	636	641	646	650	655	660
905	665	670	674	679	684	689	694	698	703	708
906	713	718	722	727	732	737	742	746	751	756
907	761	766	770	775	780	785	789	794	799	804
908	809	813	818	823	828	832	837	842	847	852
909	856	861	866	871	875	880	885	890	895	899
910	904	909	914	918	923	928	933	938	942	947
911	952	957	961	966	971	976	980	985	990	995
912	999	*004	*009	*014	*019	*023	*028	*033	*038	*042
913	96 047	052	057	061	066	071	076	080	085	090
914	095	099	104	109	114	118	123	128	133	137
915	142	147	152	156	161	166	171	175	180	185
916	190	194	199	204	209	213	218	223	227	232
917	237	242	246	251	256	261	265	270	275	280
918	284	289	294	298	303	308	313	317	322	327
919	332	336	341	346	350	355	360	365	369	374
920	379	384	388	393	398	402	407	412	417	421
921	426	431	435	440	445	450	454	459	464	468
922	473	478	483	487	492	497	501	506	511	515
923	520	525	530	534	539	544	548	553	558	562
924	567	572	577	581	586	591	595	600	605	609
925	614	619	624	628	633	638	642	647	652	656
926	661	666	670	675	680	685	689	694	699	703
927	708	713	717	722	727	731	736	741	745	750
928	755	759	764	769	774	778	783	788	792	797
929	802	806	811	816	820	825	830	834	839	844
930	848	853	858	862	867	872	876	881	886	890
931	895	900	904	909	914	918	923	928	932	937
932	942	946	951	956	960	965	970	974	979	984
933	988	993	997	*002	*007	*011	*016	*021	*025	*030
934	97 035	039	044	049	053	058	063	067	072	077
935	081	086	090	095	100	104	109	114	118	123
936	128	132	137	142	146	151	155	160	165	169
937	174	179	183	188	192	197	202	206	211	216
938	220	225	230	234	239	243	248	253	257	262
939	267	271	276	280	285	290	294	299	304	308
940	313	317	322	327	331	336	340	345	350	354
941	359	364	368	373	377	382	387	391	396	400
942	405	410	414	419	424	428	433	437	442	447
943	451	456	460	465	470	474	479	483	488	493
944	497	502	506	511	516	520	525	529	534	539
945	543	548	552	557	562	566	571	575	580	585
946	589	594	598	603	607	612	617	621	626	630
947	635	640	644	649	653	658	663	667	672	676
948	681	685	690	695	699	704	708	713	717	722
949	727	731	736	740	745	749	754	759	763	768
950	772	777	782	786	791	795	800	804	809	813
N.	0	1	2	3	4	5	6	7	8	9

Proportional parts

	5
1	0.5
2	1.0
3	1.5
4	2.0
5	2.5
6	3.0
7	3.5
8	4.0
9	4.5

	4
1	0.4
2	0.8
3	1.2
4	1.6
5	2.0
6	2.4
7	2.8
8	3.2
9	3.6

Proportional parts

N.	0	1	2	3	4	5	6	7	8	9
950	97 772	777	782	786	791	795	800	804	809	813
951	818	823	827	832	836	841	845	850	855	859
952	864	868	873	877	882	886	891	896	900	905
953	909	914	918	923	928	932	937	941	946	950
954	955	959	964	968	973	978	982	987	991	996
955	98 000	005	009	014	019	023	028	032	037	041
956	046	050	055	059	064	068	073	078	082	087
957	091	096	100	105	109	114	118	123	127	132
958	137	141	146	150	155	159	164	168	173	177
959	182	186	191	195	200	204	209	214	218	223
960	227	232	236	241	245	250	254	259	263	268
961	272	277	281	286	290	295	299	304	308	313
962	318	322	327	331	336	340	345	349	354	358
963	363	367	372	376	381	385	390	394	399	403
964	408	412	417	421	426	430	435	439	444	448
965	453	457	462	466	471	475	480	484	489	493
966	498	502	507	511	516	520	525	529	534	538
967	543	547	552	556	561	565	570	574	579	583
968	588	592	597	601	605	610	614	619	623	628
969	632	637	641	646	650	655	659	664	668	673
970	677	682	686	691	695	700	704	709	713	717
971	722	726	731	735	740	744	749	753	758	762
972	767	771	776	780	784	789	793	798	802	807
973	811	816	820	825	829	834	838	843	847	851
974	856	860	865	869	874	878	883	887	892	896
975	900	905	909	914	918	923	927	932	936	941
976	945	949	954	958	963	967	972	976	981	985
977	989	994	998	*003	*007	*012	*016	*021	*025	*029
978	99 034	038	043	047	052	056	061	065	069	074
979	078	083	087	092	096	100	105	109	114	118
980	123	127	131	136	140	145	149	154	158	162
981	167	171	176	180	185	189	193	198	202	207
982	211	216	220	224	229	233	238	242	247	251
983	255	260	264	269	273	277	282	286	291	295
984	300	304	308	313	317	322	326	330	335	339
985	344	348	352	357	361	366	370	374	379	383
986	388	392	396	401	405	410	414	419	423	427
987	432	436	441	445	449	454	458	463	467	471
988	476	480	484	489	493	498	502	506	511	515
989	520	524	528	533	537	542	546	550	555	559
990	564	568	572	577	581	585	590	594	599	603
991	607	612	616	621	625	629	634	638	642	647
992	651	656	660	664	669	673	677	682	686	691
993	695	699	704	708	712	717	721	726	730	734
994	739	743	747	752	756	760	765	769	774	778
995	782	787	791	795	800	804	808	813	817	822
996	826	830	835	839	843	848	852	856	861	865
997	870	874	878	883	887	891	896	900	904	909
998	913	917	922	926	930	935	939	944	948	952
999	957	961	965	970	974	978	983	987	991	996
1000	00 000	004	009	013	017	022	026	030	035	039
N.	0	1	2	3	4	5	6	7	8	9

Proportional parts

	5
1	0.5
2	1.0
3	1.5
4	2.0
5	2.5
6	3.0
7	3.5
8	4.0
9	4.5

	4
1	0.4
2	0.8
3	1.2
4	1.6
5	2.0
6	2.4
7	2.8
8	3.2
9	3.6

Proportional parts

N.	0	1	2	3	4	5	6	7	8	9	d.
1000	000 0000	0434	0869	1303	1737	2171	2605	3039	3473	3907	434
1001	4341	4775	5208	5642	6076	6510	6943	7377	7810	8244	434
1002	8677	9111	9544	9977	*0411	*0844	*1277	*1710	*2143	*2576	433
1003	001 3009	3442	3875	4308	4741	5174	5607	6039	6472	6905	433
1004	7337	7770	8202	8635	9067	9499	9932	*0364	*0796	*1228	432
1005	002 1661	2093	2525	2957	3389	3821	4253	4685	5116	5548	432
1006	5980	6411	6843	7275	7706	8138	8569	9001	9432	9863	431
1007	003 0295	0726	1157	1588	2019	2451	2882	3313	3744	4174	431
1008	4605	5036	5467	5898	6328	6759	7190	7620	8051	8481	431
1009	8912	9342	9772	*0203	*0633	*1063	*1493	*1924	*2354	*2784	430
1010	004 3214	3644	4074	4504	4933	5363	5793	6223	6652	7082	430
1011	7512	7941	8371	8800	9229	9659	*0088	*0517	*0947	*1376	429
1012	005 1805	2234	2663	3092	3521	3950	4379	4808	5237	5666	429
1013	6094	6523	6952	7380	7809	8238	8666	9094	9523	9951	429
1014	006 0380	0808	1236	1664	2092	2521	2949	3377	3805	4233	428
1015	4660	5088	5516	5944	6372	6799	7227	7655	8082	8510	428
1016	8937	9365	9792	*0219	*0647	*1074	*1501	*1928	*2355	*2782	427
1017	007 3210	3637	4064	4490	4917	5344	5771	6198	6624	7051	427
1018	7478	7904	8331	8757	9184	9610	*0037	*0463	*0889	*1316	426
1019	008 1742	2168	2594	3020	3446	3872	4298	4724	5150	5576	426
1020	6002	6427	6853	7279	7704	8130	8556	8981	9407	9832	426
1021	009 0257	0683	1108	1533	1959	2384	2809	3234	3659	4084	425
1022	4509	4934	5359	5784	6208	6633	7058	7483	7907	8332	425
1023	8756	9181	9605	*0030	*0454	*0878	*1303	*1727	*2151	*2575	424
1024	010 3000	3424	3848	4272	4696	5120	5544	5967	6391	6815	424
1025	7239	7662	8086	8510	8933	9357	9780	*0204	*0627	*1050	424
1026	011 1474	1897	2320	2743	3166	3590	4013	4436	4859	5282	423
1027	5704	6127	6550	6973	7396	7818	8241	8664	9086	9509	423
1028	9931	*0354	*0776	*1198	*1621	*2043	*2465	*2887	*3310	*3732	422
1029	012 4154	4576	4998	5420	5842	6264	6685	7107	7529	7951	422
1030	8372	8794	9215	9637	*0059	*0480	*0901	*1323	*1744	*2165	422
1031	013 2587	3008	3429	3850	4271	4692	5113	5534	5955	6376	421
1032	6797	7218	7639	8059	8480	8901	9321	9742	*0162	*0583	421
1033	014 1003	1424	1844	2264	2685	3105	3525	3945	4365	4785	420
1034	5205	5625	6045	6465	6885	7305	7725	8144	8564	8984	420
1035	9403	9823	*0243	*0662	*1082	*1501	*1920	*2340	*2759	*3178	420
1036	015 3598	4017	4436	4855	5274	5693	6112	6531	6950	7369	419
1037	7788	8206	8625	9044	9462	9881	*0300	*0718	*1137	*1555	419
1038	016 1974	2392	2810	3229	3647	4065	4483	4901	5319	5737	418
1039	6155	6573	6991	7409	7827	8245	8663	9080	9498	9916	418
1040	017 0333	0751	1168	1586	2003	2421	2838	3256	3673	4090	417
1041	4507	4924	5342	5759	6176	6593	7010	7427	7844	8260	417
1042	8677	9094	9511	9927	*0344	*0761	*1177	*1594	*2010	*2427	417
1043	018 2843	3259	3676	4092	4508	4925	5341	5757	6173	6589	416
1044	7005	7421	7837	8253	8669	9084	9500	9916	*0332	*0747	416
1045	019 1163	1578	1994	2410	2825	3240	3656	4071	4486	4902	415
1046	5317	5732	6147	6562	6977	7392	7807	8222	8637	9052	415
1047	9467	9882	*0296	*0711	*1126	*1540	*1955	*2369	*2784	*3198	415
1048	020 3613	4027	4442	4856	5270	5684	6099	6513	6927	7341	414
1049	7755	8169	8583	8997	9411	9824	*0238	*0652	*1066	*1479	414
1050	021 1893	2307	2720	3134	3547	3961	4374	4787	5201	5614	413
N.	0	1	2	3	4	5	6	7	8	9	d.

N.	0	1	2	3	4	5	6	7	8	9	d.
1050	021 1893	2307	2720	3134	3547	3961	4374	4787	5201	5614	413
1051	6027	6440	6854	7267	7680	8093	8506	8919	9332	9745	413
1052	022 0157	0570	0983	1396	1808	2221	2634	3046	3459	3871	413
1053	4284	4696	5109	5521	5933	6345	6758	7170	7582	7994	412
1054	8406	8818	9230	9642	*0054	*0466	*0878	*1289	*1701	*2113	412
1055	023 2525	2936	3348	3759	4171	4582	4994	5405	5817	6228	411
1056	6639	7050	7462	7873	8284	8695	9106	9517	9928	*0339	411
1057	024 0750	1161	1572	1982	2393	2804	3214	3625	4036	4446	411
1058	4857	5267	5678	6088	6498	6909	7319	7729	8139	8549	410
1059	8960	9370	9780	*0190	*0600	*1010	*1419	*1829	*2239	*2649	410
1060	025 3059	3468	3878	4288	4697	5107	5516	5926	6335	6744	410
1061	7154	7563	7972	8382	8791	9200	9609	*0018	*0427	*0836	409
1062	026 1245	1654	2063	2472	2881	3289	3698	4107	4515	4924	409
1063	5333	5741	6150	6558	6967	7375	7783	8192	8600	9008	408
1064	9416	9824	*0233	*0641	*1049	*1457	*1865	*2273	*2680	*3088	408
1065	027 3496	3904	4312	4719	5127	5535	5942	6350	6757	7165	408
1066	7572	7979	8387	8794	9201	9609	*0016	*0423	*0830	*1237	407
1067	028 1644	2051	2458	2865	3272	3679	4086	4492	4899	5306	407
1068	5713	6119	6526	6932	7339	7745	8152	8558	8964	9371	406
1069	9777	*0183	*0590	*0996	*1402	*1808	*2214	*2620	*3026	*3432	406
1070	029 3838	4244	4649	5055	5461	5867	6272	6678	7084	7489	406
1071	7895	8300	8706	9111	9516	9922	*0327	*0732	*1138	*1543	405
1072	030 1948	2353	2758	3163	3568	3973	4378	4783	5188	5592	405
1073	5997	6402	6807	7211	7616	8020	8425	8830	9234	9638	405
1074	031 0043	0447	0851	1256	1660	2064	2468	2872	3277	3681	404
1075	4085	4489	4893	5296	5700	6104	6508	6912	7315	7719	404
1076	8123	8526	8930	9333	9737	*0140	*0544	*0947	*1350	*1754	403
1077	032 2157	2560	2963	3367	3770	4173	4576	4979	5382	5785	403
1078	6188	6590	6993	7396	7799	8201	8604	9007	9409	9812	403
1079	033 0214	0617	1019	1422	1824	2226	2629	3031	3433	3835	402
1080	4238	4640	5042	5444	5846	6248	6650	7052	7453	7855	402
1081	8257	8659	9060	9462	9864	*0265	*0667	*1068	*1470	*1871	402
1082	034 2273	2674	3075	3477	3878	4279	4680	5081	5482	5884	401
1083	6285	6686	7087	7487	7888	8289	8690	9091	9491	9892	401
1084	035 0293	0693	1094	1495	1895	2296	2696	3096	3497	3897	400
1085	4297	4698	5098	5498	5898	6298	6698	7098	7498	7898	400
1086	8298	8698	9098	9498	9898	*0297	*0697	*1097	*1496	*1896	400
1087	036 2295	2695	3094	3494	3893	4293	4692	5091	5491	5890	399
1088	6289	6688	7087	7486	7885	8284	8683	9082	9481	9880	399
1089	037 0279	0678	1076	1475	1874	2272	2671	3070	3468	3867	399
1090	4265	4663	5062	5460	5858	6257	6655	7053	7451	7849	398
1091	8248	8646	9044	9442	9839	*0237	*0635	*1033	*1431	*1829	398
1092	038 2226	2624	3022	3419	3817	4214	4612	5009	5407	5804	398
1093	6202	6599	6996	7393	7791	8188	8585	8982	9379	9776	397
1094	039 0173	0570	0967	1364	1761	2158	2554	2951	3348	3745	397
1095	4141	4538	4934	5331	5727	6124	6520	6917	7313	7709	397
1096	8106	8502	8898	9294	9690	*0086	*0482	*0878	*1274	*1670	396
1097	040 2066	2462	2858	3254	3650	4045	4441	4837	5232	5628	396
1098	6023	6419	6814	7210	7605	8001	8396	8791	9187	9582	395
1099	9977	*0372	*0767	*1162	*1557	*1952	*2347	*2742	*3137	*3532	395
1100	041 3927	4322	4716	5111	5506	5900	6295	6690	7084	7479	395
N.	0	1	2	3	4	5	6	7	8	9	d.

N.	0	1	2	3	4	5	6	7	8	9	d.
1100	041 3927	4322	4716	5111	5506	5900	6295	6690	7084	7479	395
1101	7873	8268	8662	9056	9451	9845	*0239	*0633	*1028	*1422	394
1102	042 1816	2210	2604	2998	3392	3786	4180	4574	4968	5361	394
1103	5755	6149	6543	6936	7330	7723	8117	8510	8904	9297	394
1104	9691	*0084	*0477	*0871	*1264	*1657	*2050	*2444	*2837	*3230	393
1105	043 3623	4016	4409	4802	5195	5587	5980	6373	6766	7159	393
1106	7551	7944	8337	8729	9122	9514	9907	*0299	*0692	*1084	393
1107	044 1476	1869	2261	2653	3045	3437	3829	4222	4614	5006	392
1108	5398	5790	6181	6573	6965	7357	7749	8140	8532	8924	392
1109	9315	9707	*0099	*0490	*0882	*1273	*1664	*2056	*2447	*2839	392
1110	045 3230	3621	4012	4403	4795	5186	5577	5968	6359	6750	391
1111	7141	7531	7922	8313	8704	9095	9485	9876	*0267	*0657	391
1112	046 1048	1438	1829	2219	2610	3000	3391	3781	4171	4561	390
1113	4952	5342	5732	6122	6512	6902	7292	7682	8072	8462	390
1114	8852	9242	9632	*0021	*0411	*0801	*1190	*1580	*1970	*2359	390
1115	047 2749	3138	3528	3917	4306	4696	5085	5474	5864	6253	389
1116	6642	7031	7420	7809	8198	8587	8976	9365	9754	*0143	389
1117	048 0532	0921	1309	1698	2087	2475	2864	3253	3641	4030	389
1118	4418	4806	5195	5583	5972	6360	6748	7136	7525	7913	388
1119	8301	8689	9077	9465	9853	*0241	*0629	*1017	*1405	*1792	388
1120	049 2180	2568	2956	3343	3731	4119	4506	4894	5281	5669	388
1121	6056	6444	6831	7218	7606	7993	8380	8767	9154	9541	387
1122	9929	*0316	*0703	*1090	*1477	*1863	*2250	*2637	*3024	*3411	387
1123	050 3798	4184	4571	4958	5344	5731	6117	6504	6890	7277	387
1124	7663	8049	8436	8822	9208	9595	9981	*0367	*0753	*1139	386
1125	051 1525	1911	2297	2683	3069	3455	3841	4227	4612	4998	386
1126	5384	5770	6155	6541	6926	7312	7697	8083	8468	8854	386
1127	9239	9624	*0010	*0395	*0780	*1166	*1551	*1936	*2321	*2706	385
1128	052 3091	3476	3861	4246	4631	5016	5400	5785	6170	6555	385
1129	6939	7324	7709	8093	8478	8862	9247	9631	*0016	*0400	385
1130	053 0784	1169	1553	1937	2321	2706	3090	3474	3858	4242	384
1131	4626	5010	5394	5778	6162	6546	6929	7313	7697	8081	384
1132	8464	8848	9232	9615	9999	*0382	*0766	*1149	*1532	*1916	384
1133	054 2299	2682	3066	3449	3832	4215	4598	4981	5365	5748	383
1134	6131	6514	6896	7279	7662	8045	8428	8811	9193	9576	383
1135	9959	*0341	*0724	*1106	*1489	*1871	*2254	*2636	*3019	*3401	382
1136	055 3783	4166	4548	4930	5312	5694	6077	6459	6841	7223	382
1137	7605	7987	8369	8750	9132	9514	9896	*0278	*0659	*1041	382
1138	056 1423	1804	2186	2567	2949	3330	3712	4093	4475	4856	381
1139	5237	5619	6000	6381	6762	7143	7524	7905	8287	8668	381
1140	9049	9429	9810	*0191	*0572	*0953	*1334	*1714	*2095	*2476	381
1141	057 2856	3237	3618	3998	4379	4759	5140	5520	5900	6281	381
1142	6661	7041	7422	7802	8182	8562	8942	9322	9702	*0082	380
1143	058 0462	0842	1222	1602	1982	2362	2741	3121	3501	3881	380
1144	4260	4640	5019	5399	5778	6158	6537	6917	7296	7676	380
1145	8055	8434	8813	9193	9572	9951	*0330	*0709	*1088	*1467	379
1146	059 1846	2225	2604	2983	3362	3741	4119	4498	4877	5256	379
1147	5634	6013	6391	6770	7148	7527	7905	8284	8662	9041	379
1148	9419	9797	*0175	*0554	*0932	*1310	*1688	*2066	*2444	*2822	378
1149	060 3200	3578	3956	4334	4712	5090	5468	5845	6223	6601	378
1150	6978	7356	7734	8111	8489	8866	9244	9621	9999	*0376	378
N	0	1	2	3	4	5	6	7	8	9	d.

N.	0	1	2	3	4	5	6	7	8	9	d.
1150	060 6978	7356	7734	8111	8489	8866	9244	9621	9999	*0376	378
1151	061 0753	1131	1508	1885	2262	2639	3017	3394	3771	4148	377
1152	4525	4902	5279	5656	6032	6409	6786	7163	7540	7916	377
1153	8293	8670	9046	9423	9799	*0176	*0552	*0929	*1305	*1682	377
1154	062 2058	2434	2811	3187	3563	3939	4316	4692	5068	5444	376
1155	5820	6196	6572	6948	7324	7699	8075	8451	8827	9203	376
1156	9578	9954	*0330	*0705	*1081	*1456	*1832	*2207	*2583	*2958	376
1157	063 3334	3709	4084	4460	4835	5210	5585	5960	6335	6711	375
1158	7086	7461	7836	8211	8585	8960	9335	9710	*0085	*0460	375
1159	064 0834	1209	1584	1958	2333	2708	3082	3457	3831	4205	375
1160	4580	4954	5329	5703	6077	6451	6826	7200	7574	7948	374
1161	8322	8696	9070	9444	9818	*0192	*0566	*0940	*1314	*1688	374
1162	065 2061	2435	2809	3182	3556	3930	4303	4677	5050	5424	374
1163	5797	6171	6544	6917	7291	7664	8037	8410	8784	9157	373
1164	9530	9903	*0276	*0649	*1022	*1395	*1768	*2141	*2514	*2886	373
1165	066 3259	3632	4005	4377	4750	5123	5495	5868	6241	6613	373
1166	6986	7358	7730	8103	8475	8847	9220	9592	9964	*0336	372
1167	067 0709	1081	1453	1825	2197	2569	2941	3313	3685	4057	372
1168	4428	4800	5172	5544	5915	6287	6659	7030	7402	7774	372
1169	8145	8517	8888	9259	9631	*0002	*0374	*0745	*1116	*1487	371
1170	068 1859	2230	2601	2972	3343	3714	4085	4456	4827	5198	371
1171	5569	5940	6311	6681	7052	7423	7794	8164	8535	8906	371
1172	9276	9647	*0017	*0388	*0758	*1129	*1499	*1869	*2240	*2610	370
1173	069 2980	3350	3721	4091	4461	4831	5201	5571	5941	6311	370
1174	6681	7051	7421	7791	8160	8530	8900	9270	9639	*0009	370
1175	070 0379	0748	1118	1487	1857	2226	2596	2965	3335	3704	369
1176	4073	4442	4812	5181	5550	5919	6288	6658	7027	7396	369
1177	7765	8134	8503	8871	9240	9609	9978	*0347	*0715	*1084	369
1178	071 1453	1822	2190	2559	2927	3296	3664	4033	4401	4770	369
1179	5138	5506	5875	6243	6611	6979	7348	7716	8084	8452	368
1180	8820	9188	9556	9924	*0292	*0660	*1028	*1396	*1763	*2131	368
1181	072 2499	2867	3234	3602	3970	4337	4705	5072	5440	5807	368
1182	6175	6542	6910	7277	7644	8011	8379	8746	9113	9480	367
1183	9847	*0215	*0582	*0949	*1316	*1683	*2050	*2416	*2783	*3150	367
1184	073 3517	3884	4251	4617	4984	5351	5717	6084	6450	6817	367
1185	7184	7550	7916	8283	8649	9016	9382	9748	*0114	*0481	366
1186	074 0847	1213	1579	1945	2311	2677	3043	3409	3775	4141	366
1187	4507	4873	5239	5605	5970	6336	6702	7068	7433	7799	366
1188	8164	8530	8895	9261	9626	9992	*0357	*0723	*1088	*1453	365
1189	075 1819	2184	2549	2914	3279	3644	4010	4375	4740	5105	365
1190	5470	5835	6199	6564	6929	7294	7659	8024	8388	8753	365
1191	9118	9482	9847	*0211	*0576	*0940	*1305	*1669	*2034	*2398	364
1192	076 2763	3127	3491	3855	4220	4584	4948	5312	5676	6040	364
1193	6404	6768	7132	7496	7860	8224	8588	8952	9316	9680	364
1194	077 0043	0407	0771	1134	1498	1862	2225	2589	2952	3316	364
1195	3679	4042	4406	4769	5133	5496	5859	6222	6585	6949	363
1196	7312	7675	8038	8401	8764	9127	9490	9853	*0216	*0579	363
1197	078 0942	1304	1667	2030	2393	2755	3118	3480	3843	4206	363
1198	4568	4931	5293	5656	6018	6380	6743	7105	7467	7830	362
1199	8192	8554	8916	9278	9640	*0003	*0365	*0727	*1089	*1451	362
1200	079 1812	2174	2536	2898	3260	3622	3983	4345	4707	5068	362
N.	0	1	2	3	4	5	6	7	8	9	d.

LOGARITHMS OF THE TRIGONOMETRIC FUNCTIONS

Logarithms of the functions are given for each minute from $0-360°$.

The quantity -10 is to be appended to all logarithms of the sine and cosine, to logarithms of the tangent from 0–45° and of the cotangent from $45-90°$.

With degrees indicated at either side of the top of the page use the column headings at the top. With degrees stated at the bottom of the page use the column designations at the bottom.

With degrees at the left (top or bottom) use the minute column at the left, and with degrees on the right side of the page use the minute column at the right.

The method of determining the functions of small angles by the auxiliary quantities S and T is explained on page 230.

LOGARITHMS OF THE TRIGONOMETRIC FUNCTIONS
Values of S and T

Min.	Values of S, – 10 to be appended					Values of T, – 10 to be appended					Sec.
	0°	1°	2°	3°	4°	0°	1°	2°	3°	4°	
0′	4.68 558	555	549	538	522	4.68 558	562	575	597	628	0″
1	558	555	549	537	522	558	562	575	598	629	60
2	558	555	548	537	522	558	562	576	598	629	120
3	558	555	548	537	521	558	562	576	599	630	180
4	558	555	548	537	521	558	563	576	599	631	240
5	558	555	548	537	521	558	563	577	599	631	300
6	558	555	548	536	520	558	563	577	600	632	360
7	558	555	548	536	520	558	563	577	600	632	420
8	557	555	548	536	520	558	563	578	601	633	480
9	557	555	547	536	520	558	563	578	601	634	540
10	4.68 557	555	547	535	519	4.68 558	564	578	602	634	**600**
11	557	554	547	535	519	558	564	579	602	635	660
12	557	554	547	535	519	558	564	579	603	635	720
13	557	554	547	535	518	558	564	579	603	636	780
14	557	554	547	534	518	558	564	580	604	637	840
15	557	554	546	534	518	558	564	580	604	637	900
16	557	554	546	534	517	558	565	580	605	638	960
17	557	554	546	534	517	558	565	581	605	639	1020
18	557	554	546	534	517	558	565	581	606	639	1080
19	557	554	546	533	516	558	565	581	606	640	1140
20	4.68 557	554	546	533	516	4.68 558	565	582	607	640	**1200**
21	557	554	545	533	516	558	566	582	607	641	1260
22	557	553	545	533	515	558	566	582	608	642	1320
23	557	553	545	532	515	558	566	583	608	642	1380
24	557	553	545	532	515	558	566	583	609	643	1440
25	557	553	545	532	515	558	566	583	609	644	1500
26	557	553	544	532	514	558	567	584	610	644	1560
27	557	553	544	531	514	558	567	584	610	645	1620
28	557	553	544	531	514	558	567	584	611	646	1680
29	557	553	544	531	513	559	567	585	611	646	1740
30	4.68 557	553	544	531	513	4.68 559	567	585	612	647	**1800**
31	557	552	544	530	513	559	568	585	612	648	1860
32	557	552	543	530	512	559	568	586	613	648	1920
33	557	552	543	530	512	559	568	586	613	649	1980
34	557	552	543	529	512	559	568	587	614	650	2040
35	557	552	543	529	511	559	569	587	614	650	2100
36	557	552	543	529	511	559	569	587	615	651	2160
37	557	552	542	529	511	559	569	588	615	652	2220
38	557	552	542	528	510	559	569	588	616	652	2280
39	557	552	542	528	510	559	570	589	616	653	2340
40	4.68 557	551	542	528	510	4.68 559	570	589	617	654	**2400**
41	557	551	542	528	509	560	570	589	617	654	2460
42	556	551	541	527	509	560	570	590	618	655	2520
43	556	551	541	527	508	560	571	590	619	656	2580
44	556	551	541	527	508	560	571	591	619	656	2640
45	556	551	541	527	508	560	571	591	620	657	2700
46	556	551	541	526	507	560	571	591	620	658	2760
47	556	551	540	526	507	560	572	592	621	659	2820
48	556	550	540	526	507	560	572	592	621	659	2880
49	556	550	540	525	506	560	572	593	622	660	2940
50	4.68 556	550	540	525	506	4.68 561	572	593	622	661	**3000**
51	556	550	540	525	506	561	573	593	623	661	3060
52	556	550	539	525	505	561	573	594	624	662	3120
53	556	550	539	524	505	561	573	594	624	663	3180
54	556	550	539	524	505	561	573	595	625	664	3240
55	556	549	539	524	504	561	574	595	625	664	3300
56	556	549	539	523	504	561	574	596	626	665	3360
57	556	549	538	523	503	562	574	596	626	666	3420
58	555	549	538	523	503	562	575	596	627	667	3480
59	555	549	538	523	503	562	575	597	628	667	3540
60	4.68 555	549	538	522	502	4.68 562	575	597	628	668	**3600**

0° (180°) (359°) **179°**

″	′	L. Sin.	d.	C. S.	C. T.	L. Tan	c.d.	L. Cot.	L. Cos.	′
0	**0**	—		—	—	—		—	0.00 000	**60**
60	1	6.46 373	30103	5.31 443	5.31 443	6.46 373	30103	3.53 627	0.00 000	59
120	2	6.76 476	17609	5.31 443	5.31 443	6.76 476	17609	3.23 524	0.00 000	58
180	3	6.94 085	12494	5.31 443	5.31 443	6.94 085	12494	3.05 915	0.00 000	57
240	4	7.06 579	9691	5.31 443	5.31 442	7.06 579	9691	2.93 421	0.00 000	56
300	5	7.16 270	7918	5.31 443	5.31 442	7.16 270	7918	2.83 730	0.00 000	55
360	6	7.24 188	6694	5.31 443	5.31 442	7.24 188	6694	2.75 812	0.00 000	54
420	7	7.30 882	5800	5.31 443	5.31 442	7.30 882	5800	2.69 118	0.00 000	53
480	8	7.36 682	5115	5.31 443	5.31 442	7.36 682	5115	2.63 318	0.00 000	52
540	9	7.41 797	4576	5.31 443	5.31 442	7.41 797	4576	2.58 203	0.00 000	51
600	**10**	7.46 373	4139	5.31 443	5.31 442	7.46 373	4139	2.53 627	0.00 000	**50**
660	11	7.50 512	3779	5.31 443	5.31 442	7.50 512	3779	2.49 488	0.00 000	49
720	12	7.54 291	3476	5.31 443	5.31 442	7.54 291	3476	2.45 709	0.00 000	48
780	13	7.57 767	3218	5.31 443	5.31 442	7.57 767	3219	2.42 233	0.00 000	47
840	14	7.60 985	2997	5.31 443	5.31 442	7.60 986	2996	2.39 014	0.00 000	46
900	15	7.63 982	2802	5.31 443	5.31 442	7.63 982	2803	2.36 018	0.00 000	45
960	16	7.66 784	2633	5.31 443	5.31 442	7.66 785	2633	2.33 215	0.00 000	44
1020	17	7.69 417	2483	5.31 443	5.31 442	7.69 418	2482	2.30 582	9.99 999	43
1080	18	7.71 900	2348	5.31 443	5.31 442	7.71 900	2348	2.28 100	9.99 999	42
1140	19	7.74 248	2227	5.31 443	5.31 442	7.74 248	2228	2.25 752	9.99 999	41
1200	**20**	7.76 475	2119	5.31 443	5.31 442	7.76 476	2119	2.23 524	9.99 999	**40**
1260	21	7.78 594	2021	5.31 443	5.31 442	7.78 595	2020	2.21 405	9.99 999	39
1320	22	7.80 615	1930	5.31 443	5.31 442	7.80 615	1931	2.19 385	9.99 999	38
1380	23	7.82 545	1848	5.31 443	5.31 442	7.82 546	1848	2.17 454	9.99 999	37
1440	24	7.84 393	1773	5.31 443	5.31 442	7.84 394	1773	2.15 606	9.99 999	36
1500	25	7,86 166	1704	5.31 443	5.31 442	7.86 167	1704	2.13 833	9.99 999	35
1560	26	7.87 870	1639	5.31 443	5.31 442	7.87 871	1639	2.12 129	9.99 999	34
1620	27	7.89 509	1579	5.31 443	5.31 442	7.89 510	1579	2.10 490	9.99 999	33
1680	28	7.91 088	1524	5.31 443	5.31 442	7.91 089	1524	2.08 911	9.99 999	32
1740	29	7.92 612	1472	5.31 443	5.31 441	7.92 613	1473	2.07 387	9.99 998	31
1800	**30**	7.94 084	1424	5.31 443	5.31 441	7.94 086	1424	2.05 914	9.99 998	**30**
1860	31	7.95 508	1379	5.31 443	5.31 441	7.95 510	1379	2.04 490	9.99 998	29
1920	32	7.96 887	1336	5.31 443	5.31 441	7.96 889	1336	2.03 111	9.99 998	28
1980	33	7.98 223	1297	5.31 443	5.31 441	7.98 225	1297	2.01 775	9.99 998	27
2040	34	7.99 520	1259	5.31 443	5.31 441	7.99 522	1259	2.00 478	9.99 998	26
2100	35	8.00 779	1223	5.31 443	5.31 441	8.00 781	1223	1.99 219	9.99 998	25
2160	36	8.02 002	1190	5.31 443	5.31 441	8.02 004	1190	1.97 996	9.99 998	24
2220	37	8.03 192	1158	5.31 443	5.31 441	8.03 194	1159	1.96 806	9.99 997	23
2280	38	8.04 350	1128	5.31 443	5.31 441	8.04 353	1128	1.95 647	9.99 997	22
2340	39	8.05 478	1100	5.31 443	5.31 441	8.05 481	1100	1.94 519	9.99 997	21
2400	**40**	8.06 578	1072	5.31 443	5.31 441	8.06 581	1072	1.93 419	9.99 997	**20**
2460	41	8.07 650	1046	5.31 444	5.31 440	8.07 653	1047	1.92 347	9.99 997	19
2520	42	8.08 696	1022	5.31 444	5.31 440	8.08 700	1022	1.91 300	9.99 997	18
2580	43	8.09 718	999	5.31 444	5.31 440	8.09 722	998	1.90 278	9.99 997	17
2640	44	8.10 717	976	5.31 444	5.31 440	8.10 720	976	1.89 280	9.99 996	16
2700	45	8.11 693	954	5.31 444	5.31 440	8.11 696	955	1.88 304	9.99 996	15
2760	46	8.12 647	934	5.31 444	5.31 440	8.12 651	934	1.87 349	9.99 996	14
2820	47	8.13 581	914	5.31 444	5.31 440	8.13 585	915	1.86 415	9.99 996	13
2880	48	8.14 495	896	5.31 444	5.31 440	8.14 500	895	1.85 500	9.99 996	12
2940	49	8.15 391	877	5.31 444	5.31 440	8.15 395	878	1.84 605	9.99 996	11
3000	**50**	8.16 268	860	5.31 444	5.31 439	8.16 273	860	1.83 727	9.99 995	**10**
3060	51	8.17 128	843	5.31 444	5.31 439	8.17 133	843	1.82 867	9.99 995	9
3120	52	8.17 971	827	5.31 444	5.31 439	8.17 976	828	1.82 024	9.99 995	8
3180	53	8.18 798	812	5.31 444	5.31 439	8.18 804	812	1.81 196	9.99 995	7
3240	54	8.19 610	797	5.31 444	5.31 439	8.19 616	797	1.80 384	9.99 995	6
3300	55	8.20 407	782	5.31 444	5.31 439	8.20 413	782	1.79 587	9.99 994	5
3360	56	8.21 189	769	5.31 444	5.31 439	8.21 195	769	1.78 805	9.99 994	4
3420	57	8.21 958	755	5.31 445	5.31 439	8.21 964	756	1.78 036	9.99 994	3
3480	58	8.22 713	743	5.31 445	5.31 438	8.22 720	742	1.77 280	9.99 994	2
3540	59	8.23 456	730	5.31 445	5.31 438	8.23 462	730	1.76 538	9.99 994	1
3600	**60**	8.24 186		5.31 445	5.31 438	8.24 192		1.75 808	9.99 993	**0**
″	′	L. Cos.	d.	C. S.	C. T.	L. Cot.	c. d.	L. Tan.	L. Sin.	′

90° (270°) (269°) **89°**

1° (181°) (358°) **178°**

″	′	L. Sin.	d.	C. S.	C. T.	L. Tan.	c.d.	L. Cot.	L. Cos.	′
3600	**0**	8.24 186	717	5.31 445	5.31 438	8.24 192	718	1.75 808	9.99 993	**60**
3660	1	8.24 903	706	5.31 445	5.31 438	8.24 910	706	1.75 090	9.99 993	59
3720	2	8.25 609	695	5.31 445	5.31 438	8.25 616	696	1.74 384	9.99 993	58
3780	3	8.26 304	684	5.31 445	5.31 438	8.26 312	684	1.73 688	9.99 993	57
3840	4	8.26 988	673	5.31 445	5.31 437	8.26 996	673	1.73 004	9.99 992	56
3900	5	8.27 661	663	5.31 445	5.31 437	8.27 669	663	1.72 331	9.99 992	55
3960	6	8.28 324	653	5.31 445	5.31 437	8.28 332	654	1.71 668	9.99 992	54
4020	7	8.28 977	644	5.31 445	5.31 437	8.28 986	643	1.71 014	9.99 992	53
4080	8	8.29 621	634	5.31 445	5.31 437	8.29 629	634	1.70 371	9.99 992	52
4140	9	8.30 255	624	5.31 445	5.31 437	8.30 263	625	1.69 737	9.99 991	51
4200	**10**	8.30 879	616	5.31 446	5.31 437	8.30 888	617	1.69 112	9.99 991	**50**
4260	11	8.31 495	608	5.31 446	5.31 436	8.31 505	607	1.68 495	9.99 991	49
4320	12	8.32 103	599	5.31 446	5.31 436	8.32 112	599	1.67 888	9.99 990	48
4380	13	8.32 702	590	5.31 446	5.31 436	8.32 711	591	1.67 289	9.99 990	47
4440	14	8.33 292	583	5.31 446	5.31 436	8.33 302	584	1.66 698	9.99 990	46
4500	15	8.33 875	575	5.31 446	5.31 436	8.33 886	575	1.66 114	9.99 990	45
4560	16	8.34 450	568	5.31 446	5.31 435	8.34 461	568	1.65 539	9.99 989	44
4620	17	8.35 018	560	5.31 446	5.31 435	8.35 029	561	1.64 971	9.99 989	43
4680	18	8.35 578	553	5.31 446	5.31 435	8.35 590	553	1.64 410	9.99 989	42
4740	19	8.36 131	547	5.31 446	5.31 435	8.36 143	546	1.63 857	9.99 989	41
4800	**20**	8.36 678	539	5.31 446	5.31 435	8.36 689	540	1.63 311	9.99 988	**40**
4860	21	8.37 217	533	5.31 447	5.31 434	8.37 229	533	1.62 771	9.99 988	39
4920	22	8.37 750	526	5.31 447	5.31 434	8.37 762	527	1.62 238	9.99 988	38
4980	23	8.38 276	520	5.31 447	5.31 434	8.38 289	520	1.61 711	9.99 987	37
5040	24	8.38 796	514	5.31 447	5.31 434	8.38 809	514	1.61 191	9.99 987	36
5100	25	8.39 310	508	5.31 447	5.31 434	8.39 323	509	1.60 677	9.99 987	35
5160	26	8.39 818	502	5.31 447	5.31 433	8.39 832	502	1.60 168	9.99 986	34
5220	27	8.40 320	496	5.31 447	5.31 433	8.40 334	496	1.59 666	9.99 986	33
5280	28	8.40 816	491	5.31 447	5.31 433	8.40 830	491	1.59 170	9.99 986	32
5340	29	8.41 307	485	5.31 447	5.31 433	8.41 321	486	1.58 679	9.99 985	31
5400	**30**	8.41 792	480	5.31 447	5.31 433	8.41 807	480	1.58 193	9.99 985	**30**
5460	31	8.42 272	474	5.31 448	5.31 432	8.42 287	475	1.57 713	9.99 985	29
5520	32	8.42 746	470	5.31 448	5.31 432	8.42 762	470	1.57 238	9.99 984	28
5580	33	8.43 216	464	5.31 448	5.31 432	8.43 232	464	1.56 768	9.99 984	27
5640	34	8.43 680	459	5.31 448	5.31 432	8.43 696	460	1.56 304	9.99 984	26
5700	35	8.44 139	455	5.31 448	5.31 431	8.44 156	455	1.55 844	9.99 983	25
5760	36	8.44 594	450	5.31 448	5.31 431	8.44 611	450	1.55 389	9.99 983	24
5820	37	8.45 044	445	5.31 448	5.31 431	8.45 061	446	1.54 939	9.99 983	23
5880	38	8.45 489	441	5.31 448	5.31 431	8.45 507	441	1.54 493	9.99 982	22
5940	39	8.45 930	436	5.31 449	5.31 431	8.45 948	437	1.54 052	9.99 982	21
6000	**40**	8.46 366	433	5.31 449	5.31 430	8.46 385	432	1.53 615	9.99 982	**20**
6060	41	8.46 799	427	5.31 449	5.31 430	8.46 817	428	1.53 183	9.99 981	19
6120	42	8.47 226	424	5.31 449	5.31 430	8.47 245	424	1.52 755	9.99 981	18
6180	43	8.47 650	419	5.31 449	5.31 430	8.47 669	420	1.52 331	9.99 981	17
6240	44	8.48 069	416	5.31 449	5.31 429	8.48 089	416	1.51 911	9.99 980	16
6300	45	8.48 485	411	5.31 449	5.31 429	8.48 505	412	1.51 495	9.99 980	15
6360	46	8.48 896	408	5.31 449	5.31 429	8.48 917	408	1.51 083	9.99 979	14
6420	47	8.49 304	404	5.31 450	5.31 428	8.49 325	404	1.50 675	9.99 979	13
6480	48	8.49 708	400	5.31 450	5.31 428	8.49 729	401	1.50 271	9.99 979	12
6540	49	8.50 108	396	5.31 450	5.31 428	8.50 130	397	1.49 870	9.99 978	11
6600	**50**	8.50 504	393	5.31 450	5.31 428	8.50 527	393	1.49 473	9.99 978	**10**
6660	51	8.50 897	390	5.31 450	5.31 427	8.50 920	390	1.49 080	9.99 977	9
6720	52	8.51 287	386	5.31 450	5.31 427	8.51 310	386	1.48 690	9.99 977	8
6780	53	8.51 673	382	5.31 450	5.31 427	8.51 696	383	1.48 304	9.99 977	7
6840	54	8.52 055	379	5.31 450	5.31 427	8.52 079	380	1.47 921	9.99 976	6
6900	55	8.52 434	376	5.31 451	5.31 426	8.52 459	376	1.47 541	9.99 976	5
6960	56	8.52 810	373	5.31 451	5.31 426	8.52 835	373	1.47 165	9.99 975	4
7020	57	8.53 183	369	5.31 451	5.31 426	8.53 208	370	1.46 792	9.99 975	3
7080	58	8.53 552	367	5.31 451	5.31 425	8.53 578	367	1.46 422	9.99 974	2
7140	59	8.53 919	363	5.31 451	5.31 425	8.53 945	363	1.46 055	9.99 974	1
7200	**60**	8.54 282		5.31 451	5.31 425	8.54 308		1.45 692	9.99 974	**0**
″	′	L. Cos.	d.	C. S.	C. T.	L. Cot.	c.d.	L. Tan.	L. Sin.	′

91° (271°) (268°) **88°**

2° (182°) (357°) **177°**

″	′	L. Sin.	d.	C. S.	C. T.	L. Tan.	c.d.	L. Cot.	L. Cos.	′
7200	**0**	8.54 282	360	5.31 451	5.31 425	8.54 308	361	1.45 692	9.99 974	**60**
7260	1	8.54 642	357	5.31 451	5.31 425	8.54 669	358	1.45 331	9.99 973	59
7320	2	8.54 999	355	5.31 452	5.31 424	8.55 027	355	1.44 973	9.99 973	58
7380	3	8.55 354	351	5.31 452	5.31 424	8.55 382	352	1.44 618	9.99 972	57
7440	4	8.55 705	349	5.31 452	5.31 424	8.55 734	349	1.44 266	9.99 972	56
7500	5	8.56 054	346	5.31 452	5.31 423	8.56 083	346	1.43 917	9.99 971	55
7560	6	8.56 400	343	5.31 452	5.31 423	8.56 429	344	1.43 571	9.99 971	54
7620	7	8.56 743	341	5.31 452	5.31 423	8.56 773	341	1.43 227	9.99 970	53
7680	8	8.57 084	337	5.31 453	5.31 422	8.57 114	338	1.42 886	9.99 970	52
7740	9	8.57 421	336	5.31 453	5.31 422	8.57 452	336	1.42 548	9.99 969	51
7800	**10**	8.57 757	332	5.31 453	5.31 422	8.57 788	333	1.42 212	9.99 969	**50**
7860	11	8.58 089	330	5.31 453	5.31 421	8.58 121	330	1.41 879	9.99 968	49
7920	12	8.58 419	328	5.31 453	5.31 421	8.58 451	328	1.41 549	9.99 968	48
7980	13	8.58 747	325	5.31 453	5.31 421	8.58 779	326	1.41 221	9.99 967	47
8040	14	8.59 072	323	5.31 454	5.31 421	8.59 105	323	1.40 895	9.99 967	46
8100	15	8.59 395	320	5.31 454	5.31 420	8.59 428	321	1.40 572	9.99 967	45
8160	16	8.59 715	318	5.31 454	5.31 420	8.59 749	319	1.40 251	9.99 966	44
8220	17	8.60 033	316	5.31 454	5.31 420	8.60 068	316	1.39 932	9.99 966	43
8280	18	8.60 349	313	5.31 454	5.31 419	8.60 384	314	1.39 616	9.99 965	42
8340	19	8.60 662	311	5.31 454	5.31 419	8.60 698	311	1.39 302	9.99 964	41
8400	**20**	8.60 973	309	5.31 455	5.31 418	8.61 009	310	1.38 991	9.99 964	**40**
8460	21	8.61 282	307	5.31 455	5.31 418	8.61 319	307	1.38 681	9.99 963	39
8520	22	8.61 589	305	5.31 455	5.31 418	8.61 626	305	1.38 374	9.99 963	38
8580	23	8.61 894	302	5.31 455	5.31 417	8.61 931	303	1.38 069	9.99 962	37
8640	24	8.62 196	301	5.31 455	5.31 417	8.62 234	301	1.37 766	9.99 962	36
8700	25	8.62 497	298	5.31 455	5.31 417	8.62 535	299	1.37 465	9.99 961	35
8760	26	8.62 795	296	5.31 456	5.31 416	8.62 834	297	1.37 166	9.99 961	34
8820	27	8.63 091	294	5.31 456	5.31 416	8.63 131	295	1.36 869	9.99 960	33
8880	28	8.63 385	293	5.31 456	5.31 416	8.63 426	292	1.36 574	9.99 960	32
8940	29	8.63 678	290	5.31 456	5.31 415	8.63 718	291	1.36 282	9.99 959	31
9000	**30**	8.63 968	288	5.31 456	5.31 415	8.64 009	289	1.35 991	9.99 959	**30**
9060	31	8.64 256	287	5.31 456	5.31 415	8.64 298	287	1.35 702	9.99 958	29
9120	32	8.64 543	284	5.31 457	5.31 414	8.64 585	285	1.35 415	9.99 958	28
9180	33	8.64 827	283	5.31 457	5.31 414	8.64 870	284	1.35 130	9.99 957	27
9240	34	8.65 110	281	5.31 457	5.31 413	8.65 154	281	1.34 846	9.99 956	26
9300	35	8.65 391	279	5.31 457	5.31 413	8.65 435	280	1.34 565	9.99 956	25
9360	36	8.65 670	277	5.31 457	5.31 413	8.65 715	278	1.34 285	9.99 955	24
9420	37	8.65 947	276	5.31 458	5.31 412	8.65 993	276	1.34 007	9.99 955	23
9480	38	8.66 223	274	5.31 458	5.31 412	8.66 269	274	1.33 731	9.99 954	22
9540	39	8.66 497	272	5.31 458	5.31 412	8.66 543	273	1.33 457	9.99 954	21
9600	**40**	8.66 769	270	5.31 458	5.31 411	8.66 816	271	1.33 184	9.99 953	**20**
9660	41	8.67 039	269	5.31 458	5.31 411	8.67 087	269	1.32 913	9.99 952	19
9720	42	8.67 308	267	5.31 459	5.31 410	8.67 356	268	1.32 644	9.99 952	18
9780	43	8.67 575	266	5.31 459	5.31 410	8.67 624	266	1.32 376	9.99 951	17
9840	44	8.67 841	263	5.31 459	5.31 410	8.67 890	264	1.32 110	9.99 951	16
9900	45	8.68 104	263	5.31 459	5.31 409	8.68 154	263	1.31 846	9.99 950	15
9960	46	8.68 367	260	5.31 459	5.31 409	8.68 417	261	1.31 583	9.99 949	14
10020	47	8.68 627	259	5.31 460	5.31 408	8.68 678	260	1.31 322	9.99 949	13
10080	48	8.68 886	258	5.31 460	5.31 408	8.68 938	258	1.31 062	9.99 948	12
10140	49	8.69 144	256	5.31 460	5.31 408	8.69 196	257	1.30 804	9.99 948	11
10200	**50**	8.69 400	254	5.31 460	5.31 407	8.69 453	255	1.30 547	9.99 947	**10**
10260	51	8.69 654	253	5.31 460	5.31 407	8.69 708	254	1.30 292	9.99 946	9
10320	52	8.69 907	252	5.31 461	5.31 406	8.69 962	252	1.30 038	9.99 946	8
10380	53	8.70 159	250	5.31 461	5.31 406	8.70 214	251	1.29 786	9.99 945	7
10440	54	8.70 409	249	5.31 461	5.31 405	8.70 465	249	1.29 535	9.99 944	6
10500	55	8.70 658	247	5.31 461	5.31 405	8.70 714	248	1.29 286	9.99 944	5
10560	56	8.70 905	246	5.31 461	5.31 405	8.70 962	246	1.29 038	9.99 943	4
10620	57	8.71 151	244	5.31 462	5.31 404	8.71 208	245	1.28 792	9.99 942	3
10680	58	8.71 395	243	5.31 462	5.31 404	8.71 453	244	1.28 547	9.99 942	2
10740	59	8.71 638	242	5.31 462	5.31 403	8.71 697	243	1.28 303	9.99 941	1
10800	**60**	8.71 880		5.31 462	5.31 403	8.71 940		1.28 060	9.99 940	**0**
″	′	L. Cos.	d.	C. S.	C. T.	L. Cot.	c.d.	L. Tan.	L. Sin.	′

92° (272°) (267°) **87°**

′	L. Sin.	d.	L. Tan.	c.d.	L. Cot.	L. Cos.	′
0	8.71 880	240	8.71 940	241	1.28 060	9.99 940	**60**
1	8.72 120	239	8.72 181	239	1.27 819	9.99 940	59
2	8.72 359	238	8.72 420	239	1.27 580	9.99 939	58
3	8.72 597	237	8.72 659	237	1.27 341	9.99 938	57
4	8.72 834	235	8.72 896	236	1.27 104	9.99 938	56
5	8.73 069	234	8.73 132	234	1.26 868	9.99 937	55
6	8.73 303	232	8.73 366	234	1.26 634	9.99 936	54
7	8.73 535	232	8.73 600	232	1.26 400	9.99 936	53
8	8.73 767	230	8.73 832	231	1.26 168	9.99 935	52
9	8.73 997	229	8.74 063	229	1.25 937	9.99 934	51
10	8.74 226	228	8.74 292	229	1.25 708	9.99 934	**50**
11	8.74 454	226	8.74 521	227	1.25 479	9.99 933	49
12	8.74 680	226	8.74 748	226	1.25 252	9.99 932	48
13	8.74 906	224	8.74 974	225	1.25 026	9.99 932	47
14	8.75 130	223	8.75 199	224	1.24 801	9.99 931	46
15	8.75 353	222	8.75 423	222	1.24 577	9.99 930	45
16	8.75 575	220	8.75 645	222	1.24 355	9.99 929	44
17	8.75 795	220	8.75 867	220	1.24 133	9.99 929	43
18	8.76 015	219	8.76 087	219	1.23 913	9.99 928	42
19	8.76 234	217	8.76 306	219	1.23 694	9.99 927	41
20	8.76 451	216	8.76 525	217	1.23 475	9.99 926	**40**
21	8.76 667	216	8.76 742	216	1.23 258	9.99 926	39
22	8.76 883	214	8.76 958	215	1.23 042	9.99 925	38
23	8.77 097	213	8.77 173	214	1.22 827	9.99 924	37
24	8.77 310	212	8.77 387	213	1.22 613	9.99 923	36
25	8.77 522	211	8.77 600	211	1.22 400	9.99 923	35
26	8.77 733	210	8.77 811	211	1.22 189	9.99 922	34
27	8.77 943	209	8.78 022	210	1.21 978	9.99 921	33
28	8.78 152	208	8.78 232	209	1.21 768	9.99 920	32
29	8.78 360	208	8.78 441	208	1.21 559	9.99 920	31
30	8.78 568	206	8.78 649	206	1.21 351	9.99 919	**30**
31	8.78 774	205	8.78 855	206	1.21 145	9.99 918	29
32	8.78 979	204	8.79 061	205	1.20 939	9.99 917	28
33	8.79 183	203	8.79 266	204	1.20 734	9.99 917	27
34	8.79 386	202	8.79 470	203	1.20 530	9.99 916	26
35	8.79 588	201	8.79 673	202	1.20 327	9.99 915	25
36	8.79 789	201	8.79 875	201	1.20 125	9.99 914	24
37	8.79 990	199	8.80 076	201	1.19 924	9.99 913	23
38	8.80 189	199	8.80 277	199	1.19 723	9.99 913	22
39	8.80 388	197	8.80 476	198	1.19 524	9.99 912	21
40	8.80 585	197	8.80 674	198	1.19 326	9.99 911	**20**
41	8.80 782	196	8.80 872	196	1.19 128	9.99 910	19
42	8.80 978	195	8.81 068	196	1.18 932	9.99 909	18
43	8.81 173	194	8.81 264	195	1.18 736	9.99 909	17
44	8.81 367	193	8.81 459	194	1.18 541	9.99 908	16
45	8.81 560	192	8.81 653	193	1.18 347	9.99 907	15
46	8.81 752	192	8.81 846	192	1.18 154	9.99 906	14
47	8.81 944	190	8.82 038	192	1.17 962	9.99 905	13
48	8.82 134	190	8.82 230	190	1.17 770	9.99 904	12
49	8.82 324	189	8.82 420	190	1.17 580	9.99 904	11
50	8.82 513	188	8.82 610	189	1.17 390	9.99 903	**10**
51	8.82 701	187	8.82 799	188	1.17 201	9.99 902	9
52	8.82 888	187	8.82 987	188	1.17 013	9.99 901	8
53	8.83 075	186	8.83 175	186	1.16 825	9.99 900	7
54	8.83 261	185	8.83 361	186	1.16 639	9.99 899	6
55	8.83 446	184	8.83 547	185	1.16 453	9.99 898	5
56	8.83 630	183	8.83 732	184	1.16 268	9.99 898	4
57	8.83 813	183	8.83 916	184	1.16 084	9.99 897	3
58	8.83 996	181	8.84 100	182	1.15 900	9.99 896	2
59	8.84 177	181	8.84 282	182	1.15 718	9.99 895	1
60	8.84 358		8.84 464		1.15 536	9.99 894	**0**
′	L. Cos.	d.	L. Cot.	c.d	L. Tan.	L. Sin.	′

P. P.

″	**241**	**239**	**237**	**235**	**234**
1	4.0	4.0	4.0	3.9	3.9
2	8.0	8.0	7.9	7.8	7.8
3	12.0	12.0	11.8	11.8	11.7
4	16.1	15.9	15.8	15.7	15.6
5	20.1	19.9	19.8	19.6	19.5
6	24.1	23.9	23.7	23.5	23.4
7	28.1	27.9	27.6	27.4	27.3
8	32.1	31.9	31.6	31.3	31.2
9	36.2	35.8	35.6	35.2	35.1

″	**232**	**229**	**227**	**225**	**223**
1	3.9	3.8	3.8	3.8	3.7
2	7.7	7.6	7.6	7.5	7.4
3	11.6	11.4	11.4	11.2	11.2
4	15.5	15.3	15.1	15.0	14.9
5	19.3	19.1	18.9	18.8	18.6
6	23.2	22.9	22.7	22.5	22.3
7	27.1	26.7	26.5	26.2	26.0
8	30.9	30.5	30.3	30.0	29.7
9	34.8	34.4	34.0	33.8	33.4

″	**222**	**220**	**217**	**215**	**213**
1	3.7	3.7	3.6	3.6	3.6
2	7.4	7.3	7.2	7.2	7.1
3	11.1	11.0	10.8	10.8	10.6
4	14.8	14.7	14.5	14.3	14.2
5	18.5	18.3	18.1	17.9	17.8
6	22.2	22.0	21.7	21.5	21.3
7	25.9	25.7	25.3	25.1	24.8
8	29.6	29.3	28.9	28.7	28.4
9	33.3	33.0	32.6	32.2	32.0

″	**211**	**208**	**206**	**203**	**201**
1	3.5	3.5	3.4	3.4	3.4
2	7.0	6.9	6.9	6.8	6.7
3	10.6	10.4	10.3	10.2	10.0
4	14.1	13.9	13.7	13.5	13.4
5	17.6	17.3	17.2	16.9	16.8
6	21.1	20.8	20.6	20.3	20.1
7	24.6	24.3	24.0	23.7	23.4
8	28.1	27.7	27.5	27.1	26.8
9	31.6	31.2	30.9	30.4	30.2

″	**199**	**197**	**195**	**193**	**192**
1	3.3	3.3	3.2	3.2	3.2
2	6.6	6.6	6.5	6.4	6.4
3	10.0	9.8	9.8	9.6	9.6
4	13.3	13.1	13.0	12.9	12.8
5	16.6	16.4	16.2	16.1	16.0
6	19.9	19.7	19.5	19.3	19.2
7	23.2	23.0	22.8	22.5	22.4
8	26.5	26.3	26.0	25.7	25.6
9	29.8	29.6	29.2	29.0	28.8

″	**189**	**187**	**185**	**183**	**181**
1	3.2	3.1	3.1	3.0	3.0
2	6.3	6.2	6.2	6.1	6.0
3	9.4	9.4	9.2	9.2	9.0
4	12.6	12.5	12.3	12.2	12.1
5	15.8	15.6	15.4	15.2	15.1
6	18.9	18.7	18.5	18.3	18.1
7	22.0	21.8	21.6	21.4	21.1
8	25.2	24.9	24.7	24.4	24.1
9	28.4	28.0	27.8	27.4	27.2
10	31.5	31.2	30.8	30.5	30.2

P. P.

4° (184°) (355°) **175°**

′	L. Sin.	d.	L. Tan.	c.d.	L. Cot.	L. Cos.	′	P. P.					
0	8.84 358	181	8.84 464	182	1.15 536	9.99 894	**60**	″	**182**	**181**	**179**	**178**	**17**
1	8.84 539	179	8.84 646	180	1.15 354	9.99 893	59	1	3.0	3.0	3.0	3.0	3
2	8.84 718	179	8.84 826	180	1.15 174	9.99 892	58	2	6.1	6.0	6.0	5.9	5
3	8.84 897	178	8.85 006	179	1.14 994	9.99 891	57	3	9.1	9.0	9.0	8.9	8
4	8.85 075	177	8.85 185	178	1.14 815	9.99 891	56	4	12.1	12.1	11.9	11.9	11
5	8.85 252	177	8.85 363	177	1.14 637	9.99 890	55	5	15.2	15.1	14.9	14.8	14
6	8.85 429	176	8.85 540	177	1.14 460	9.99 889	54	6	18.2	18.1	17.9	17.8	17
7	8.85 605	175	8.85 717	176	1.14 283	9.99 888	53	7	21.2	21.1	20.9	20.8	20
8	8.85 780	175	8.85 893	176	1.14 107	9.99 887	52	8	24.3	24.1	23.9	23.7	23
9	8.85 955	173	8.86 069	174	1.13 931	9.99 886	51	9	27.3	27.2	26.8	26.7	26
10	8.86 128	173	8.86 243	174	1.13 757	9.99 885	**50**	″	**176**	**175**	**174**	**173**	**17**
11	8.86 301	173	8.86 417	174	1.13 583	9.99 884	49	1	2.9	2.9	2.9	2.9	2
12	8.86 474	171	8.86 591	172	1.13 409	9.99 883	48	2	5.9	5.8	5.8	5.8	5.
13	8.86 645	171	8.86 763	172	1.13 237	9.99 882	47	3	8.8	8.8	8.7	8.6	8
14	8.86 816	171	8.86 935	171	1.13 065	9.99 881	46	4	11.7	11.7	11.6	11.5	11.
15	8.86 987	169	8.87 106	171	1.12 894	9.99 880	45	5	14.7	14.6	14.5	14.4	14.
16	8.87 156	169	8.87 277	170	1.12 723	9.99 879	44	6	17.6	17.5	17.4	17.3	17.
17	8.87 325	169	8.87 447	169	1.12 553	9.99 879	43	7	20.5	20.4	20.3	20.2	20.
18	8.87 494	167	8.87 616	169	1.12 384	9.99 878	42	8	23.5	23.3	23.2	23.1	22.
19	8.87 661	168	8.87 785	168	1.12 215	9.99 877	41	9	26.4	26.2	26.1	26.0	25.
20	8.87 829	166	8.87 953	167	1.12 047	9.99 876	**40**	″	**171**	**170**	**169**	**168**	**16**
21	8.87 995	166	8.88 120	167	1.11 880	9.99 875	39	1	2.8	2.8	2.8	2.8	2.
22	8.88 161	165	8.88 287	166	1.11 713	9.99 874	38	2	5.7	5.7	5.6	5.6	5.
23	8.88 326	164	8.88 453	165	1.11 547	9.99 873	37	3	8.6	8.5	8.4	8.4	8.
24	8.88 490	164	8.88 618	165	1.11 382	9.99 872	36	4	11.4	11.3	11.3	11.2	11.
25	8.88 654	163	8.88 783	165	1.11 217	9.99 871	35	5	14.2	14.2	14.1	14.0	13.
26	8.88 817	163	8.88 948	163	1.11 052	9.99 870	34	6	17.1	17.0	16.9	16.8	16.
27	8.88 980	162	8.89 111	163	1.10 889	9.99 869	33	7	20.0	19.8	19.7	19.6	19.
28	8.89 142	162	8.89 274	163	1.10 726	9.99 868	32	8	22.8	22.7	22.5	22.4	22.
29	8.89 304	160	8.89 437	161	1.10 563	9.99 867	31	9	25.6	25.5	25.4	25.2	25.
30	8.89 464	161	8.89 598	162	1.10 402	9.99 866	**30**	″	**166**	**165**	**164**	**163**	**16**
31	8.89 625	159	8.89 760	160	1.10 240	9.99 865	29	1	2.8	2.8	2.7	2.7	2.
32	8.89 784	159	8.89 920	160	1.10 080	9.99 864	28	2	5.5	5.5	5.5	5.4	5.
33	8.89 943	159	8.90 080	160	1.09 920	9.99 863	27	3	8.3	8.2	8.2	8.2	8.
34	8.90 102	158	8.90 240	159	1.09 760	9.99 862	26	4	11.1	11.0	10.9	10.9	10.
35	8.90 260	157	8.90 399	158	1.09 601	9.99 861	25	5	13.8	13.8	13.7	13.6	13.
36	8.90 417	157	8.90 557	158	1.09 443	9.99 860	24	6	16.6	16.5	16.4	16.3	16.
37	8.90 574	156	8.90 715	157	1.09 285	9.99 859	23	7	19.4	19.2	19.1	19.0	18.
38	8.90 730	155	8.90 872	157	1.09 128	9.99 858	22	8	22.1	22.0	21.9	21.7	21.
39	8.90 885	155	8.91 029	156	1.08 971	9.99 857	21	9	24.9	24.8	24.6	24.4	24.
40	8.91 040	155	8.91 185	155	1.08 815	9.99 856	**20**	″	**161**	**160**	**159**	**158**	**15**
41	8.91 195	154	8.91 340	155	1.08 660	9.99 855	19	1	2.7	2.7	2.6	2.6	2.
42	8.91 349	153	8.91 495	155	1.08 505	9.99 854	18	2	5.4	5.3	5.3	5.3	5.
43	8.91 502	153	8.91 650	153	1.08 350	9.99 853	17	3	8.0	8.0	8.0	7.9	7.
44	8.91 655	152	8.91 803	154	1.08 197	9.99 852	16	4	10.7	10.7	10.6	10.5	10.
45	8.91 807	152	8.91 957	153	1.08 043	9.99 851	15	5	13.4	13.3	13.2	13.2	13.
46	8.91 959	151	8.92 110	152	1.07 890	9.99 850	14	6	16.1	16.0	15.9	15.8	15.
47	8.92 110	151	8.92 262	152	1.07 738	9.99 848	13	7	18.8	18.7	18.6	18.4	18.
48	8.92 261	150	8.92 414	151	1.07 586	9.99 847	12	8	21.5	21.3	21.2	21.1	20.
49	8.92 411	150	8.92 565	151	1.07 435	9.99 846	11	9	24.2	24.0	23.8	23.7	23.
50	8.92 561	149	8.92 716	150	1.07 284	9.99 845	**10**	″	**156**	**155**	**154**	**153**	**15**
51	8.92 710	149	8.92 866	150	1.07 134	9.99 844	9	1	2.6	2.6	2.6	2.6	2.
52	8.92 859	148	8.93 016	149	1.06 984	9.99 843	8	2	5.2	5.2	5.1	5.1	5.
53	8.93 007	147	8.93 165	148	1.06 835	9.99 842	7	3	7.8	7.8	7.7	7.6	7.
54	8.93 154	147	8.93 313	149	1.06 687	9.99 841	6	4	10.4	10.3	10.3	10.2	10.
55	8.93 301	147	8.93 462	147	1.06 538	9.99 840	5	5	13.0	12.9	12.8	12.8	12.
56	8.93 448	146	8.93 609	147	1.06 391	9.99 839	4	6	15.6	15.5	15.4	15.3	15.
57	8.93 594	146	8.93 756	147	1.06 244	9.99 838	3	7	18.2	18.1	18.0	17.8	17.
58	8.93 740	145	8.93 903	146	1.06 097	9.99 837	2	8	20.8	20.7	20.5	20.4	20.
59	8.93 885	145	8.94 049	146	1.05 951	9.99 836	1	9	23.4	23.2	23.1	23.0	22.
60	8.94 030		8.94 195		1.05 805	9.99 834	**0**	10	26.0	25.8	25.7	25.5	25.
′	L. Cos.	d.	L. Cot.	c.d.	L. Tan.	L. Sin.	′	P. P.					

94° (274°) (265°) **85°**

′	L. Sin.	d.	L. Tan.	c.d.	L. Cot.	L. Cos.	′	P. P.					
0	8.94 030	144	8.94 195	145	1.05 805	9.99 834	**60**	″	**151**	**149**	**148**	**147**	**146**
1	8.94 174	143	8.94 340	145	1.05 660	9.99 833	59	1	2.5	2.5	2.5	2.4	2.4
2	8.94 317	144	8.94 485	145	1.05 515	9.99 832	58	2	5.0	5.0	4.9	4.9	4.9
3	8.94 461	142	8.94 630	143	1.05 370	9.99 831	57	3	7.6	7.4	7.4	7.4	7.3
4	8.94 603	143	8.94 773	144	1.05 227	9.99 830	56	4	10.1	9.9	9.9	9.8	9.7
5	8.94 746	141	8.94 917	143	1.05 083	9.99 829	55	5	12.6	12.4	12.3	12.2	12.2
6	8.94 887	142	8.95 060	142	1.04 940	9.99 828	54	6	15.1	14.9	14.8	14.7	14.6
7	8.95 029	141	8.95 202	142	1.04 798	9.99 827	53	7	17.6	17.4	17.3	17.2	17.0
8	8.95 170	140	8.95 344	142	1.04 656	9.99 825	52	8	20.1	19.9	19.7	19.6	19.5
9	8.95 310	140	8.95 486	141	1.04 514	9.99 824	51	9	22.6	22.4	22.2	22.0	21.9
10	8.95 450	139	8.95 627	140	1.04 373	9.99 823	**50**	″	**145**	**144**	**143**	**142**	**141**
11	8.95 589	139	8.95 767	141	1.04 233	9.99 822	49	1	2.4	2.4	2.4	2.4	2.4
12	8.95 728	139	8.95 908	139	1.04 092	9.99 821	48	2	4.8	4.8	4.8	4.7	4.7
13	8.95 867	138	8.96 047	140	1.03 953	9.99 820	47	3	7.2	7.2	7.2	7.1	7.0
14	8.96 005	138	8.96 187	138	1.03 813	9.99 819	46	4	9.7	9.6	9.5	9.5	9.4
15	8.96 143	137	8.96 325	139	1.03 675	9.99 817	45	5	12.1	12.0	11.9	11.8	11.8
16	8.96 280	137	8.96 464	138	1.03 536	9.99 816	44	6	14.5	14.4	14.3	14.2	14.1
17	8.96 417	136	8.96 602	137	1.03 398	9.99 815	43	7	16.9	16.8	16.7	16.6	16.4
18	8.96 553	136	8.96 739	138	1.03 261	9.99 814	42	8	19.3	19.2	19.1	18.9	18.8
19	8.96 689	136	8.96 877	136	1.03 123	9.99 813	41	9	21.8	21.6	21.4	21.3	21.2
20	8.96 825	135	8.97 013	137	1.02 987	9.99 812	**40**	″	**140**	**139**	**138**	**137**	**136**
21	8.96 960	135	8.97 150	135	1.02 850	9.99 810	39	1	2.3	2.3	2.3	2.3	2.3
22	8.97 095	134	8.97 285	136	1.02 715	9.99 809	38	2	4.7	4.6	4.6	4.6	4.5
23	8.97 229	134	8.97 421	135	1.02 579	9.99 808	37	3	7.0	7.0	6.9	6.8	6.8
24	8.97 363	133	8.97 556	135	1.02 444	9.99 807	36	4	9.3	9.3	9.2	9.1	9.1
25	8.97 496	133	8.97 691	134	1.02 309	9.99 806	35	5	11.7	11.6	11.5	11.4	11.3
26	8.97 629	133	8.97 825	134	1.02 175	9.99 804	34	6	14.0	13.9	13.8	13.7	13.6
27	8.97 762	132	8.97 959	133	1.02 041	9.99 803	33	7	16.3	16.2	16.1	16.0	15.9
28	8.97 894	132	8.98 092	133	1.01 908	9.99 802	32	8	18.7	18.5	18.4	18.3	18.1
29	8.98 026	131	8.98 225	133	1.01 775	9.99 801	31	9	21.0	20.8	20.7	20.6	20.4
30	8.98 157	131	8.98 358	132	1.01 642	9.99 800	**30**	″	**135**	**134**	**133**	**132**	**131**
31	8.98 288	131	8.98 490	132	1.01 510	9.99 798	29	1	2.2	2.2	2.2	2.2	2.2
32	8.98 419	130	8.98 622	131	1.01 378	9.99 797	28	2	4.5	4.5	4.4	4.4	4.4
33	8.98 549	130	8.98 753	131	1.01 247	9.99 796	27	3	6.8	6.7	6.6	6.6	6.6
34	8.98 679	129	8.98 884	131	1.01 116	9.99 795	26	4	9.0	8.9	8.9	8.8	8.7
35	8.98 808	129	8.99 015	130	1.00 985	9.99 793	25	5	11.2	11.2	11.1	11.0	10.9
36	8.98 937	129	8.99 145	130	1.00 855	9.99 792	24	6	13.5	13.4	13.3	13.2	13.1
37	8.99 066	128	8.99 275	130	1.00 725	9.99 791	23	7	15.8	15.6	15.5	15.4	15.3
38	8.99 194	128	8.99 405	129	1.00 595	9.99 790	22	8	18.0	17.9	17.7	17.6	17.5
39	8.99 322	128	8.99 534	128	1.00 466	9.99 788	21	9	20.2	20.1	20.0	19.8	19.6
40	8.99 450	127	8.99 662	129	1.00 338	9.99 787	**20**	″	**130**	**129**	**128**	**127**	**126**
41	8.99 577	127	8.99 791	128	1.00 209	9.99 786	19	1	2.2	2.2	2.1	2.1	2.1
42	8.99 704	126	8.99 919	127	1.00 081	9.99 785	18	2	4.3	4.3	4.3	4.2	4.2
43	8.99 830	126	9.00 046	128	0.99 954	9.99 783	17	3	6.5	6.4	6.4	6.4	6.3
44	8.99 956	126	9.00 174	127	0.99 826	9.99 782	16	4	8.7	8.6	8.5	8.5	8.4
45	9.00 082	125	9.00 301	126	0.99 699	9.99 781	15	5	10.8	10.8	10.7	10.6	10.5
46	9.00 207	125	9.00 427	126	0.99 573	9.99 780	14	6	13.0	12.9	12.8	12.7	12.6
47	9.00 332	124	9.00 553	126	0.99 447	9.99 778	13	7	15.2	15.0	14.9	14.8	14.7
48	9.00 456	125	9.00 679	126	0.99 321	9.99 777	12	8	17.3	17.2	17.1	16.9	16.8
49	9.00 581	123	9.00 805	125	0.99 195	9.99 776	11	9	19.5	19.4	19.2	19.0	18.9
50	9.00 704	124	9.00 930	125	0.99 070	9.99 775	**10**	″	**125**	**124**	**123**	**122**	**121**
51	9.00 828	123	9.01 055	124	0.98 945	9.99 773	9	1	2.1	2.1	2.0	2.0	2.0
52	9.00 951	123	9.01 179	124	0.98 821	9.99 772	8	2	4.2	4.1	4.1	4.1	4.0
53	9.01 074	122	9.01 303	124	0.98 697	9.99 771	7	3	6.2	6.2	6.2	6.1	6.0
54	9.01 196	122	9.01 427	123	0.98 573	9.99 769	6	4	8.3	8.3	8.2	8.1	8.1
55	9.01 318	122	9.01 550	123	0.98 450	9.99 768	5	5	10.4	10.3	10.2	10.2	10.1
56	9.01 440	121	9.01 673	123	0.98 327	9.99 767	4	6	12.5	12.4	12.3	12.2	12.1
57	9.01 561	121	9.01 796	122	0.98 204	9.99 765	3	7	14.6	14.5	14.4	14.2	14.1
58	9.01 682	121	9.01 918	122	0.98 082	9.99 764	2	8	16.7	16.5	16.4	16.3	16.1
59	9.01 803	120	9.02 040	122	0.97 960	9.99 763	1	9	18.8	18.6	18.4	18.3	18.2
60	9.01 923		9.02 162		0.97 838	9.99 761	**0**	10	20.8	20.7	20.5	20.3	20.2
′	L. Cos.	d.	L. Cot.	c.d.	L. Tan.	L. Sin.	′	P. P.					

6° (186°) (353°) **173°**

′	L. Sin.	d.	L. Tan.	c.d.	L. Cot.	L. Cos.	′
0	9.01 923	120	9.02 162	121	0.97 838	9.99 761	**60**
1	9.02 043	120	9.02 283	121	0.97 717	9.99 760	59
2	9.02 163	120	9.02 404	121	0.97 596	9.99 759	58
3	9.02 283	119	9.02 525̇	120	0.97 475̄	9.99 757	57
4	9.02 402	118	9.02 645̇	121	0.97 355̄	9.99 756	56
5	9.02 520	119	9.02 766	119	0.97 234	9.99 755̄	55
6	9.02 639	118	9.02 885̇	120	0.97 115̄	9.99 753	54
7	9.02 757	117	9.03 005̄	119	0.96 995̇	9.99 752	53
8	9.02 874	118	9.03 124	118	0.96 876	9.99 751	52
9	9.02 992	117	9.03 242	119	0.96 758	9.99 749	51
10	9.03 109	117	9.03 361	118	0.96 639	9.99 748	**50**
11	9.03 226	116	9.03 479	118	0.96 521	9.99 747	49
12	9.03 342	116	9.03 597	117	0.96 403	9.99 745̇	48
13	9.03 458	116	9.03 714	118	0.96 286	9.99 744	47
14	9.03 574	116	9.03 832	116	0.96 168	9.99 742	46
15	9.03 690	115	9.03 948	117	0.96 052	9.99 741	45
16	9.03 805̄	115	9.04 065̇	116	0.95 935̄	9.99 740	44
17	9.03 920	114	9.04 181	116	0.95 819	9.99 738	43
18	9.04 034	115	9.04 297	116	0.95 703	9.99 737	42
19	9.04 149	113	9.04 413	115	0.95 587	9.99 736	41
20	9.04 262	114	9.04 528	115	0.95 472	9.99 734	**40**
21	9.04 376	114	9.04 643	115	0.95 357	9.99 733	39
22	9.04 490	113	9.04 758	115	0.95 242	9.99 731	38
23	9.04 603	112	9.04 873	114	0.95 127	9.99 730	37
24	9.04 715̇	113	9.04 987	114	0.95 013	9.99 728	36
25	9.04 828	112	9.05 101	113	0.94 899	9.99 727	35
26	9.04 940	112	9.05 214	114	0.94 786	9.99 726	34
27	9.05 052	112	9.05 328	113	0.94 672	9.99 724	33
28	9.05 164	111	9.05 441	112	0.94 559	9.99 723	32
29	9.05 275̄	111	9.05 553	113	0.94 447	9.99 721	31
30	9.05 386	111	9.05 666	112	0.94 334	9.99 720	**30**
31	9.05 497	110	9.05 778	112	0.94 222	9.99 718	29
32	9.05 607	110	9.05 890	112	0.94 110	9.99 717	28
33	9.05 717	110	9.06 002	111	0.93 998	9.99 716	27
34	9.05 827	110	9.06 113	111	0.93 887	9.99 714	26
35	9.05 937	109	9.06 224	111	0.93 776	9.99 713	25
36	9.06 046	109	9.06 335̄	110	0.93 665̇	9.99 711	24
37	9.06 155̇	109	9.06 445̇	111	0.93 555̄	9.99 710	23
38	9.06 264	108	9.06 556	110	0.93 444	9.99 708	22
39	9.06 372	109	9.06 666	109	0.93 334	9.99 707	21
40	9.06 481	108	9.06 775̇	110	0.93 225̄	9.99 705̇	**20**
41	9.06 589	107	9.06 885̄	109	0.93 115̇	9.99 704	19
42	9.06 696	108	9.06 994	109	0.93 006	9.99 702	18
43	9.06 804	107	9.07 103	108	0.92 897	9.99 701	17
44	9.06 911	107	9.07 211	109	0.92 789	9.99 699	16
45	9.07 018	106	9.07 320	108	0.92 680	9.99 698	15
46	9.07 124	107	9.07 428	108	0.92 572	9.99 696	14
47	9.07 231	106	9.07 536	107	0.92 464	9.99 695̄	13
48	9.07 337	105	9.07 643	108	0.92 357	9.99 693	12
49	9.07 442	106	9.07 751	107	0.92 249	9.99 692	11
50	9.07 548	105	9.07 858	106	0.92 142	9.99 690	**10**
51	9.07 653	105	9.07 964	107	0.92 036	9.99 689	9
52	9.07 758	105	9.08 071	106	0.91 929	9.99 687	8
53	9.07 863	105	9.08 177	106	0.91 823	9.99 686	7
54	9.07 968	104	9.08 283	106	0.91 717	9.99 684	6
55	9.08 072	104	9.08 389	106	0.91 611	9.99 683	5
56	9.08 176	104	9.08 495̄	105	0.91 505̇	9.99 681	4
57	9.08 280	103	9.08 600	105	0.91 400	9.99 680	3
58	9.08 383	103	9.08 705̇	105	0.91 295̄	9.99 678	2
59	9.08 486	103	9.08 810	104	0.91 190	9.99 677	1
60	9.08 589		9.08 914		0.91 086	9.99 675̇	**0**
′	L. Cos.	d.	L. Cot.	c.d.	L. Tan.	L. Sin.	′

P. P.

″				
″	**121**	**120**	**119**	**118**
1	2.0	2.0	2.0	2.0
2	4.0	4.0	4.0	3.9
3	6.0	6.0	6.0	5.9
4	8.1	8.0	7.9	7.9
5	10.1	10.0	9.9	9.8
6	12.1	12.0	11.9	11.8
7	14.1	14.0	13.9	13.8
8	16.1	16.0	15.9	15.7
9	18.2	18.0	17.8	17.7
10	20.2	20.0	19.8	19.7
20	40.3	40.0	39.7	39.3
30	60.5	60.0	59.5	59.0
40	80.7	80.0	79.3	78.7
50	100.8	100.0	99.2	98.3
″	**117**	**116**	**115**	**114**
1	2.0	1.9	1.9	1.9
2	3.9	3.9	3.8	3.8
3	5.8	5.8	5.8	5.7
4	7.8	7.7	7.7	7.6
5	9.8	9.7	9.6	9.5
6	11.7	11.6	11.5	11.4
7	13.6	13.5̇	13.4	13.3
8	15.6	15.5̄	15.3	15.2
9	17.6	17.4	17.2	17.1
10	19.5	19.3	19.2	19.0
20	39.0	38.7	38.3	38.0
30	58.5	58.0	57.5	57.0
40	78.0	77.3	76.7	76.0
50	97.5	96.7	95.8	95.0
″	**113**	**112**	**111**	**110**
1	1.9	1.9	1.8	1.8
2	3.8	3.7	3.7	3.7
3	5.6	5.6	5.6	5.5
4	7.5̇	7.5̄	7.4	7.3
5	9.4	9.3	9.2	9.2
6	11.3	11.2	11.1	11.0
7	13.2	13.1	13.0	12.8
8	15.1	14.9	14.8	14.7
9	17.0	16.8	16.6	16.5
10	18.8	18.7	18.5	18.3
20	37.7	37.3	37.0	36.7
30	56.5	56.0	55.5	55.0
40	75.3	74.7	74.0	73.3
50	94.2	93.3	92.5	91.7
″	**109**	**108**	**107**	**106**
1	1.8	1.8	1.8	1.8
2	3.6	3.6	3.6	3.5̇
3	5.4	5.4	5.4	5.3
4	7.3	7.2	7.1	7.1
5	9.1	9.0	8.9	8.8
6	10.9	10.8	10.7	10.6
7	12.7	12.6	12.5̄	12.4
8	14.5̇	14.4	14.3	14.1
9	16.4	16.2	16.0	15.9
10	18.2	18.0	17.8	17.7
20	36.3	36.0	35.7	35.3
30	54.5	54.0	53.5	53.0
40	72.7	72.0	71.3	70.7
50	90.8	90.0	89.2	88.3

96° (276°) (263°) **83°**

LOGARITHMS OF THE TRIGONOMETRIC FUNCTIONS

7° (187°) (352°) **172°**

′	L. Sin.	d.	L. Tan.	c.d.	L. Cot.	L. Cos.	′	″	P. P.			
0	9.08 589	103	9.08 914	105	0.91 086	9.99 675	**60**	″	**105**	**104**	**103**	**102**
1	9.08 692	103	9.09 019	104	0.90 981	9.99 674	59	1	1.8	1.7	1.7	1.7
2	9.08 795	102	9.09 123	104	0.90 877	9.99 672	58	2	3.5	3.5	3.4	3.4
3	9.08 897	102	9.09 227	103	0.90 773	9.99 670	57	3	5.2	5.2	5.2	5.1
4	9.08 999	102	9.09 330	104	0.90 670	9.99 669	56	4	7.0	6.9	6.9	6.8
5	9.09 101	101	9.09 434	103	0.90 566	9.99 667	55	5	8.8	8.7	8.6	8.5
6	9.09 202	102	9.09 537	103	0.90 463	9.99 666	54	6	10.5	10.4	10.3	10.2
7	9.09 304	101	9.09 640	102	0.90 360	9.99 664	53	7	12.2	12.1	12.0	11.9
8	9.09 405	101	9.09 742	103	0.90 258	9.99 663	52	8	14.0	13.9	13.7	13.6
9	9.09 506	100	9.09 845	102	0.90 155	9.99 661	51	9	15.8	15.6	15.4	15.3
10	9.09 606	101	9.09 947	102	0.90 053	9.99 659	**50**	10	17.5	17.3	17.2	17.0
11	9.09 707	100	9.10 049	101	0.89 951	9.99 658	49	20	35.0	34.7	34.3	34.0
12	9.09 807	100	9.10 150	102	0.89 850	9.99 656	48	30	52.5	52.0	51.5	51.0
13	9.09 907	99	9.10 252	101	0.89 748	9.99 655	47	40	70.0	69.3	68.7	68.0
14	9.10 006	100	9.10 353	101	0.89 647	9.99 653	46	50	87.5	86.7	85.8	85.0
15	9.10 106	99	9.10 454	101	0.89 546	9.99 651	45	″	**101**	**100**	**99**	**98**
16	9.10 205	99	9.10 555	101	0.89 445	9.99 650	44	1	1.7	1.7	1.6	1.6
17	9.10 304	98	9.10 656	100	0.89 344	9.99 648	43	2	3.4	3.3	3.3	3.3
18	9.10 402	99	9.10 756	100	0.89 244	9.99 647	42	3	5.0	5.0	5.0	4.9
19	9.10 501	98	9.10 856	100	0.89 144	9.99 645	41	4	6.7	6.7	6.6	6.5
20	9.10 599	98	9.10 956	100	0.89 044	9.99 643	**40**	5	8.4	8.3	8.2	8.2
21	9.10 697	98	9.11 056	99	0.88 944	9.99 642	39	6	10.1	10.0	9.9	9.8
22	9.10 795	98	9.11 155	99	0.88 845	9.99 640	38	7	11.8	11.7	11.6	11.4
23	9.10 893	97	9.11 254	99	0.88 746	9.99 638	37	8	13.5	13.3	13.2	13.1
24	9.10 990	97	9.11 353	99	0.88 647	9.99 637	36	9	15.2	15.0	14.8	14.7
25	9.11 087	97	9.11 452	99	0.88 548	9.99 635	35	10	16.8	16.7	16.5	16.3
26	9.11 184	97	9.11 551	98	0.88 449	9.99 633	34	20	33.7	33.3	33.0	32.7
27	9.11 281	96	9.11 649	98	0.88 351	9.99 632	33	30	50.5	50.0	49.5	49.0
28	9.11 377	97	9.11 747	98	0.88 253	9.99 630	32	40	67.3	66.7	66.0	65.3
29	9.11 474	96	9.11 845	98	0.88 155	9.99 629	31	50	84.2	83.3	82.5	81.7
30	9.11 570	96	9.11 943	97	0.88 057	9.99 627	**30**	″	**97**	**96**	**95**	**94**
31	9.11 666	95	9.12 040	98	0.87 960	9.99 625	29	1	1.6	1.6	1.6	1.6
32	9.11 761	96	9.12 138	97	0.87 862	9.99 624	28	2	3.2	3.2	3.2	3.1
33	9.11 857	95	9.12 235	97	0.87 765	9.99 622	27	3	4.8	4.8	4.8	4.7
34	9.11 952	95	9.12 332	96	0.87 668	9.99 620	26	4	6.5	6.4	6.3	6.3
35	9.12 047	95	9.12 428	97	0.87 572	9.99 618	25	5	8.1	8.0	7.9	7.8
36	9.12 142	94	9.12 525	96	0.87 475	9.99 617	24	6	9.7	9.6	9.5	9.4
37	9.12 236	95	9.12 621	96	0.87 379	9.99 615	23	7	11.3	11.2	11.1	11.0
38	9.12 331	94	9.12 717	96	0.87 283	9.99 613	22	8	12.9	12.8	12.7	12.5
39	9.12 425	94	9.12 813	96	0.87 187	9.99 612	21	9	14.6	14.4	14.2	14.1
40	9.12 519	93	9.12 909	95	0.87 091	9.99 610	**20**	10	16.2	16.0	15.8	15.7
41	9.12 612	94	9.13 004	95	0.86 996	9.99 608	19	20	32.3	32.0	31.7	31.3
42	9.12 706	93	9.13 099	95	0.86 901	9.99 607	18	30	48.5	48.0	47.5	47.0
43	9.12 799	93	9.13 194	95	0.86 806	9.99 605	17	40	64.7	64.0	63.3	62.7
44	9.12 892	93	9.13 289	95	0.86 711	9.99 603	16	50	80.8	80.0	79.2	78.3
45	9.12 985	93	9.13 384	94	0.86 616	9.99 601	15	″	**93**	**92**	**91**	**90**
46	9.13 078	93	9.13 478	95	0.86 522	9.99 600	14	1	1.6	1.5	1.5	1.5
47	9.13 171	92	9.13 573	94	0.86 427	9.99 598	13	2	3.1	3.1	3.0	3.0
48	9.13 263	92	9.13 667	94	0.86 333	9.99 596	12	3	4.6	4.6	4.6	4.5
49	9.13 355	92	9.13 761	93	0.86 239	9.99 595	11	4	6.2	6.1	6.1	6.0
50	9.13 447	92	9.13 854	94	0.86 146	9.99 593	**10**	5	7.8	7.7	7.6	7.5
51	9.13 539	91	9.13 948	93	0.86 052	9.99 591	9	6	9.3	9.2	9.1	9.0
52	9.13 630	92	9.14 041	93	0.85 959	9.99 589	8	7	10.8	10.7	10.6	10.5
53	9.13 722	91	9.14 134	93	0.85 866	9.99 588	7	8	12.4	12.3	12.1	12.0
54	9.13 813	91	9.14 227	93	0.85 773	9.99 586	6	9	14.0	13.8	13.6	13.5
55	9.13 904	90	9.14 320	92	0.85 680	9.99 584	5	10	15.5	15.3	15.2	15.0
56	9.13 994	91	9.14 412	92	0.85 588	9.99 582	4	20	31.0	30.7	30.3	30.0
57	9.14 085	90	9.14 504	93	0.85 496	9.99 581	3	30	46.5	46.0	45.5	45.0
58	9.14 175	91	9.14 597	91	0.85 403	9.99 579	2	40	62.0	61.3	60.7	60.0
59	9.14 266	90	9.14 688	92	0.85 312	9.99 577	1	50	77.5	76.7	75.8	75.0
60	9.14 356		9.14 780		0.85 220	9.99 575	**0**					
′	L. Cos.	d.	L. Cot.	c.d.	L. Tan.	L. Sin.	′		P. P.			

97° (277°) (262°) **82°**

8° (188°) (351°) **171°**

′	L. Sin.	d.	L. Tan.	c.d.	L. Cot.	L. Cos.	′
0	9.14 356	89	9.14 780	92	0.85 220	9.99 575̇	**60**
1	9.14 445̇	90	9.14 872	91	0.85 128	9.99 574	59
2	9.14 535̄	89	9.14 963	91	0.85 037	9.99 572	58
3	9.14 624	90	9.15 054	91	0.84 946	9.99 570	57
4	9.14 714	89	9.15 145̇	91	0.84 855̄	9.99 568	56
5	9.14 803	88	9.15 236	91	0.84 764	9.99 566	55
6	9.14 891	89	9.15 327	90	0.84 673	9.99 565̄	54
7	9.14 980	89	9.15 417	91	0.84 583	9.99 563	53
8	9.15 069	88	9.15 508	90	0.84 492	9.99 561	52
9	9.15 157	88	9.15 598	90	0.84 402	9.99 559	51
10	9.15 245̇	88	9.15 688	89	0.84 312	9.99 557	**50**
11	9.15 333	88	9.15 777	90	0.84 223	9.99 556	49
12	9.15 421	87	9.15 867	89	0.84 133	9.99 554	48
13	9.15 508	88	9.15 956	90	0.84 044	9.99 552	47
14	9.15 596	87	9.16 046	89	0.83 954	9.99 550	46
15	9.15 683	87	9.16 135̄	89	0.83 865̇	9.99 548	45
16	9.15 770	87	9.16 224	88	0.83 776	9.99 546	44
17	9.15 857	87	9.16 312	89	0.83 688	9.99 545̄	43
18	9.15 944	86	9.16 401	88	0.83 599	9.99 543	42
19	9.16 030	86	9.16 489	88	0.83 511	9.99 541	41
20	9.16 116	87	9.16 577	88	0.83 423	9.99 539	**40**
21	9.16 203	86	9.16 665̇	88	0.83 335̄	9.99 537	39
22	9.16 289	85	9.16 753	88	0.83 247	9.99 535̇	38
23	9.16 374	86	9.16 841	87	0.83 159	9.99 533	37
24	9.16 460	85	9.16 928	88	0.83 072	9.99 532	36
25	9.16 545̇	86	9.17 016	87	0.82 984	9.99 530	35
26	9.16 631	85	9.17 103	87	0.82 897	9.99 528	34
27	9.16 716	85	9.17 190	87	0.82 810	9.99 526	33
28	9.16 801	85	9.17 277	86	0.82 723	9.99 524	32
29	9.16 886	84	9.17 363	87	0.82 637	9.99 522	31
30	9.16 970	85	9.17 450	86	0.82 550	9.99 520	**30**
31	9.17 055̄	84	9.17 536	86	0.82 464	9.99 518	29
32	9.17 139	84	9.17 622	86	0.82 378	9.99 517	28
33	9.17 223	84	9.17 708	86	0.82 292	9.99 515̄	27
34	9.17 307	84	9.17 794	86	0.82 206	9.99 513	26
35	9.17 391	83	9.17 880	85	0.82 120	9.99 511	25
36	9.17 474	84	9.17 965̇	86	0.82 035̄	9.99 509	24
37	9.17 558	83	9.18 051	85	0.81 949	9.99 507	23
38	9.17 641	83	9.18 136	85	0.81 864	9.99 505̇	22
39	9.17 724	83	9.18 221	85	0.81 779	9.99 503	21
40	9.17 807	83	9.18 306	85	0.81 694	9.99 501	**20**
41	9.17 890	83	9.18 391	84	0.81 609	9.99 499	19
42	9.17 973	82	9.18 475̇	85	0.81 525̄	9.99 497	18
43	9.18 055̇	82	9.18 560	84	0.81 440	9.99 495̇	17
44	9.18 137	83	9.18 644	84	0.81 356	9.99 494	16
45	9.18 220	82	9.18 728	84	0.81 272	9.99 492	15
46	9.18 302	81	9.18 812	84	0.81 188	9.99 490	14
47	9.18 383	82	9.18 896	83	0.81 104	9.99 488	13
48	9.18 465̇	82	9.18 979	84	0.81 021	9.99 486	12
49	9.18 547	81	9.19 063	83	0.80 937	9.99 484	11
50	9.18 628	81	9.19 146	83	0.80 854	9.99 482	**10**
51	9.18 709	81	9.19 229	83	0.80 771	9.99 480	9
52	9.18 790	81	9.19 312	83	0.80 688	9.99 478	8
53	9.18 871	81	9.19 395̇	83	0.80 605̄	9.99 476	7
54	9.18 952	81	9.19 478	83	0.80 522	9.99 474	6
55	9.19 033	80	9.19 561	82	0.80 439	9.99 472	5
56	9.19 113	80	9.19 643	82	0.80 357	9.99 470	4
57	9.19 193	80	9.19 725̇	82	0.80 275̄	9.99 468	3
58	9.19 273	80	9.19 807	82	0.80 193	9.99 466	2
59	9.19 353	80	9.19 889	82	0.80 111	9.99 464	1
60	9.19 433		9.19 971		0.80 029	9.99 462	**0**
′	L. Cos.	d.	L. Cot.	c.d.	L. Tan.	L. Sin.	′

P. P.

″	**92**	**91**	**90**
1	1.5̇	1.5̇	1.5
2	3.1	3.0	3.0
3	4.6	4.6	4.5
4	6.1	6.1	6.0
5	7.7	7.6	7.5
6	9.2	9.1	9.0
7	10.7	10.6	10.5
8	12.3	12.1	12.0
9	13.8	13.6	13.5
10	15.3	15.2	15.0
20	30.7	30.3	30.0
30	46.0	45.5	45.0
40	61.3	60.7	60.0
50	76.7	75.8	75.0
″	**89**	**88**	**87**
1	1.5̄	1.5̄	1.4
2	3.0	2.9	2.9
3	4.4	4.4	4.4
4	5.9	5.9	5.8
5	7.4	7.3	7.2
6	8.9	8.8	8.7
7	10.4	10.3	10.2
8	11.9	11.7	11.6
9	13.4	13.2	13.0
10	14.8	14.7	14.5
20	29.7	29.3	29.0
30	44.5	44.0	43.5
40	59.3	58.7	58.0
50	74.2	73.3	72.5
″	**86**	**85**	**84**
1	1.4	1.4	1.4
2	2.9	2.8	2.8
3	4.3	4.2	4.2
4	5.7	5.7	5.6
5	7.2	7.1	7.0
6	8.6	8.5	8.4
7	10.0	9.9	9.8
8	11.5̄	11.3	11.2
9	12.9	12.8	12.6
10	14.3	14.2	14.0
20	28.7	28.3	28.0
30	43.0	42.5	42.0
40	57.3	56.7	56.0
50	71.7	70.8	70.0
″	**83**	**82**	**81**
1	1.4	1.4	1.4
2	2.8	2.7	2.7
3	4.2	4.1	4.0
4	5.5̇	5.5̄	5.4
5	6.9	6.8	6.8
6	8.3	8.2	8.1
7	9.7	9.6	9.4
8	11.1	10.9	10.8
9	12.4	12.3	12.2
10	13.8	13.7	13.5
20	27.7	27.3	27.0
30	41.5	41.0	40.5
40	55.3	54.7	54.0
50	69.2	68.3	67.5

P. P.

98° (278°) (261°) **81°**

9° (189°) (350°) **170°**

′	L. Sin.	d.	L. Tan.	c.d.	L. Cot.	L. Cos.	′
0	9.19 433	80	9.19 971	82	0.80 029	9.99 462	**60**
1	9.19 513	79	9.20 053	81	0.79 947	9.99 460	59
2	9.19 592	80	9.20 134	82	0.79 866	9.99 458	58
3	9.19 672	79	9.20 216	81	0.79 784	9.99 456	57
4	9.19 751	79	9.20 297	81	0.79 703	9.99 454	56
5	9.19 830	79	9.20 378	81	0.79 622	9.99 452	55
6	9.19 909	79	9.20 459	81	0.79 541	9.99 450	54
7	9.19 988	79	9.20 540	81	0.79 460	9.99 448	53
8	9.20 067	78	9.20 621	80	0.79 379	9.99 446	52
9	9.20 145	78	9.20 701	81	0.79 299	9.99 444	51
10	9.20 223	79	9.20 782	80	0.79 218	9.99 442	**50**
11	9.20 302	78	9.20 862	80	0.79 138	9.99 440	49
12	9.20 380	78	9.20 942	80	0.79 058	9.99 438	48
13	9.20 458	77	9.21 022	80	0.78 978	9.99 436	47
14	9.20 535	78	9.21 102	80	0.78 898	9.99 434	46
15	9.20 613	78	9.21 182	79	0.78 818	9.99 432	45
16	9.20 691	77	9.21 261	80	0.78 739	9.99 429	44
17	9.20 768	77	9.21 341	79	0.78 659	9.99 427	43
18	9.20 845	77	9.21 420	79	0.78 580	9.99 425	42
19	9.20 922	77	9.21 499	79	0.78 501	9.99 423	41
20	9.20 999	77	9.21 578	79	0.78 422	9.99 421	**40**
21	9.21 076	77	9.21 657	79	0.78 343	9.99 419	39
22	9.21 153	76	9.21 736	78	0.78 264	9.99 417	38
23	9.21 229	77	9.21 814	79	0.78 186	9.99 415	37
24	9.21 306	76	9.21 893	78	0.78 107	9.99 413	36
25	9.21 382	76	9.21 971	78	0.78 029	9.99 411	35
26	9.21 458	76	9.22 049	78	0.77 951	9.99 409	34
27	9.21 534	76	9.22 127	78	0.77 873	9.99 407	33
28	9.21 610	75	9.22 205	78	0.77 795	9.99 404	32
29	9.21 685	76	9.22 283	78	0.77 717	9.99 402	31
30	9.21 761	75	9.22 361	77	0.77 639	9.99 400	**30**
31	9.21 836	76	9.22 438	78	0.77 562	9.99 398	29
32	9.21 912	75	9.22 516	77	0.77 484	9.99 396	28
33	9.21 987	75	9.22 593	77	0.77 407	9.99 394	27
34	9.22 062	75	9.22 670	77	0.77 330	9.99 392	26
35	9.22 137	74	9.22 747	77	0.77 253	9.99 390	25
36	9.22 211	75	9.22 824	77	0.77 176	9.99 388	24
37	9.22 286	75	9.22 901	76	0.77 099	9.99 385	23
38	9.22 361	74	9.22 977	77	0.77 023	9.99 383	22
39	9.22 435	74	9.23 054	76	0.76 946	9.99 381	21
40	9.22 509	74	9.23 130	76	0.76 870	9.99 379	**20**
41	9.22 583	74	9.23 206	77	0.76 794	9.99 377	19
42	9.22 657	74	9.23 283	76	0.76 717	9.99 375	18
43	9.22 731	74	9.23 359	76	0.76 641	9.99 372	17
44	9.22 805	73	9.23 435	75	0.76 565	9.99 370	16
45	9.22 878	74	9.23 510	76	0.76 490	9.99 368	15
46	9.22 952	73	9.23 586	75	0.76 414	9.99 366	14
47	9.23 025	73	9.23 661	76	0.76 339	9.99 364	13
48	9.23 098	73	9.23 737	75	0.76 263	9.99 362	12
49	9.23 171	73	9.23 812	75	0.76 188	9.99 359	11
50	9.23 244	73	9.23 887	75	0.76 113	9.99 357	**10**
51	9.23 317	73	9.23 962	75	0.76 038	9.99 355	9
52	9.23 390	72	9.24 037	75	0.75 963	9.99 353	8
53	9.23 462	73	9.24 112	74	0.75 888	9.99 351	7
54	9.23 535	72	9.24 186	75	0.75 814	9.99 348	6
55	9.23 607	72	9.24 261	74	0.75 739	9.99 346	5
56	9.23 679	73	9.24 335	75	0.75 665	9.99 344	4
57	9.23 752	71	9.24 410	74	0.75 590	9.99 342	3
58	9.23 823	72	9.24 484	74	0.75 516	9.99 340	2
59	9.23 895	72	9.24 558	74	0.75 442	9.99 337	1
60	9.23 967		9.24 632		0.75 368	9.99 335	**0**
′	L. Cos.	d.	L. Cot.	c.d.	L. Tan.	L. Sin.	′

P. P.

″	**80**	**79**	**78**	**77**
1	1.3	1.3	1.3	1.3
2	2.7	2.6	2.6	2.6
3	4.0	4.0	3.9	3.8
4	5.3	5.3	5.2	5.1
5	6.7	6.6	6.5	6.4
6	8.0	7.9	7.8	7.7
7	9.3	9.2	9.1	9.0
8	10.7	10.5	10.4	10.3
9	12.0	11.8	11.7	11.6
10	13.3	13.2	13.0	12.8
20	26.7	26.3	26.0	25.7
30	40.0	39.5	39.0	38.5
40	53.3	52.7	52.0	51.3
50	66.7	65.8	65.0	64.2

″	**76**	**75**	**74**	**73**
1	1.3	1.2	1.2	1.2
2	2.5	2.5	2.5	2.4
3	3.8	3.8	3.7	3.6
4	5.1	5.0	4.9	4.9
5	6.3	6.2	6.2	6.1
6	7.6	7.5	7.4	7.3
7	8.9	8.8	8.6	8.5
8	10.1	10.0	9.9	9.7
9	11.4	11.2	11.1	11.0
10	12.7	12.5	12.3	12.2
20	25.3	25.0	24.7	24.3
30	38.0	37.5	37.0	36.5
40	50.7	50.0	49.3	48.7
50	63.3	62.5	61.7	60.8

″	**72**	**71**	**3**	**2**
1	1.2	1.2	0.0	0.0
2	2.4	2.4	0.1	0.1
3	3.6	3.6	0.2	0.1
4	4.8	4.7	0.2	0.1
5	6.0	5.9	0.2	0.2
6	7.2	7.1	0.3	0.2
7	8.4	8.3	0.4	0.2
8	9.6	9.5	0.4	0.3
9	10.8	10.6	0.4	0.3
10	12.0	11.8	0.5	0.3
20	24.0	23.7	1.0	0.7
30	36.0	35.5	1.5	1.0
40	48.0	47.3	2.0	1.3
50	60.0	59.2	2.5	1.7

	3/79	**3/78**	**3/77**
0	13.2	13.0	12.8
1	39.5	39.0	38.5
2	65.8	65.0	64.2
3			

	3/76	**3/75**	**3/74**
0	12.7	12.5	12.3
1	38.0	37.5	37.0
2	63.3	62.5	61.7
3			

P. P.

99° (279°) (260°) **80°**

10° (190°) (349°) **169°**

′	L. Sin.	d.	L. Tan.	c.d.	L. Cot.	L. Cos.	d.	′
0	9.23 967	72	9.24 632	74	0.75 368	9.99 335	2	**60**
1	9.24 039	71	9.24 706	73	0.75 294	9.99 333	2	59
2	9.24 110	71	9.24 779	74	0.75 221	9.99 331	3	58
3	9.24 181	72	9.24 853	73	0.75 147	9.99 328	2	57
4	9.24 253	71	9.24 926	74	0.75 074	9.99 326	2	56
5	9.24 324	71	9.25 000	73	0.75 000	9.99 324	2	55
6	9.24 395	71	9.25 073	73	0.74 927	9.99 322	3	54
7	9.24 466	70	9.25 146	73	0.74 854	9.99 319	2	53
8	9.24 536	71	9.25 219	73	0.74 781	9.99 317	2	52
9	9.24 607	70	9.25 292	73	0.74 708	9.99 315	2	51
10	9.24 677	71	9.25 365	72	0.74 635	9.99 313	3	**50**
11	9.24 748	70	9.25 437	73	0.74 563	9.99 310	2	49
12	9.24 818	70	9.25 510	72	0.74 490	9.99 308	2	48
13	9.24 888	70	9.25 582	73	0.74 418	9.99 306	2	47
14	9.24 958	70	9.25 655	72	0.74 345	9.99 304	3	46
15	9.25 028	70	9.25 727	72	0.74 273	9.99 301	2	45
16	9.25 098	70	9.25 799	72	0.74 201	9.99 299	2	44
17	9.25 168	69	9.25 871	72	0.74 129	9.99 297	3	43
18	9.25 237	70	9.25 943	72	0.74 057	9.99 294	2	42
19	9.25 307	69	9.26 015	71	0.73 985	9.99 292	2	41
20	9.25 376	69	9.26 086	72	0.73 914	9.99 290	2	**40**
21	9.25 445	69	9.26 158	71	0.73 842	9.99 288	3	39
22	9.25 514	69	9.26 229	72	0.73 771	9.99 285	2	38
23	9.25 583	69	9.26 301	71	0.73 699	9.99 283	2	37
24	9.25 652	69	9.26 372	71	0.73 628	9.99 281	3	36
25	9.25 721	69	9.26 443	71	0.73 557	9.99 278	2	35
26	9.25 790	68	9.26 514	71	0.73 486	9.99 276	2	34
27	9.25 858	69	9.26 585	70	0.73 415	9.99 274	3	33
28	9.25 927	68	9.26 655	71	0.73 345	9.99 271	2	32
29	9.25 995	68	9.26 726	71	0.73 274	9.99 269	2	31
30	9.26 063	68	9.26 797	70	0.73 203	9.99 267	3	**30**
31	9.26 131	68	9.26 867	70	0.73 133	9.99 264	2	29
32	9.26 199	68	9.26 937	71	0.73 063	9.99 262	2	28
33	9.26 267	68	9.27 008	70	0.72 992	9.99 260	3	27
34	9.26 335	68	9.27 078	70	0.72 922	9.99 257	2	26
35	9.26 403	67	9.27 148	70	0.72 852	9.99 255	3	25
36	9.26 470	68	9.27 218	70	0.72 782	9.99 252	2	24
37	9.26 538	67	9.27 288	69	0.72 712	9.99 250	2	23
38	9.26 605	67	9.27 357	70	0.72 643	9.99 248	3	22
39	9.26 672	67	9.27 427	69	0.72 573	9.99 245	2	21
40	9.26 739	67	9.27 496	70	0.72 504	9.99 243	2	**20**
41	9.26 806	67	9.27 566	69	0.72 434	9.99 241	3	19
42	9.26 873	67	9.27 635	69	0.72 365	9.99 238	2	18
43	9.26 940	67	9.27 704	69	0.72 296	9.99 236	3	17
44	9.27 007	66	9.27 773	69	0.72 227	9.99 233	2	16
45	9.27 073	67	9.27 842	69	0.72 158	9.99 231	2	15
46	9.27 140	66	9.27 911	69	0.72 089	9.99 229	3	14
47	9.27 206	67	9.27 980	69	0.72 020	9.99 226	2	13
48	9.27 273	66	9.28 049	68	0.71 951	9.99 224	3	12
49	9.27 339	66	9.28 117	69	0.71 883	9.99 221	2	11
50	9.27 405	66	9.28 186	68	0.71 814	9.99 219	2	**10**
51	9.27 471	66	9.28 254	69	0.71 746	9.99 217	3	9
52	9.27 537	65	9.28 323	68	0.71 677	9.99 214	2	8
53	9.27 602	66	9.28 391	68	0.71 609	9.99 212	3	7
54	9.27 668	66	9.28 459	68	0.71 541	9.99 209	2	6
55	9.27 734	65	9.28 527	68	0.71 473	9.99 207	3	5
56	9.27 799	65	9.28 595	67	0.71 405	9.99 204	2	4
57	9.27 864	66	9.28 662	68	0.71 338	9.99 202	2	3
58	9.27 930	65	9.28 730	68	0.71 270	9.99 200	3	2
59	9.27 995	65	9.28 798	67	0.71 202	9.99 197	2	1
60	9.28 060		9.28 865		0.71 135	9.99 195		**0**
′	L. Cos.	d.	L. Cot.	c.d.	L. Tan.	L. Sin.	d.	′

P. P.

″	**74**	**73**	**72**
1	1.2	1.2	1.2
2	2.5	2.4	2.4
3	3.7	3.6	3.6
4	4.9	4.9	4.8
5	6.2	6.1	6.0
6	7.4	7.3	7.2
7	8.6	8.5	8.4
8	9.9	9.7	9.6
9	11.1	11.0	10.8
10	12.3	12.2	12.0
20	24.7	24.3	24.0
30	37.0	36.5	36.0
40	49.3	48.7	48.0
50	61.7	60.8	60.0

″	**71**	**70**	**69**
1	1.2	1.2	1.2
2	2.4	2.3	2.3
3	3.6	3.5	3.4
4	4.7	4.7	4.6
5	5.9	5.8	5.8
6	7.1	7.0	6.9
7	8.3	8.2	8.0
8	9.5	9.3	9.2
9	10.6	10.5	10.4
10	11.8	11.7	11.5
20	23.7	23.3	23.0
30	35.5	35.0	34.5
40	47.3	46.7	46.0
50	59.2	58.3	57.5

″	**68**	**67**	**66**
1	1.1	1.1	1.1
2	2.3	2.2	2.2
3	3.4	3.4	3.3
4	4.5	4.5	4.4
5	5.7	5.6	5.5
6	6.8	6.7	6.6
7	7.9	7.8	7.7
8	9.1	8.9	8.8
9	10.2	10.0	9.9
10	11.3	11.2	11.0
20	22.7	22.3	22.0
30	34.0	33.5	33.0
40	45.3	44.7	44.0
50	56.7	55.8	55.0

	3/74	**3/73**	**3/72**
0			
1	12.3	12.2	12.0
2	37.0	36.5	36.0
3	61.7	60.8	60.0

	3/71	**3/70**	**3/69**	**3/68**
0				
1	11.8	11.7	11.5	11.3
2	35.5	35.0	34.5	34.0
3	59.2	58.3	57.5	56.7

P. P.

100° (280°) (259°) **79°**

11° (191°) | (348°) **168°**

′	L. Sin.	d.	L. Tan.	c.d.	L. Cot.	L. Cos.	d.	′
0	9.28 060	65	9.28 865	68	0.71 135	9.99 195	3	**60**
1	9.28 125	65	9.28 933	67	0.71 067	9.99 192	2	59
2	9.28 190	64	9.29 000	67	0.71 000	9.99 190	3	58
3	9.28 254	65	9.29 067	67	0.70 933	9.99 187	2	57
4	9.28 319	65	9.29 134	67	0.70 866	9.99 185	3	56
5	9.28 384	64	9.29 201	67	0.70 799	9.99 182	2	55
6	9.28 448	64	9.29 268	67	0.70 732	9.99 180	3	54
7	9.28 512	65	9.29 335	67	0.70 665	9.99 177	2	53
8	9.28 577	64	9.29 402	66	0.70 598	9.99 175	3	52
9	9.28 641	64	9.29 468	67	0.70 532	9.99 172	2	51
10	9.28 705	64	9.29 535	66	0.70 465	9.99 170	3	**50**
11	9.28 769	64	9.29 601	67	0.70 399	9.99 167	2	49
12	9.28 833	63	9.29 668	66	0.70 332	9.99 165	3	48
13	9.28 896	64	9.29 734	66	0.70 266	9.99 162	2	47
14	9.28 960	64	9.29 800	66	0.70 200	9.99 160	3	46
15	9.29 024	63	9.29 866	66	0.70 134	9.99 157	2	45
16	9.29 087	63	9.29 932	66	0.70 068	9.99 155	3	44
17	9.29 150	64	9.29 998	66	0.70 002	9.99 152	2	43
18	9.29 214	63	9.30 064	66	0.69 936	9.99 150	3	42
19	9.29 277	63	9.30 130	65	0.69 870	9.99 147	2	41
20	9.29 340	63	9.30 195	66	0.69 805	9.99 145	3	**40**
21	9.29 403	63	9.30 261	65	0.69 739	9.99 142	2	39
22	9.29 466	63	9.30 326	65	0.69 674	9.99 140	3	38
23	9.29 529	62	9.30 391	66	0.69 609	9.99 137	2	37
24	9.29 591	63	9.30 457	65	0.69 543	9.99 135	3	36
25	9.29 654	62	9.30 522	65	0.69 478	9.99 132	2	35
26	9.29 716	63	9.30 587	65	0.69 413	9.99 130	3	34
27	9.29 779	62	9.30 652	65	0.69 348	9.99 127	3	33
28	9.29 841	62	9.30 717	65	0.69 283	9.99 124	2	32
29	9.29 903	63	9.30 782	64	0.69 218	9.99 122	3	31
30	9.29 966	62	9.30 846	65	0.69 154	9.99 119	2	**30**
31	9.30 028	62	9.30 911	64	0.69 089	9.99 117	3	29
32	9.30 090	61	9.30 975	65	0.69 025	9.99 114	2	28
33	9.30 151	62	9.31 040	64	0.68 960	9.99 112	3	27
34	9.30 213	62	9.31 104	64	0.68 896	9.99 109	3	26
35	9.30 275	61	9.31 168	65	0.68 832	9.99 106	2	25
36	9.30 336	62	9.31 233	64	0.68 767	9.99 104	3	24
37	9.30 398	61	9.31 297	64	0.68 703	9.99 101	2	23
38	9.30 459	62	9.31 361	64	0.68 639	9.99 099	3	22
39	9.30 521	61	9.31 425	64	0.68 575	9.99 096	3	21
40	9.30 582	61	9.31 489	63	0.68 511	9.99 093	2	**20**
41	9.30 643	61	9.31 552	64	0.68 448	9.99 091	3	19
42	9.30 704	61	9.31 616	63	0.68 384	9.99 088	2	18
43	9.30 765	61	9.31 679	64	0.68 321	9.99 086	3	17
44	9.30 826	61	9.31 743	63	0.68 257	9.99 083	3	16
45	9.30 887	60	9.31 806	64	0.68 194	9.99 080	2	15
46	9.30 947	61	9.31 870	63	0.68 130	9.99 078	3	14
47	9.31 008	60	9.31 933	63	0.68 067	9.99 075	3	13
48	9.31 068	61	9.31 996	63	0.68 004	9.99 072	2	12
49	9.31 129	60	9.32 059	63	0.67 941	9.99 070	3	11
50	9.31 189	61	9.32 122	63	0.67 878	9.99 067	3	**10**
51	9.31 250	60	9.32 185	63	0.67 815	9.99 064	2	9
52	9.31 310	60	9.32 248	63	0.67 752	9.99 062	3	8
53	9.31 370	60	9.32 311	62	0.67 689	9.99 059	3	7
54	9.31 430	60	9.32 373	63	0.67 627	9.99 056	2	6
55	9.31 490	59	9.32 436	62	0.67 564	9.99 054	3	5
56	9.31 549	60	9.32 498	63	0.67 502	9.99 051	3	4
57	9.31 609	60	9.32 561	62	0.67 439	9.99 048	2	3
58	9.31 669	59	9.32 623	62	0.67 377	9.99 046	3	2
59	9.31 728	60	9.32 685	62	0.67 315	9.99 043	3	1
60	9.31 788		9.32 747		0.67 253	9.99 040		**0**
′	L. Cos.	d.	L. Cot.	c.d.	L. Tan.	L. Sin.	d.	′

P. P.

″	65	64	63
1	1.1	1.1	1.0
2	2.2	2.1	2.1
3	3.2	3.2	3.2
4	4.3	4.3	4.2
5	5.4	5.3	5.2
6	6.5	6.4	6.3
7	7.6	7.5	7.4
8	8.7	8.5	8.4
9	9.8	9.6	9.4
10	10.8	10.7	10.5
20	21.7	21.3	21.0
30	32.5	32.0	31.5
40	43.3	42.7	42.0
50	54.2	53.3	52.5
″	**62**	**61**	**60**
1	1.0	1.0	1.0
2	2.1	2.0	2.0
3	3.1	3.0	3.0
4	4.1	4.1	4.0
5	5.2	5.1	5.0
6	6.2	6.1	6.0
7	7.2	7.1	7.0
8	8.3	8.1	8.0
9	9.3	9.2	9.0
10	10.3	10.2	10.0
20	20.7	20.3	20.0
30	31.0	30.5	30.0
40	41.3	40.7	40.0
50	51.7	50.8	50.0
″	**59**	**3**	**2**
1	1.0	0.0	0.0
2	2.0	0.1	0.1
3	3.0	0.2	0.1
4	3.9	0.2	0.1
5	4.9	0.2	0.2
6	5.9	0.3	0.2
7	6.9	0.4	0.2
8	7.9	0.4	0.3
9	8.8	0.4	0.3
10	9.8	0.5	0.3
20	19.7	1.0	0.7
30	29.5	1.5	1.0
40	39.3	2.0	1.3
50	49.2	2.5	1.7

	3/67	3/66	3/65
0	11.2	11.0	10.8
1	33.5	33.0	32.5
2	55.8	55.0	54.2
3			

	3/64	3/63	3/62
0	10.7	10.5	10.3
1	32.0	31.5	31.0
2	53.3	52.5	51.7
3			

P. P.

101° (281°) | (258°) **78°**

LOGARITHMS OF THE TRIGONOMETRIC FUNCTIONS

12° (192°) — (347°) **167°**

′	L. Sin.	d.	L. Tan.	c.d.	L. Cot.	L. Cos.	d.	′
0	9.31 788	59	9.32 747	63	0.67 253	9.99 040	2	**60**
1	9.31 847	60	9.32 810	62	0.67 190	9.99 038	3	59
2	9.31 907	59	9.32 872	61	0.67 128	9.99 035	3	58
3	9.31 966	59	9.32 933	62	0.67 067	9.99 032	2	57
4	9.32 025	59	9.32 995	62	0.67 005	9.99 030	3	56
5	9.32 084	59	9.33 057	62	0.66 943	9.99 027	3	55
6	9.32 143	59	9.33 119	61	0.66 881	9.99 024	2	54
7	9.32 202	59	9.33 180	62	0.66 820	9.99 022	3	53
8	9.32 261	58	9.33 242	61	0.66 758	9.99 019	3	52
9	9.32 319	59	9.33 303	62	0.66 697	9.99 016	3	51
10	9.32 378	59	9.33 365	61	0.66 635	9.99 013	2	**50**
11	9.32 437	58	9.33 426	61	0.66 574	9.99 011	3	49
12	9.32 495	58	9.33 487	61	0.66 513	9.99 008	3	48
13	9.32 553	59	9.33 548	61	0.66 452	9.99 005	3	47
14	9.32 612	58	9.33 609	61	0.66 391	9.99 002	2	46
15	9.32 670	58	9.33 670	61	0.66 330	9.99 000	3	45
16	9.32 728	58	9.33 731	61	0.66 269	9.98 997	3	44
17	9.32 786	58	9.33 792	61	0.66 208	9.98 994	3	43
18	9.32 844	58	9.33 853	60	0.66 147	9.98 991	2	42
19	9.32 902	58	9.33 913	61	0.66 087	9.98 989	3	41
20	9.32 960	58	9.33 974	60	0.66 026	9.98 986	3	**40**
21	9.33 018	57	9.34 034	61	0.65 966	9.98 983	3	39
22	9.33 075	58	9.34 095	60	0.65 905	9.98 980	2	38
23	9.33 133	57	9.34 155	60	0.65 845	9.98 978	3	37
24	9.33 190	58	9.34 215	61	0.65 785	9.98 975	3	36
25	9.33 248	57	9.34 276	60	0.65 724	9.98 972	3	35
26	9.33 305	57	9.34 336	60	0.65 664	9.98 969	2	34
27	9.33 362	58	9.34 396	60	0.65 604	9.98 967	3	33
28	9.33 420	57	9.34 456	60	0.65 544	9.98 964	3	32
29	9.33 477	57	9.34 516	60	0.65 484	9.98 961	3	31
30	9.33 534	57	9.34 576	59	0.65 424	9.98 958	3	**30**
31	9.33 591	56	9.34 635	60	0.65 365	9.98 955	2	29
32	9.33 647	57	9.34 695	60	0.65 305	9.98 953	3	28
33	9.33 704	57	9.34 755	59	0.65 245	9.98 950	3	27
34	9.33 761	57	9.34 814	60	0.65 186	9.98 947	3	26
35	9.33 818	56	9.34 874	59	0.65 126	9.98 944	3	25
36	9.33 874	57	9.34 933	59	0.65 067	9.98 941	3	24
37	9.33 931	56	9.34 992	59	0.65 008	9.98 938	2	23
38	9.33 987	56	9.35 051	60	0.64 949	9.98 936	3	22
39	9.34 043	57	9.35 111	59	0.64 889	9.98 933	3	21
40	9.34 100	56	9.35 170	59	0.64 830	9.98 930	3	**20**
41	9.34 156	56	9.35 229	59	0.64 771	9.98 927	3	19
42	9.34 212	56	9.35 288	59	0.64 712	9.98 924	3	18
43	9.34 268	56	9.35 347	58	0.64 653	9.98 921	2	17
44	9.34 324	56	9.35 405	59	0.64 595	9.98 919	3	16
45	9.34 380	56	9.35 464	59	0.64 536	9.98 916	3	15
46	9.34 436	55	9.35 523	58	0.64 477	9.98 913	3	14
47	9.34 491	56	9.35 581	59	0.64 419	9.98 910	3	13
48	9.34 547	55	9.35 640	58	0.64 360	9.98 907	3	12
49	9.34 602	56	9.35 698	59	0.64 302	9.98 904	3	11
50	9.34 658	55	9.35 757	58	0.64 243	9.98 901	3	**10**
51	9.34 713	56	9.35 815	58	0.64 185	9.98 898	2	9
52	9.34 769	55	9.35 873	58	0.64 127	9.98 896	3	8
53	9.34 824	55	9.35 931	58	0.64 069	9.98 893	3	7
54	9.34 879	55	9.35 989	58	0.64 011	9.98 890	3	6
55	9.34 934	55	9.36 047	58	0.63 953	9.98 887	3	5
56	9.34 989	55	9.36 105	58	0.63 895	9.98 884	3	4
57	9.35 044	55	9.36 163	58	0.63 837	9.98 881	3	3
58	9.35 099	55	9.36 221	58	0.63 779	9.98 878	3	2
59	9.35 154	55	9.36 279	57	0.63 721	9.98 875	3	1
60	9.35 209		9.36 336		0.63 664	9.98 872		**0**
′	L. Cos.	d.	L. Cot.	c.d.	L. Tan.	L. Sin.	d.	′

P. P.

″	**63**	**62**	**61**
1	1.0	1.0	1.0
2	2.1	2.1	2.0
3	3.2	3.1	3.0
4	4.2	4.1	4.1
5	5.2	5.2	5.1
6	6.3	6.2	6.1
7	7.4	7.2	7.1
8	8.4	8.3	8.1
9	9.4	9.3	9.2
10	10.5	10.3	10.2
20	21.0	20.7	20.3
30	31.5	31.0	30.5
40	42.0	41.3	40.7
50	52.5	51.7	50.8
″	**60**	**59**	**58**
1	1.0	1.0	1.0
2	2.0	2.0	1.9
3	3.0	3.0	2.9
4	4.0	3.9	3.9
5	5.0	4.9	4.8
6	6.0	5.9	5.8
7	7.0	6.9	6.8
8	8.0	7.9	7.7
9	9.0	8.8	8.7
10	10.0	9.8	9.7
20	20.0	19.7	19.3
30	30.0	29.5	29.0
40	40.0	39.3	38.7
50	50.0	49.2	48.3
″	**57**	**56**	**55**
1	1.0	0.9	0.9
2	1.9	1.9	1.8
3	2.8	2.8	2.8
4	3.8	3.7	3.7
5	4.8	4.7	4.6
6	5.7	5.6	5.5
7	6.6	6.5	6.4
8	7.6	7.5	7.3
9	8.6	8.4	8.2
10	9.5	9.3	9.2
20	19.0	18.7	18.3
30	28.5	28.0	27.5
40	38.0	37.3	36.7
50	47.5	46.7	45.8

	3/**62**	3/**61**	3/**60**
0			
1	10.3	10.2	10.0
2	31.0	30.5	30.0
3	51.7	50.8	50.0

	3/**59**	3/**58**	3/**57**
0			
1	9.8	9.7	9.5
2	29.5	29.0	28.5
3	49.2	48.3	47.5

P. P.

102° (282°) — (257°) **77°**

13° (193°) (346°) **166°**

′	L. Sin.	d.	L. Tan.	c.d.	L. Cot.	L. Cos.	d.	′
0	9.35 209	54	9.36 336	58	0.63 664	9.98 872	3	**60**
1	9.35 263	55	9.36 394	58	0.63 606	9.98 869	2	59
2	9.35 318	55	9.36 452	57	0.63 548	9.98 867	3	58
3	9.35 373	54	9.36 509	57	0.63 491	9.98 864	3	57
4	9.35 427	54	9.36 566	58	0.63 434	9.98 861	3	56
5	9.35 481	55	9.36 624	57	0.63 376	9.98 858	3	55
6	9.35 536	54	9.36 681	57	0.63 319	9.98 855	3	54
7	9.35 590	54	9.36 738	57	0.63 262	9.98 852	3	53
8	9.35 644	54	9.36 795	57	0.63 205	9.98 849	3	52
9	9.35 698	54	9.36 852	57	0.63 148	9.98 846	3	51
10	9.35 752	54	9.36 909	57	0.63 091	9.98 843	3	**50**
11	9.35 806	54	9.36 966	57	0.63 034	9.98 840	3	49
12	9.35 860	54	9.37 023	57	0.62 977	9.98 837	3	48
13	9.35 914	54	9.37 080	57	0.62 920	9.98 834	3	47
14	9.35 968	54	9.37 137	56	0.62 863	9.98 831	3	46
15	9.36 022	53	9.37 193	57	0.62 807	9.98 828	3	45
16	9.36 075	54	9.37 250	56	0.62 750	9.98 825	3	44
17	9.36 129	53	9.37 306	57	0.62 694	9.98 822	3	43
18	9.36 182	54	9.37 363	56	0.62 637	9.98 819	3	42
19	9.36 236	53	9.37 419	57	0.62 581	9.98 816	3	41
20	9.36 289	53	9.37 476	56	0.62 524	9.98 813	3	**40**
21	9.36 342	53	9.37 532	56	0.62 468	9.98 810	3	39
22	9.36 395	54	9.37 588	56	0.62 412	9.98 807	3	38
23	9.36 449	53	9.37 644	56	0.62 356	9.98 804	3	37
24	9.36 502	53	9.37 700	56	0.62 300	9.98 801	3	36
25	9.36 555	53	9.37 756	56	0.62 244	9.98 798	3	35
26	9.36 608	52	9.37 812	56	0.62 188	9.98 795	3	34
27	9.36 660	53	9.37 868	56	0.62 132	9.98 792	3	33
28	9.36 713	53	9.37 924	56	0.62 076	9.98 789	3	32
29	9.36 766	53	9.37 980	55	0.62 020	9.98 786	3	31
30	9.36 819	52	9.38 035	56	0.61 965	9.98 783	3	**30**
31	9.36 871	53	9.38 091	56	0.61 909	9.98 780	3	29
32	9.36 924	52	9.38 147	55	0.61 853	9.98 777	3	28
33	9.36 976	52	9.38 202	55	0.61 798	9.98 774	3	27
34	9.37 028	53	9.38 257	56	0.61 743	9.98 771	3	26
35	9.37 081	52	9.38 313	55	0.61 687	9.98 768	3	25
36	9.37 133	52	9.38 368	55	0.61 632	9.98 765	3	24
37	9.37 185	52	9.38 423	56	0.61 577	9.98 762	3	23
38	9.37 237	52	9.38 479	55	0.61 521	9.98 759	3	22
39	9.37 289	52	9.38 534	55	0.61 466	9.98 756	3	21
40	9.37 341	52	9.38 589	55	0.61 411	9.98 753	3	**20**
41	9.37 393	52	9.38 644	55	0.61 356	9.98 750	4	19
42	9.37 445	52	9.38 699	55	0.61 301	9.98 746	3	18
43	9.37 497	52	9.38 754	54	0.61 246	9.98 743	3	17
44	9.37 549	51	9.38 808	55	0.61 192	9.98 740	3	16
45	9.37 600	52	9.38 863	55	0.61 137	9.98 737	3	15
46	9.37 652	51	9.38 918	54	0.61 082	9.98 734	3	14
47	9.37 703	52	9.38 972	55	0.61 028	9.98 731	3	13
48	9.37 755	51	9.39 027	55	0.60 973	9.98 728	3	12
49	9.37 806	52	9.39 082	54	0.60 918	9.98 725	3	11
50	9.37 858	51	9.39 136	54	0.60 864	9.98 722	3	**10**
51	9.37 909	51	9.39 190	55	0.60 810	9.98 719	4	9
52	9.37 960	51	9.39 245	54	0.60 755	9.98 715	3	8
53	9.38 011	51	9.39 299	54	0.60 701	9.98 712	3	7
54	9.38 062	51	9.39 353	54	0.60 647	9.98 709	3	6
55	9.38 113	51	9.39 407	54	0.60 593	9.98 706	3	5
56	9.38 164	51	9.39 461	54	0.60 539	9.98 703	3	4
57	9.38 215	51	9.39 515	54	0.60 485	9.98 700	3	3
58	9.38 266	51	9.39 569	54	0.60 431	9.98 697	3	2
59	9.38 317	51	9.39 623	54	0.60 377	9.98 694	4	1
60	9.38 368		9.39 677		0.60 323	9.98 690		**0**
′	L. Cos.	d.	L. Cot.	c.d.	L. Tan.	L. Sin.	d.	′

P. P.

″	**57**	**56**	**55**
1	1.0	0.9	0.9
2	1.9	1.9	1.8
3	2.8	2.8	2.8
4	3.8	3.7	3.7
5	4.8	4.7	4.6
6	5.7	5.6	5.5
7	6.6	6.5	6.4
8	7.6	7.5	7.3
9	8.6	8.4	8.2
10	9.5	9.3	9.2
20	19.0	18.7	18.3
30	28.5	28.0	27.5
40	38.0	37.3	36.7
50	47.5	46.7	45.8

″	**54**	**53**	**52**
1	0.9	0.9	0.9
2	1.8	1.8	1.7
3	2.7	2.6	2.6
4	3.6	3.5	3.5
5	4.5	4.4	4.3
6	5.4	5.3	5.2
7	6.3	6.2	6.1
8	7.2	7.1	6.9
9	8.1	8.0	7.8
10	9.0	8.8	8.7
20	18.0	17.7	17.3
30	27 0	26.5	26.0
40	36.0	35.3	34.7
50	45.0	44.2	43.3

″	**51**	**4**	**3**	**2**
1	0.8	0.1	0.0	0.0
2	1.7	0.1	0.1	0.1
3	2.6	0.2	0.2	0.1
4	3.4	0.3	0.2	0.1
5	4.2	0.3	0.2	0.2
6	5.1	0.4	0.3	0.2
7	6.0	0.5	0.4	0.2
8	6.8	0.5	0.4	0.3
9	7.6	0.6	0.4	0.3
10	8.5	0.7	0.5	0.3
20	17.0	1.3	1.0	0.7
30	25.5	2.0	1.5	1.0
40	34.0	2.7	2.0	1.3
50	42.5	3.3	2.5	1.7

	4/55	**4/54**	**3/58**	**3/57**
0	6.9	6.8	9.7	9.5
1	20.6	20.2	29.0	28.5
2	34.4	33.8	48.3	47.5
3	48.1	47.2	—	—
4				

	3/56	**3/55**	**3/54**
0			
1	9.3	9.2	9.0
2	28.0	27.5	27.0
3	46.7	45.8	45.0

P. P.

103° (283°) (256°) **76°**

14° (194°) (345°) **165°**

′	L. Sin.	d.	L. Tan.	c.d.	L. Cot.	L. Cos.	d.	′
0	9.38 368	50	9.39 677	54	0.60 323	9.98 690	3	**60**
1	9.38 418	51	9.39 731	54	0.60 269	9.98 687	3	59
2	9.38 469	50	9.39 785̄	53	0.60 215̄	9.98 684	3	58
3	9.38 519	51	9.39 838	54	0.60 162	9.98 681	3	57
4	9.38 570	50	9.39 892	53	0.60 108	9.98 678	3	56
5	9.38 620	50	9.39 945̄	54	0.60 055̄	9.98 675̄	4	55
6	9.38 670	51	9.39 999	53	0.60 001	9.98 671	3	54
7	9.38 721	50	9.40 052	54	0.59 948	9.98 668	3	53
8	9.38 771	50	9.40 106	53	0.59 894	9.98 665̄	3	52
9	9.38 821	50	9.40 159	53	0.59 841	9.98 662	3	51
10	9.38 871	50	9.40 212	54	0.59 788	9.98 659	3	**50**
11	9.38 921	50	9.40 266	53	0.59 734	9.98 656	4	49
12	9.38 971	50	9.40 319	53	0.59 681	9.98 652	3	48
13	9.39 021	50	9.40 372	53	0.59 628	9.98 649	3	47
14	9.39 071	50	9.40 425̄	53	0.59 575̄	9.98 646	3	46
15	9.39 121	49	9.40 478	53	0.59 522	9.98 643	3	45
16	9.39 170	50	9.40 531	53	0.59 469	9.98 640	4	44
17	9.39 220	50	9.40 584	52	0.59 416	9.98 636	3	43
18	9.39 270	49	9.40 636	53	0.59 364	9.98 633	3	42
19	9.39 319	50	9.40 689	53	0.59 311	9.98 630	3	41
20	9.39 369	49	9.40 742	53	0.59 258	9.98 627	4	**40**
21	9.39 418	49	9.40 795̄	52	0.59 205̄	9.98 623	3	39
22	9.39 467	50	9.40 847	53	0.59 153	9.98 620	3	38
23	9.39 517	49	9.40 900	52	0.59 100	9.98 617	3	37
24	9.39 566	49	9.40 952	53	0.59 048	9.98 614	4	36
25	9.39 615̄	49	9.41 005̄	52	0.58 995̄	9.98 610	3	35
26	9.39 664	49	9.41 057	52	0.58 943	9.98 607	3	34
27	9.39 713	49	9.41 109	52	0.58 891	9.98 604	3	33
28	9.39 762	49	9.41 161	53	0.58 839	9.98 601	4	32
29	9.39 811	49	9.41 214	52	0.58 786	9.98 597	3	31
30	9.39 860	49	9.41 266	52	0.58 734	9.98 594	3	**30**
31	9.39 909	49	9.41 318	52	0.58 682	9.98 591	3	29
32	9.39 958	48	9.41 370	52	0.58 630	9.98 588	4	28
33	9.40 006	49	9.41 422	52	0.58 578	9.98 584	3	27
34	9.40 055̄	48	9.41 474	52	0.58 526	9.98 581	3	26
35	9.40 103	49	9.41 526	52	0.58 474	9.98 578	4	25
36	9.40 152	48	9.41 578	51	0.58 422	9.98 574	3	24
37	9.40 200	49	9.41 629	52	0.58 371	9.98 571	3	23
38	9.40 249	48	9.41 681	52	0.58 319	9.98 568	3	22
39	9.40 297	49	9.41 733	51	0.58 267	9.98 565̄	4	21
40	9.40 346	48	9.41 784	52	0.58 216	9.98 561	3	**20**
41	9.40 394	48	9.41 836	51	0.58 164	9.98 558	3	19
42	9.40 442	48	9.41 887	52	0.58 113	9.98 555̄	4	18
43	9.40 490	48	9.41 939	51	0.58 061	9.98 551	3	17
44	9.40 538	48	9.41 990	51	0.58 010	9.98 548	3	16
45	9.40 586	48	9.42 041	52	0.57 959	9.98 545̄	4	15
46	9.40 634	48	9.42 093	51	0.57 907	9.98 541	3	14
47	9.40 682	48	9.42 144	51	0.57 856	9.98 538	3	13
48	9.40 730	48	9.42 195̄	51	0.57 805̄	9.98 535̄	4	12
49	9.40 778	47	9.42 246	51	0.57 754	9.98 531	3	11
50	9.40 825̄	48	9.42 297	51	0.57 703	9.98 528	3	**10**
51	9.40 873	48	9.42 348	51	0.57 652	9.98 525̄	4	9
52	9.40 921	47	9.42 399	51	0.57 601	9.98 521	3	8
53	9.40 968	48	9.42 450	51	0.57 550	9.98 518	3	7
54	9.41 016	47	9.42 501	51	0.57 499	9.98 515̄	4	6
55	9.41 063	48	9.42 552	51	0.57 448	9.98 511	3	5
56	9.41 111	47	9.42 603	50	0.57 397	9.98 508	3	4
57	9.41 158	47	9.42 653	51	0.57 347	9.98 505̄	4	3
58	9.41 205̄	47	9.42 704	51	0.57 296	9.98 501	3	2
59	9.41 252	48	9.42 755̄	50	0.57 245̄	9.98 498	4	1
60	9.41 300		9.42 805̄		0.57 195̄	9.98 494		**0**
′	L. Cos.	d.	L. Cot.	c.d.	L. Tan.	L. Sin.	d.	′

P. P.

″	**54**	**53**	**52**
1	0.9	0.9	0.9
2	1.8	1.8	1.7
3	2.7	2.6	2.6
4	3.6	3.5	3.5
5	4.5	4.4	4.3
6	5.4	5.3	5.2
7	6.3	6.2	6.1
8	7.2	7.1	6.9
9	8.1	8.0	7.8
10	9.0	8.8	8.7
20	18.0	17.7	17.3
30	27.0	26.5	26.0
40	36.0	35.3	34.7
50	45.0	44.2	43.3

″	**51**	**50**	**49**
1	0.8	0.8	0.8
2	1.7	1.7	1.6
3	2.6	2.5	2.4
4	3.4	3.3	3.3
5	4.2	4.2	4.1
6	5.1	5.0	4.9
7	6.0	5.8	5.7
8	6.8	6.7	6.5̄
9	7.6	7.5̄	7.4
10	8.5	8.3	8.2
20	17.0	16.7	16.3
30	25.5	25.0	24.5
40	34.0	33.3	32.7
50	42.5	41.7	40.8

″	**48**	**47**	**4**	**3**
1	0.8	0.8	0.1	0.0
2	1.6	1.6	0.1	0.1
3	2.4	2.4	0.2	0.2
4	3.2	3.1	0.3	0.2
5	4.0	3.9	0.3	0.2
6	4.8	4.7	0.4	0.3
7	5.6	5.5̄	0.5̄	0.4
8	6.4	6.3	0.5̄	0.4
9	7.2	7.0	0.6	0.4
10	8.0	7.8	0.7	0.5
20	16.0	15.7	1.3	1.0
30	24.0	23.5	2.0	1.5
40	32.0	31.3	2.7	2.0
50	40.0	39.2	3.3	2.5

	4/54	**4/53**	**4/52**	**4/51**
0	6.8	6.6	6.5	6.4
1	20.2	19.9	19.5	19.1
2	33.8	33.1	32.5	31.9
3	47.2	46.4	45.5	44.6

	3/54	**3/53**	**3/52**	**3/51**
0	9.0	8.8	8.7	8.5
1	27.0	26.5	26.0	25.5
2	45.0	44.2	43.3	42.5

P. P.

104° (284°) (255°) **75°**

15° (195°) (344°) **164°**

′	L. Sin.	d.	L. Tan.	c.d.	L. Cot.	L. Cos.	d.	′
0	9.41 300	47	9.42 805	51	0.57 195	9.98 494	3	**60**
1	9.41 347	47	9.42 856	50	0.57 144	9.98 491	3	59
2	9.41 394	47	9.42 906	51	0.57 094	9.98 488	4	58
3	9.41 441	47	9.42 957	50	0.57 043	9.98 484	3	57
4	9.41 488	47	9.43 007	50	0.56 993	9.98 481	4	56
5	9.41 535	47	9.43 057	51	0.56 943	9.98 477	3	55
6	9.41 582	46	9.43 108	50	0.56 892	9.98 474	3	54
7	9.41 628	47	9.43 158	50	0.56 842	9.98 471	4	53
8	9.41 675	47	9.43 208	50	0.56 792	9.98 467	3	52
9	9.41 722	46	9.43 258	50	0.56 742	9.98 464	4	51
10	9.41 768	47	9.43 308	50	0.56 692	9.98 460	3	**50**
11	9.41 815	46	9.43 358	50	0.56 642	9.98 457	4	49
12	9.41 861	47	9.43 408	50	0.56 592	9.98 453	3	48
13	9.41 908	46	9.43 458	50	0.56 542	9.98 450	3	47
14	9.41 954	47	9.43 508	50	0.56 492	9.98 447	4	46
15	9.42 001	46	9.43 558	49	0.56 442	9.98 443	3	45
16	9.42 047	46	9.43 607	50	0.56 393	9.98 440	4	44
17	9.42 093	47	9.43 657	50	0.56 343	9.98 436	3	43
18	9.42 140	46	9.43 707	49	0.56 293	9.98 433	4	42
19	9.42 186	46	9.43 756	50	0.56 244	9.98 429	3	41
20	9.42 232	46	9.43 806	49	0.56 194	9.98 426	4	**40**
21	9.42 278	46	9.43 855	50	0.56 145	9.98 422	3	39
22	9.42 324	46	9.43 905	49	0.56 095	9.98 419	4	38
23	9.42 370	46	9.43 954	50	0.56 046	9.98 415	3	37
24	9.42 416	45	9.44 004	49	0.55 996	9.98 412	3	36
25	9.42 461	46	9.44 053	49	0.55 947	9.98 409	4	35
26	9.42 507	46	9.44 102	49	0.55 898	9.98 405	3	34
27	9.42 553	46	9.44 151	50	0.55 849	9.98 402	4	33
28	9.42 599	45	9.44 201	49	0.55 799	9.98 398	3	32
29	9.42 644	46	9.44 250	49	0.55 750	9.98 395	4	31
30	9.42 690	45	9.44 299	49	0.55 701	9.98 391	3	**30**
31	9.42 735	46	9.44 348	49	0.55 652	9.98 388	4	29
32	9.42 781	45	9.44 397	49	0.55 603	9.98 384	3	28
33	9.42 826	46	9.44 446	49	0.55 554	9.98 381	4	27
34	9.42 872	45	9.44 495	49	0.55 505	9.98 377	4	26
35	9.42 917	45	9.44 544	48	0.55 456	9.98 373	3	25
36	9.42 962	46	9.44 592	49	0.55 408	9.98 370	4	24
37	9.43 008	45	9.44 641	49	0.55 359	9.98 366	3	23
38	9.43 053	45	9.44 690	48	0.55 310	9.98 363	4	22
39	9.43 098	45	9.44 738	49	0.55 262	9.98 359	3	21
40	9.43 143	45	9.44 787	49	0.55 213	9.98 356	4	**20**
41	9.43 188	45	9.44 836	48	0.55 164	9.98 352	3	19
42	9.43 233	45	9.44 884	49	0.55 116	9.98 349	4	18
43	9.43 278	45	9.44 933	48	0.55 067	9.98 345	3	17
44	9.43 323	44	9.44 981	48	0.55 019	9.98 342	4	16
45	9.43 367	45	9.45 029	49	0.54 971	9.98 338	4	15
46	9.43 412	45	9.45 078	48	0.54 922	9.98 334	3	14
47	9.43 457	45	9.45 126	48	0.54 874	9.98 331	4	13
48	9.43 502	44	9.45 174	48	0.54 826	9.98 327	3	12
49	9.43 546	45	9.45 222	49	0.54 778	9.98 324	4	11
50	9.43 591	44	9.45 271	48	0.54 729	9.98 320	3	**10**
51	9.43 635	45	9.45 319	48	0.54 681	9.98 317	4	9
52	9.43 680	44	9.45 367	48	0.54 633	9.98 313	4	8
53	9.43 724	45	9.45 415	48	0.54 585	9.98 309	3	7
54	9.43 769	44	9.45 463	48	0.54 537	9.98 306	4	6
55	9.43 813	44	9.45 511	48	0.54 489	9.98 302	3	5
56	9.43 857	44	9.45 559	47	0.54 441	9.98 299	4	4
57	9.43 901	45	9.45 606	48	0.54 394	9.98 295	4	3
58	9.43 946	44	9.45 654	48	0.54 346	9.98 291	3	2
59	9.43 990	44	9.45 702	48	0.54 298	9.98 288	4	1
60	9.44 034		9.45 750		0.54 250	9.98 284		**0**
′	L. Cos.	d.	L. Cot.	c.d.	L. Tan.	L. Sin.	d.	′

P. P.

″	**51**	**50**	**49**
1	0.8	0.8	0.8
2	1.7	1.7	1.6
3	2.6	2.5	2.4
4	3.4	3.3	3.3
5	4.2	4.2	4.1
6	5.1	5.0	4.9
7	6.0	5.8	5.7
8	6.8	6.7	6.5
9	7.6	7.5	7.4
10	8.5	8.3	8.2
20	17.0	16.7	16.3
30	25.5	25.0	24.5
40	34.0	33.3	32.7
50	42.5	41.7	40.8

″	**48**	**47**	**46**
1	0.8	0.8	0.8
2	1.6	1.6	1.5
3	2.4	2.4	2.3
4	3.2	3.1	3.1
5	4.0	3.9	3.8
6	4.8	4.7	4.6
7	5.6	5.5	5.4
8	6.4	6.3	6.1
9	7.2	7.0	6.9
10	8.0	7.8	7.7
20	16.0	15.7	15.3
30	24.0	23.5	23.0
40	32.0	31.3	30.7
50	40.0	39.2	38.3

″	**45**	**44**	**4**	**3**
1	0.8	0.7	0.1	0.0
2	1.5	1.5	0.1	0.1
3	2.2	2.2	0.2	0.2
4	3.0	2.9	0.3	0.2
5	3.8	3.7	0.3	0.2
6	4.5	4.4	0.4	0.3
7	5.2	5.1	0.5	0.4
8	6.0	5.9	0.5	0.4
9	6.8	6.6	0.6	0.4
10	7.5	7.3	0.7	0.5
20	15.0	14.7	1.3	1.0
30	22.5	22.0	2.0	1.5
40	30.0	29.3	2.7	2.0
50	37.5	36.7	3.3	2.5

	4/50	**4/49**	**4/48**	**4/47**
0	6.2	6.1	6.0	5.9
1	18.8	18.4	18.0	17.6
2	31.2	30.6	30.0	29.4
3	43.8	42.9	42.0	41.1
4				

	3/51	**3/50**	**3/49**	**3/48**
0	8.5	8.3	8.2	8.0
1	25.5	25.0	24.5	24.0
2	42.5	41.7	40.8	40.0
3				

P. P.

105° (285°) (254°) **74°**

16° (196°) (343°) **163°**

′	L. Sin.	d.	L. Tan.	c.d.	L. Cot.	L. Cos.	d.	′
0	9.44 034	44	9.45 750	47	0.54 250	9.98 284	3	**60**
1	9.44 078	44	9.45 797	48	0.54 203	9.98 281	4	59
2	9.44 122	44	9.45 845	47	0.54 155	9.98 277	4	58
3	9.44 166	44	9.45 892	48	0.54 108	9.98 273	3	57
4	9.44 210	43	9.45 940	47	0.54 060	9.98 270	4	56
5	9.44 253	44	9.45 987	48	0.54 013	9.98 266	4	55
6	9.44 297	44	9.46 035	47	0.53 965	9.98 262	3	54
7	9.44 341	44	9.46 082	48	0.53 918	9.98 259	4	53
8	9.44 385	43	9.46 130	47	0.53 870	9.98 255	4	52
9	9.44 428	44	9.46 177	47	0.53 823	9.98 251	3	51
10	9.44 472	44	9.46 224	47	0.53 776	9.98 248	4	**50**
11	9.44 516	43	9.46 271	48	0.53 729	9.98 244	4	49
12	9.44 559	43	9.46 319	47	0.53 681	9.98 240	3	48
13	9.44 602	44	9.46 366	47	0.53 634	9.98 237	4	47
14	9.44 646	43	9.46 413	47	0.53 587	9.98 233	4	46
15	9.44 689	44	9.46 460	47	0.53 540	9.98 229	3	45
16	9.44 733	43	9.46 507	47	0.53 493	9.98 226	4	44
17	9.44 776	43	9.46 554	47	0.53 446	9.98 222	4	43
18	9.44 819	43	9.46 601	47	0.53 399	9.98 218	3	42
19	9.44 862	43	9.46 648	46	0.53 352	9.98 215	4	41
20	9.44 905	43	9.46 694	47	0.53 306	9.98 211	4	**40**
21	9.44 948	44	9.46 741	47	0.53 259	9.98 207	3	39
22	9.44 992	43	9.46 788	47	0.53 212	9.98 204	4	38
23	9.45 035	42	9.46 835	46	0.53 165	9.98 200	4	37
24	9.45 077	43	9.46 881	47	0.53 119	9.98 196	4	36
25	9.45 120	43	9.46 928	47	0.53 072	9.98 192	3	35
26	9.45 163	43	9.46 975	46	0.53 025	9.98 189	4	34
27	9.45 206	43	9.47 021	47	0.52 979	9.98 185	4	33
28	9.45 249	43	9.47 068	46	0.52 932	9.98 181	4	32
29	9.45 292	42	9.47 114	46	0.52 886	9.98 177	3	31
30	9.45 334	43	9.47 160	47	0.52 840	9.98 174	4	**30**
31	9.45 377	42	9.47 207	46	0.52 793	9.98 170	4	29
32	9.45 419	43	9.47 253	46	0.52 747	9.98 166	4	28
33	9.45 462	42	9.47 299	47	0.52 701	9.98 162	3	27
34	9.45 504	43	9.47 346	46	0.52 654	9.98 159	4	26
35	9.45 547	42	9.47 392	46	0.52 608	9.98 155	4	25
36	9.45 589	43	9.47 438	46	0.52 562	9.98 151	4	24
37	9.45 632	42	9.47 484	46	0.52 516	9.98 147	3	23
38	9.45 674	42	9.47 530	46	0.52 470	9.98 144	4	22
39	9.45 716	42	9.47 576	46	0.52 424	9.98 140	4	21
40	9.45 758	43	9.47 622	46	0.52 378	9.98 136	4	**20**
41	9.45 801	42	9.47 668	46	0.52 332	9.98 132	3	19
42	9.45 843	42	9.47 714	46	0.52 286	9.98 129	4	18
43	9.45 885	42	9.47 760	46	0.52 240	9.98 125	4	17
44	9.45 927	42	9.47 806	46	0.52 194	9.98 121	4	16
45	9.45 969	42	9.47 852	45	0.52 148	9.98 117	4	15
46	9.46 011	42	9.47 897	46	0.52 103	9.98 113	3	14
47	9.46 053	42	9.47 943	46	0.52 057	9.98 110	4	13
48	9.46 095	41	9.47 989	46	0.52 011	9.98 106	4	12
49	9.46 136	42	9.48 035	45	0.51 965	9.98 102	4	11
50	9.46 178	42	9.48 080	46	0.51 920	9.98 098	4	**10**
51	9.46 220	42	9.48 126	45	0.51 874	9.98 094	4	9
52	9.46 262	41	9.48 171	46	0.51 829	9.98 090	3	8
53	9.46 303	42	9.48 217	45	0.51 783	9.98 087	4	7
54	9.46 345	41	9.48 262	45	0.51 738	9.98 083	4	6
55	9.46 386	42	9.48 307	46	0.51 693	9.98 079	4	5
56	9.46 428	41	9.48 353	45	0.51 647	9.98 075	4	4
57	9.46 469	42	9.48 398	45	0.51 602	9.98 071	4	3
58	9.46 511	41	9.48 443	46	0.51 557	9.98 067	4	2
59	9.46 552	42	9.48 489	45	0.51 511	9.98 063	3	1
60	9.46 594		9.48 534		0.51 466	9.98 060		**0**

P. P.

″	**48**	**47**	**46**
1	0.8	0.8	0.8
2	1.6	1.6	1.5
3	2.4	2.4	2.3
4	3.2	3.1	3.1
5	4.0	3.9	3.8
6	4.8	4.7	4.6
7	5.6	5.5	5.4
8	6.4	6.3	6.1
9	7.2	7.0	6.9
10	8.0	7.8	7.7
20	16.0	15.7	15.3
30	24.0	23.5	23.0
40	32.0	31.3	30.7
50	40.0	39.2	38.3

″	**45**	**44**	**43**
1	0.8	0.7	0.7
2	1.5	1.5	1.4
3	2.2	2.2	2.2
4	3.0	2.9	2.9
5	3.8	3.7	3.6
6	4.5	4.4	4.3
7	5.2	5.1	5.0
8	6.0	5.9	5.7
9	6.8	6.6	6.4
10	7.5	7.3	7.2
20	15.0	14.7	14.3
30	22.5	22.0	21.5
40	30.0	29.3	28.7
50	37.5	36.7	35.8

″	**42**	**41**	**4**	**3**
1	0.7	0.7	0.1	0.0
2	1.4	1.4	0.1	0.1
3	2.1	2.0	0.2	0.2
4	2.8	2.7	0.3	0.2
5	3.5	3.4	0.3	0.2
6	4.2	4.1	0.4	0.3
7	4.9	4.8	0.5	0.4
8	5.6	5.5	0.5	0.4
9	6.3	6.2	0.6	0.4
10	7.0	6.8	0.7	0.5
20	14.0	13.7	1.3	1.0
30	21.0	20.5	2.0	1.5
40	28.0	27.3	2.7	2.0
50	35.0	34.2	3.3	2.5

	4/48	**4/47**	**4/46**	**4/45**
0	6.0	5.9	5.8	5.6
1	18.0	17.6	17.2	16.9
2	30.0	29.4	28.8	28.1
3	42.0	41.1	40.2	39.4

	3/48	**3/47**	**3/46**	**3/45**
0	8.0	7.8	7.7	7.5
1	24.0	23.5	23.0	22.5
2	40.0	39.2	38.3	37.5

P. P.

17° (197°) (342°) **162°**

′	L. Sin.	d.	L. Tan.	c.d.	L. Cot.	L. Cos.	d.	′
0	9.46 594	41	9.48 534	45	0.51 466	9.98 060	4	**60**
1	9.46 635̄	41	9.48 579	45	0.51 421	9.98 056	4	59
2	9.46 676	41	9.48 624	45	0.51 376	9.98 052	4	58
3	9.46 717	41	9.48 669	45	0.51 331	9.98 048	4	57
4	9.46 758	42	9.48 714	45	0.51 286	9.98 044	4	56
5	9.46 800	41	9.48 759	45	0.51 241	9.98 040	4	55
6	9.46 841	41	9.48 804	45	0.51 196	9.98 036	4	54
7	9.46 882	41	9.48 849	45	0.51 151	9.98 032	3	53
8	9.46 923	41	9.48 894	45	0.51 106	9.98 029	4	52
9	9.46 964	41	9.48 939	45	0.51 061	9.98 025̄	4	51
10	9.47 005̄	40	9.48 984	45	0.51 016	9.98 021	4	**50**
11	9.47 045̇	41	9.49 029	44	0.50 971	9.98 017	4	49
12	9.47 086	41	9.49 073	45	0.50 927	9.98 013	4	48
13	9.47 127	41	9.49 118	45	0.50 882	9.98 009	4	47
14	9.47 168	41	9.49 163	44	0.50 837	9.98 005̇	4	46
15	9.47 209	40	9.49 207	45	0.50 793	9.98 001	4	45
16	9.47 249	41	9.49 252	44	0.50 748	9.97 997	4	44
17	9.47 290	40	9.49 296	45	0.50 704	9.97 993	4	43
18	9.47 330	41	9.49 341	44	0.50 659	9.97 989	3	42
19	9.47 371	40	9.49 385̇	45	0.50 615̄	9.97 986	4	41
20	9.47 411	41	9.49 430	44	0.50 570	9.97 982	4	**40**
21	9.47 452	40	9.49 474	45	0.50 526	9.97 978	4	39
22	9.47 492	41	9.49 519	44	0.50 481	9.97 974	4	38
23	9.47 533	40	9.49 563	44	0.50 437	9.97 970	4	37
24	9.47 573	40	9.49 607	45	0.50 393	9.97 966	4	36
25	9.47 613	41	9.49 652	44	0.50 348	9.97 962	4	35
26	9.47 654	40	9.49 696	44	0.50 304	9.97 958	4	34
27	9.47 694	40	9.49 740	44	0.50 260	9.97 954	4	33
28	9.47 734	40	9.49 784	44	0.50 216	9.97 950	4	32
29	9.47 774	40	9.49 828	44	0.50 172	9.97 946	4	31
30	9.47 814	40	9.49 872	44	0.50 128	9.97 942	4	**30**
31	9.47 854	40	9.49 916	44	0.50 084	9.97 938	4	29
32	9.47 894	40	9.49 960	44	0.50 040	9.97 934	4	28
33	9.47 934	40	9.50 004	44	0.49 996	9.97 930	4	27
34	9.47 974	40	9.50 048	44	0.49 952	9.97 926	4	26
35	9.48 014	40	9.50 092	44	0.49 908	9.97 922	4	25
36	9.48 054	40	9.50 136	44	0.49 864	9.97 918	4	24
37	9.48 094	39	9.50 180	43	0.49 820	9.97 914	4	23
38	9.48 133	40	9.50 223	44	0.49 777	9.97 910	4	22
39	9.48 173	40	9.50 267	44	0.49 733	9.97 906	4	21
40	9.48 213	39	9.50 311	44	0.49 689	9.97 902	4	**20**
41	9.48 252	40	9.50 355̄	43	0.49 645̇	9.97 898	4	19
42	9.48 292	40	9.50 398	44	0.49 602	9.97 894	4	18
43	9.48 332	39	9.50 442	43	0.49 558	9.97 890	4	17
44	9.48 371	40	9.50 485̇	44	0.49 515̄	9.97 886	4	16
45	9.48 411	39	9.50 529	43	0.49 471	9.97 882	4	15
46	9.48 450	40	9.50 572	44	0.49 428	9.97 878	4	14
47	9.48 490	39	9.50 616	43	0.49 384	9.97 874	4	13
48	9.48 529	39	9.50 659	44	0.49 341	9.97 870	4	12
49	9.48 568	39	9.50 703	43	0.49 297	9.97 866	5	11
50	9.48 607	40	9.50 746	43	0.49 254	9.97 861	4	**10**
51	9.48 647	39	9.50 789	44	0.49 211	9.97 857	4	9
52	9.48 686	39	9.50 833	43	0.49 167	9.97 853	4	8
53	9.48 725̇	39	9.50 876	43	0.49 124	9.97 849	4	7
54	9.48 764	39	9.50 919	43	0.49 081	9.97 845̇	4	6
55	9.48 803	39	9.50 962	43	0.49 038	9.97 841	4	5
56	9.48 842	39	9.51 005̇	43	0.48 995̄	9.97 837	4	4
57	9.48 881	39	9.51 048	44	0.48 952	9.97 833	4	3
58	9.48 920	39	9.51 092	43	0.48 908	9.97 829	4	2
59	9.48 959	39	9.51 135̄	43	0.48 865̇	9.97 825̄	4	1
60	9.48 998		9.51 178		0.48 822	9.97 821		**0**
′	L. Cos.	d.	L. Cot.	c.d.	L. Tan.	L. Sin.	d.	′

P. P.

″	**45**	**44**	**43**
1	0.8	0.7	0.7
2	1.5	1.5̄	1.4
3	2.2	2.2	2.2
4	3.0	2.9	2.9
5	3.8	3.7	3.6
6	4.5	4.4	4.3
7	5.2	5.1	5.0
8	6.0	5.9	5.7
9	6.8	6.6	6.4
10	7.5	7.3	7.2
20	15.0	14.7	14.3
30	22.5	22.0	21.5
40	30.0	29.3	28.7
50	37.5	36.7	35.8

″	**42**	**41**	**40**
1	0.7	0.7	0.7
2	1.4	1.4	1.3
3	2.1	2.0	2.0
4	2.8	2.7	2.7
5	3.5	3.4	3.3
6	4.2	4.1	4.0
7	4.9	4.8	4.7
8	5.6	5.5̄	5.3
9	6.3	6.2	6.0
10	7.0	6.8	6.7
20	14.0	13.7	13.3
30	21.0	20.5	20.0
40	28.0	27.3	26.7
50	35.0	34.2	33.3

″	**39**	**5**	**4**	**3**
1	0.6	0.1	0.1	0.0
2	1.3	0.2	0.1	0.1
3	2.0	0.2	0.2	0.2
4	2.6	0.3	0.3	0.2
5	3.2	0.4	0.3	0.2
6	3.9	0.5	0.4	0.3
7	4.6	0.6	0.5̄	0.4
8	5.2	0.7	0.5̇	0.4
9	5.8	0.8	0.6	0.4
10	6.5	0.8	0.7	0.5
20	13.0	1.7	1.3	1.0
30	19.5	2.5	2.0	1.5
40	26.0	3.3	2.7	2.0
50	32.5	4.2	3.3	2.5

	5/43	**4/45**	**4/44**
0	4.3	5.6	5.5
1	12.9	16.9	16.5
2	21.5	28.1	27.5
3	30.1	39.4	38.5
4	38.7	—	—
5			

	4/43	**3/45**	**3/44**
0	5.4	7.5	7.3
1	16.1	22.5	22.0
2	26.9	37.5	36.7
3	37.6	—	—
4			

P. P.

107° (287°) (252°) **72°**

18° (198°) (341°) **161°**

′	L. Sin.	d.	L. Tan.	c.d.	L. Cot.	L. Cos.	d.	′
0	9.48 998	39	9.51 178	43	0.48 822	9.97 821	4	**60**
1	9.49 037	39	9.51 221	43	0.48 779	9.97 817	5	59
2	9.49 076	39	9.51 264	42	0.48 736	9.97 812	4	58
3	9.49 115	38	9.51 306	43	0.48 694	9.97 808	4	57
4	9.49 153	39	9.51 349	43	0.48 651	9.97 804	4	56
5	9.49 192	39	9.51 392	43	0.48 608	9.97 800	4	55
6	9.49 231	38	9.51 435	43	0.48 565	9.97 796	4	54
7	9.49 269	39	9.51 478	42	0.48 522	9.97 792	4	53
8	9.49 308	39	9.51 520	43	0.48 480	9.97 788	4	52
9	9.49 347	38	9.51 563	43	0.48 437	9.97 784	5	51
10	9.49 385	39	9.51 606	42	0.48 394	9.97 779	4	**50**
11	9.49 424	38	9.51 648	43	0.48 352	9.97 775	4	49
12	9.49 462	38	9.51 691	43	0.48 309	9.97 771	4	48
13	9.49 500	39	9.51 734	42	0.48 266	9.97 767	4	47
14	9.49 539	38	9.51 776	43	0.48 224	9.97 763	4	46
15	9.49 577	38	9.51 819	42	0.48 181	9.97 759	5	45
16	9.49 615	39	9.51 861	42	0.48 139	9.97 754	4	44
17	9.49 654	38	9.51 903	43	0.48 097	9.97 750	4	43
18	9.49 692	38	9.51 946	42	0.48 054	9.97 746	4	42
19	9.49 730	38	9.51 988	43	0.48 012	9.97 742	4	41
20	9.49 768	38	9.52 031	42	0.47 969	9.97 738	4	**40**
21	9.49 806	38	9.52 073	42	0.47 927	9.97 734	5	39
22	9.49 844	38	9.52 115	42	0.47 885	9.97 729	4	38
23	9.49 882	38	9.52 157	43	0.47 843	9.97 725	4	37
24	9.49 920	38	9.52 200	42	0.47 800	9.97 721	4	36
25	9.49 958	38	9.52 242	42	0.47 758	9.97 717	4	35
26	9.49 996	38	9.52 284	42	0.47 716	9.97 713	5	34
27	9.50 034	38	9.52 326	42	0.47 674	9.97 708	4	33
28	9.50 072	38	9.52 368	42	0.47 632	9.97 704	4	32
29	9.50 110	38	9.52 410	42	0.47 590	9.97 700	4	31
30	9.50 148	37	9.52 452	42	0.47 548	9.97 696	5	**30**
31	9.50 185	38	9.52 494	42	0.47 506	9.97 691	4	29
32	9.50 223	38	9.52 536	42	0.47 464	9.97 687	4	28
33	9.50 261	37	9.52 578	42	0.47 422	9.97 683	4	27
34	9.50 298	38	9.52 620	41	0.47 380	9.97 679	5	26
35	9.50 336	38	9.52 661	42	0.47 339	9.97 674	4	25
36	9.50 374	37	9.52 703	42	0.47 297	9.97 670	4	24
37	9.50 411	38	9.52 745	42	0.47 255	9.97 666	4	23
38	9.50 449	37	9.52 787	42	0.47 213	9.97 662	5	22
39	9.50 486	37	9.52 829	41	0.47 171	9.97 657	4	21
40	9.50 523	38	9.52 870	42	0.47 130	9.97 653	4	**20**
41	9.50 561	37	9.52 912	41	0.47 088	9.97 649	4	19
42	9.50 598	37	9.52 953	42	0.47 047	9.97 645	5	18
43	9.50 635	38	9.52 995	42	0.47 005	9.97 640	4	17
44	9.50 673	37	9.53 037	41	0.46 963	9.97 636	4	16
45	9.50 710	37	9.53 078	42	0.46 922	9.97 632	4	15
46	9.50 747	37	9.53 120	41	0.46 880	9.97 628	5	14
47	9.50 784	37	9.53 161	41	0.46 839	9.97 623	4	13
48	9.50 821	37	9.53 202	42	0.46 798	9.97 619	4	12
49	9.50 858	38	9.53 244	41	0.46 756	9.97 615	5	11
50	9.50 896	37	9.53 285	42	0.46 715	9.97 610	4	**10**
51	9.50 933	37	9.53 327	41	0.46 673	9.97 606	4	9
52	9.50 970	37	9.53 368	41	0.46 632	9.97 602	5	8
53	9.51 007	36	9.53 409	41	0.46 591	9.97 597	4	7
54	9.51 043	37	9.53 450	42	0.46 550	9.97 593	4	6
55	9.51 080	37	9.53 492	41	0.46 508	9.97 589	5	5
56	9.51 117	37	9.53 533	41	0.46 467	9.97 584	4	4
57	9.51 154	37	9.53 574	41	0.46 426	9.97 580	4	3
58	9.51 191	36	9.53 615	41	0.46 385	9.97 576	5	2
59	9.51 227	37	9.53 656	41	0.46 344	9.97 571	4	1
60	9.51 264		9.53 697		0.46 303	9.97 567		**0**
′	L. Cos.	d.	L. Cot.	c.d.	L. Tan.	L. Sin.	d.	′

P. P.

″	**43**	**42**	**41**
1	0.7	0.7	0.7
2	1.4	1.4	1.4
3	2.2	2.1	2.0
4	2.9	2.8	2.7
5	3.6	3.5	3.4
6	4.3	4.2	4.1
7	5.0	4.9	4.8
8	5.7	5.6	5.5
9	6.4	6.3	6.2
10	7.2	7.0	6.8
20	14.3	14.0	13.7
30	21.5	21.0	20.5
40	28.7	28.0	27.3
50	35.8	35.0	34.2
″	**39**	**38**	**37**
1	0.6	0.6	0.6
2	1.3	1.3	1.2
3	2.0	1.9	1.8
4	2.6	2.5	2.5
5	3.2	3.2	3.1
6	3.9	3.8	3.7
7	4.6	4.4	4.3
8	5.2	5.1	4.9
9	5.8	5.7	5.6
10	6.5	6.3	6.2
20	13.0	12.7	12.3
30	19.5	19.0	18.5
40	26.0	25.3	24.7
50	32.5	31.7	30.8
″	**36**	**5**	**4**
1	0.6	0.1	0.1
2	1.2	0.2	0.1
3	1.8	0.2	0.2
4	2.4	0.3	0.3
5	3.0	0.4	0.3
6	3.6	0.5	0.4
7	4.2	0.6	0.5
8	4.8	0.7	0.5
9	5.4	0.8	0.6
10	6.0	0.8	0.7
20	12.0	1.7	1.3
30	18.0	2.5	2.0
40	24.0	3.3	2.7
50	30.0	4.2	3.3

	5/43	**5/42**	**5/41**
0	4.3	4.2	4.1
1	12.9	12.6	12.3
2	21.5	21.0	20.5
3	30.1	29.4	28.7
4	38.7	37.8	36.9
5			

	4/43	**4/42**	**4/41**
0	5.4	5.2	5.1
1	16.1	15.8	15.4
2	26.9	26.2	25.6
3	37.6	36.8	35.9
4			

P. P.

108° (288°) (251°) **71°**

19° (199°) (340°) **160°**

′	L. Sin.	d.	L. Tan.	c.d.	L. Cot.	L. Cos.	d.	′
0	9.51 264	37	9.53 697	41	0.46 303	9.97 567	4	**60**
1	9.51 301	37	9.53 738	41	0.46 262	9.97 563	5	59
2	9.51 338	36	9.53 779	41	0.46 221	9.97 558	4	58
3	9.51 374	37	9.53 820	41	0.46 180	9.97 554	4	57
4	9.51 411	36	9.53 861	41	0.46 139	9.97 5̄50	5	56
5	9.51 447	37	9.53 902	41	0.46 098	9.97 545̇	4	55
6	9.51 484	36	9.53 943	41	0.46 057	9.97 541	5	54
7	9.51 520	37	9.53 984	41	0.46 016	9.97 536	4	53
8	9.51 557	36	9.54 025̄	40	0.45 975̇	9.97 532	4	52
9	9.51 593	36	9.54 065̇	41	0.45 935̄	9.97 528	5	51
10	9.51 629	37	9.54 106	41	0.45 894	9.97 523	4	**50**
11	9.51 666	36	9.54 147	40	0.45 853	9.97 519	4	49
12	9.51 702	36	9.54 187	41	0.45 813	9.97 515̄	5	48
13	9.51 738	36	9.54 228	41	0.45 772	9.97 510	4	47
14	9.51 774	37	9.54 269	40	0.45 731	9.97 506	5	46
15	9.51 811	36	9.54 309	41	0.45 691	9.97 501	4	45
16	9.51 847	36	9.54 35̄0	40	0.45 65̇0	9.97 497	5	44
17	9.51 883	36	9.54 390	41	0.45 610	9.97 492	4	43
18	9.51 919	36	9.54 431	40	0.45 569	9.97 488	4	42
19	9.51 955̇	36	9.54 471	41	0.45 529	9.97 484	5	41
20	9.51 991	36	9.54 512	40	0.45 488	9.97 479	4	**40**
21	9.52 027	36	9.54 552	41	0.45 448	9.97 475̄	5	39
22	9.52 063	36	9.54 593	40	0.45 407	9.97 470	4	38
23	9.52 099	36	9.54 633	40	0.45 367	9.97 466	5	37
24	9.52 135̄	36	9.54 673	41	0.45 327	9.97 461	4	36
25	9.52 171	36	9.54 714	40	0.45 286	9.97 457	4	35
26	9.52 207	35	9.54 754	40	0.45 246	9.97 453	5	34
27	9.52 242	36	9.54 794	41	0.45 206	9.97 448	4	33
28	9.52 278	36	9.54 835̄	40	0.45 165̇	9.97 444	5	32
29	9.52 314	36	9.54 875̄	40	0.45 125̇	9.97 439	4	31
30	9.52 35̄0	35	9.54 915̄	40	0.45 085̇	9.97 435̄	5	**30**
31	9.52 385̇	36	9.54 955̇	40	0.45 045̄	9.97 430	4	29
32	9.52 421	35	9.54 995̇	40	0.45 005̄	9.97 426	5	28
33	9.52 456	36	9.55 035̇	40	0.44 965̄	9.97 421	4	27
34	9.52 492	35	9.55 075̇	40	0.44 925̄	9.97 417	5	26
35	9.52 527	36	9.55 115̇	40	0.44 885̄	9.97 412	4	25
36	9.52 563	35	9.55 155̇	40	0.44 845̇	9.97 408	5	24
37	9.52 598	36	9.55 195̇	40	0.44 805̇	9.97 403	4	23
38	9.52 634	35	9.55 235̇	40	0.44 765̇	9.97 399	5	22
39	9.52 669	36	9.55 275̇	40	0.44 725̄	9.97 394	4	21
40	9.52 705̄	35	9.55 315̄	40	0.44 685̇	9.97 390	5	**20**
41	9.52 740	35	9.55 355̄	40	0.44 645̇	9.97 385̇	4	19
42	9.52 775̇	36	9.55 395̄	39	0.44 605̇	9.97 381	5	18
43	9.52 811	35	9.55 434	40	0.44 566	9.97 376	4	17
44	9.52 846	35	9.55 474	40	0.44 526	9.97 372	5	16
45	9.52 881	35	9.55 514	40	0.44 486	9.97 367	4	15
46	9.52 916	35	9.55 554	39	0.44 446	9.97 363	5	14
47	9.52 951	35	9.55 593	40	0.44 407	9.97 358	5	13
48	9.52 986	35	9.55 633	40	0.44 367	9.97 353	4	12
49	9.53 021	35	9.55 673	39	0.44 327	9.97 349	5	11
50	9.53 056	36	9.55 712	40	0.44 288	9.97 344	4	**10**
51	9.53 092	34	9.55 752	39	0.44 248	9.97 340	5	9
52	9.53 126	35	9.55 791	40	0.44 209	9.97 335̇	4	8
53	9.53 161	35	9.55 831	39	0.44 169	9.97 331	5	7
54	9.53 196	35	9.55 870	40	0.44 130	9.97 326	4	6
55	9.53 231	35	9.55 910	39	0.44 090	9.97 322	5	5
56	9.53 266	35	9.55 949	40	0.44 051	9.97 317	5	4
57	9.53 301	35	9.55 989	39	0.44 011	9.97 312	4	3
58	9.53 336	34	9.56 028	39	0.43 972	9.97 308	5	2
59	9.53 370	35	9.56 067	40	0.43 933	9.97 303	4	1
60	9.53 405̇		9.56 107		0.43 893	9.97 299		**0**
′	L. Cos.	d.	L. Cot.	c.d.	L. Tan.	L. Sin.	d.	′

P. P.

″	**41**	**40**	**39**
1	0.7	0.7	0.6
2	1.4	1.3	1.3
3	2.0	2.0	2.0
4	2.7	2.7	2.6
5	3.4	3.3	3.2
6	4.1	4.0	3.9
7	4.8	4.7	4.6
8	5.5̄	5.3	5.2
9	6.2	6.0	5.8
10	6.8	6.7	6.5
20	13.7	13.3	13.0
30	20.5	20.0	19.5
40	27.3	26.7	26.0
50	34.2	33.3	32.5

″	**37**	**36**	**35**
1	0.6	0.6	0.6
2	1.2	1.2	1.2
3	1.8	1.8	1.8
4	2.5̄	2.4	2.3
5	3.1	3.0	2.9
6	3.7	3.6	3.5
7	4.3	4.2	4.1
8	4.9	4.8	4.7
9	5.6	5.4	5.2
10	6.2	6.0	5.8
20	12.3	12.0	11.7
30	18.5	18.0	17.5
40	24.7	24.0	23.3
50	30.8	30.0	29.2

″	**34**	**5**	**4**
1	0.6	0.1	0.1
2	1.1	0.2	0.1
3	1.7	0.2	0.2
4	2.3	0.3	0.3
5	2.8	0.4	0.3
6	3.4	0.5	0.4
7	4.0	0.6	0.5̄
8	4.5̇	0.7	0.5̇
9	5.1	0.8	0.6
10	5.7	0.8	0.7
20	11.3	1.7	1.3
30	17.0	2.5	2.0
40	22.7	3.3	2.7
50	28.3	4.2	3.3

	5/41	**5/40**	**5/39**
0	4.1	4.0	3.9
1	12.3	12.0	11.7
2	20.5	20.0	19.5
3	28.7	28.0	27.3
4	36.9	36.0	35.1
5			

	4/41	**4/40**	**4/39**
0	5.1	5.0	4.9
1	15.4	15.0	14.6
2	25.6	25.0	24.4
3	35.9	35.0	34.1
4			

P. P.

109° (289°) (250°) **70°**

20° (200°) (339°) **159°**

′	L. Sin.	d.	L. Tan.	c.d.	L. Cot.	L. Cos.	d.	′
0	9.53 405̇	35	9.56 107	39	0.43 893	9.97 299	5	**60**
1	9.53 440	35	9.56 146	39	0.43 854	9.97 294	5	59
2	9.53 475̄	34	9.56 185̇	39	0.43 815̄	9.97 289	4	58
3	9.53 509	35	9.56 224	40	0.43 776	9.97 285̄	5	57
4	9.53 544	34	9.56 264	39	0.43 736	9.97 280	4	56
5	9.53 578	35	9.56 303	39	0.43 697	9.97 276	5	55
6	9.53 613	34	9.56 342	39	0.43 658	9.97 271	5	54
7	9.53 647	35	9.56 381	39	0.43 619	9.97 266	4	53
8	9.53 682	34	9.56 420	39	0.43 580	9.97 262	5	52
9	9.53 716	35	9.56 459	39	0.43 541	9.97 257	5	51
10	9.53 751	34	9.56 498	39	0.43 502	9.97 252	4	**50**
11	9.53 785̇	34	9.56 537	39	0.43 463	9.97 248	5	49
12	9.53 819	35	9.56 576	39	0.43 424	9.97 243	5	48
13	9.53 854	34	9.56 615̇	39	0.43 385̄	9.97 238	4	47
14	9.53 888	34	9.56 654	39	0.43 346	9.97 234	5	46
15	9.53 922	35	9.56 693	39	0.43 307	9.97 229	5	45
16	9.53 957	34	9.56 732	39	0.43 268	9.97 224	4	44
17	9.53 991	34	9.56 771	39	0.43 229	9.97 220	5	43
18	9.54 025̄	34	9.56 810	39	0.43 190	9.97 215̇	5	42
19	9.54 059	34	9.56 849	38	0.43 151	9.97 210	4	41
20	9.54 093	34	9.56 887	39	0.43 113	9.97 206	5	**40**
21	9.54 127	34	9.56 926	39	0.43 074	9.97 201	5	39
22	9.54 161	34	9.56 965̄	39	0.43 035̄	9.97 196	4	38
23	9.54 195̇	34	9.57 004	38	0.42 996	9.97 192	5	37
24	9.54 229	34	9.57 042	39	0.42 958	9.97 187	5	36
25	9.54 263	34	9.57 081	39	0.42 919	9.97 182	4	35
26	9.54 297	34	9.57 120	38	0.42 880	9.97 178	5	34
27	9.54 331	34	9.57 158	39	0.42 842	9.97 173	5	33
28	9.54 365̄	34	9.57 197	38	0.42 803	9.97 168	5	32
29	9.54 399	34	9.57 235̇	39	0.42 765̄	9.97 163	4	31
30	9.54 433	33	9.57 274	38	0.42 726	9.97 159	5	**30**
31	9.54 466	34	9.57 312	39	0.42 688	9.97 154	5	29
32	9.54 500	34	9.57 351	38	0.42 649	9.97 149	4	28
33	9.54 534	33	9.57 389	39	0.42 611	9.97 145̄	5	27
34	9.54 567	34	9.57 428	38	0.42 572	9.97 140	5	26
35	9.54 601	34	9.57 466	38	0.42 534	9.97 135̇	5	25
36	9.54 635̄	33	9.57 504	39	0.42 496	9.97 130	4	24
37	9.54 668	34	9.57 543	38	0.42 457	9.97 126	5	23
38	9.54 702	33	9.57 581	38	0.42 419	9.97 121	5	22
39	9.54 735̇	34	9.57 619	39	0.42 381	9.97 116	5	21
40	9.54 769	33	9.57 658	38	0.42 342	9.97 111	4	**20**
41	9.54 802	34	9.57 696	38	0.42 304	9.97 107	5	19
42	9.54 836	33	9.57 734	38	0.42 266	9.97 102	5	18
43	9.54 869	34	9.57 772	38	0.42 228	9.97 097	5	17
44	9.54 903	33	9.57 810	39	0.42 190	9.97 092	5	16
45	9.54 936	33	9.57 849	38	0.42 151	9.97 087	4	15
46	9.54 969	34	9.57 887	38	0.42 113	9.97 083	5	14
47	9.55 003	33	9.57 925̄	38	0.42 075̇	9.97 078	5	13
48	9.55 036	33	9.57 963	38	0.42 037	9.97 073	5	12
49	9.55 069	33	9.58 001	38	0.41 999	9.97 068	5	11
50	9.55 102	34	9.58 039	38	0.41 961	9.97 063	4	**10**
51	9.55 136	33	9.58 077	38	0.41 923	9.97 059	5	9
52	9.55 169	33	9.58 115̄	38	0.41 885̇	9.97 054	5	8
53	9.55 202	33	9.58 153	38	0.41 847	9.97 049	5	7
54	9.55 235̄	33	9.58 191	38	0.41 809	9.97 044	5	6
55	9.55 268	33	9.58 229	38	0.41 771	9.97 039	4	5
56	9.55 301	33	9.58 267	37	0.41 733	9.97 035̄	5	4
57	9.55 334	33	9.58 304	38	0.41 696	9.97 030	5	3
58	9.55 367	33	9.58 342	38	0.41 658	9.97 025̄	5	2
59	9.55 400	33	9.58 380	38	0.41 620	9.97 020	5	1
60	9.55 433		9.58 418		0.41 582	9.97 015̇		**0**
′	L. Cos.	d.	L. Cot.	c.d.	L. Tan.	L. Sin.	d.	′

P. P.

″	**40**	**39**	**38**
1	0.7	0.6	0.6
2	1.3	1.3	1.3
3	2.0	2.0	1.9
4	2.7	2.6	2.5̇
5	3.3	3.2	3.2
6	4.0	3.9	3.8
7	4.7	4.6	4.4
8	5.3	5.2	5.1
9	6.0	5.8	5.7
10	6.7	6.5	6.3
20	13.3	13.0	12.7
30	20.0	19.5	19.0
40	26.7	26.0	25.3
50	33.3	32.5	31.7

″	**37**	**35**	**34**
1	0.6	0.6	0.6
2	1.2	1.2	1.1
3	1.8	1.8	1.7
4	2.5̄	2.3	2.3
5	3.1	2.9	2.8
6	3.7	3.5	3.4
7	4.3	4.1	4.0
8	4.9	4.7	4.5̇
9	5.6	5.2	5.1
10	6.2	5.8	5.7
20	12.3	11.7	11.3
30	18.5	17.5	17.0
40	24.7	23.3	22.7
50	30.8	29.2	28.3

″	**33**	**5**	**4**
1	0.6	0.1	0.1
2	1.1	0.2	0.1
3	1.6	0.2	0.2
4	2.2	0.3	0.3
5	2.8	0.4	0.3
6	3.3	0.5	0.4
7	3.8	0.6	0.5̄
8	4.4	0.7	0.5̇
9	5̄.0	0.8	0.6
10	5.5	0.8	0.7
20	11.0	1.7	1.3
30	16.5	2.5	2.0
40	22.0	3.3	2.7
50	27.5	4.2	3.3

	5 / **40**	**5** / **39**	**5** / **38**
0	4.0	3.9	3.8
1	12.0	11.7	11.4
2	20.0	19.5	19.0
3	28.0	27.3	26.6
4	36.0	35.1	34.2
5			

	5 / **37**	**4** / **39**	**4** / **38**
0	3.7	4.9	4.8
1	11.1	14.6	14.2
2	18.5	24.4	23.8
3	25.9	34.1	33.2
4	33.3	—	—
5			

P. P.

110° (290°) (249°) **69°**

21° (201°) (338°) **158°**

′	L. Sin.	d.	L. Tan.	c.d.	L. Cot.	L. Cos.	d.	′
0	9.55 433	33	9.58 418	37	0.41 582	9.97 015	5	**60**
1	9.55 466	33	9.58 455	38	0.41 545	9.97 010	5	59
2	9.55 499	33	9.58 493	38	0.41 507	9.97 005	4	58
3	9.55 532	32	9.58 531	38	0.41 469	9.97 001	5	57
4	9.55 564	33	9.58 569	37	0.41 431	9.96 996	5	56
5	9.55 597	33	9.58 606	38	0.41 394	9.96 991	5	55
6	9.55 630	33	9.58 644	37	0.41 356	9.96 986	5	54
7	9.55 663	32	9.58 681	38	0.41 319	9.96 981	5	53
8	9.55 695	33	9.58 719	38	0.41 281	9.96 976	5	52
9	9.55 728	33	9.58 757	37	0.41 243	9.96 971	5	51
10	9.55 761	32	9.58 794	38	0.41 206	9.96 966	4	**50**
11	9.55 793	33	9.58 832	37	0.41 168	9.96 962	5	49
12	9.55 826	32	9.58 869	38	0.41 131	9.96 957	5	48
13	9.55 858	33	9.58 907	37	0.41 093	9.96 952	5	47
14	9.55 891	32	9.58 944	37	0.41 056	9.96 947	5	46
15	9.55 923	33	9.58 981	38	0.41 019	9.96 942	5	45
16	9.55 956	32	9.59 019	37	0.40 981	9.96 937	5	44
17	9.55 988	33	9.59 056	38	0.40 944	9.96 932	5	43
18	9.56 021	32	9.59 094	37	0.40 906	9.96 927	5	42
19	9.56 053	32	9.59 131	37	0.40 869	9.96 922	5	41
20	9.56 085	33	9.59 168	37	0.40 832	9.96 917	5	**40**
21	9.56 118	32	9.59 205	38	0.40 795	9.96 912	5	39
22	9.56 150	32	9.59 243	37	0.40 757	9.96 907	4	38
23	9.56 182	33	9.59 280	37	0.40 720	9.96 903	5	37
24	9.56 215	32	9.59 317	37	0.40 683	9.96 898	5	36
25	9.56 247	32	9.59 354	37	0.40 646	9.96 893	5	35
26	9.56 279	32	9.59 391	38	0.40 609	9.96 888	5	34
27	9.56 311	32	9.59 429	37	0.40 571	9.96 883	5	33
28	9.56 343	32	9.59 466	37	0.40 534	9.96 878	5	32
29	9.56 375	33	9.59 503	37	0.40 497	9.96 873	5	31
30	9.56 408	32	9.59 540	37	0.40 460	9.96 868	5	**30**
31	9.56 440	32	9.59 577	37	0.40 423	9.96 863	5	29
32	9.56 472	32	9.59 614	37	0.40 386	9.96 858	5	28
33	9.56 504	32	9.59 651	37	0.40 349	9.96 853	5	27
34	9.56 536	32	9.59 688	37	0.40 312	9.96 848	5	26
35	9.56 568	31	9.59 725	37	0.40 275	9.96 843	5	25
36	9.56 599	32	9.59 762	37	0.40 238	9.96 838	5	24
37	9.56 631	32	9.59 799	36	0.40 201	9.96 833	5	23
38	9.56 663	32	9.59 835	37	0.40 165	9.96 828	5	22
39	9.56 695	32	9.59 872	37	0.40 128	9.96 823	5	21
40	9.56 727	32	9.59 909	37	0.40 091	9.96 818	5	**20**
41	9.56 759	31	9.59 946	37	0.40 054	9.96 813	5	19
42	9.56 790	32	9.59 983	36	0.40 017	9.96 808	5	18
43	9.56 822	32	9.60 019	37	0.39 981	9.96 803	5	17
44	9.56 854	32	9.60 056	37	0.39 944	9.96 798	5	16
45	9.56 886	31	9.60 093	37	0.39 907	9.96 793	5	15
46	9.56 917	32	9.60 130	36	0.39 870	9.96 788	5	14
47	9.56 949	31	9.60 166	37	0.39 834	9.96 783	5	13
48	9.56 980	32	9.60 203	37	0.39 797	9.96 778	6	12
49	9.57 012	32	9.60 240	36	0.39 760	9.96 772	5	11
50	9.57 044	31	9.60 276	37	0.39 724	9.96 767	5	**10**
51	9.57 075	32	9.60 313	36	0.39 687	9.96 762	5	9
52	9.57 107	31	9.60 349	37	0.39 651	9.96 757	5	8
53	9.57 138	31	9.60 386	36	0.39 614	9.96 752	5	7
54	9.57 169	32	9.60 422	37	0.39 578	9.96 747	5	6
55	9.57 201	31	9.60 459	36	0.39 541	9.96 742	5	5
56	9.57 232	32	9.60 495	37	0.39 505	9.96 737	5	4
57	9.57 264	31	9.60 532	36	0.39 468	9.96 732	5	3
58	9.57 295	31	9.60 568	37	0.39 432	9.96 727	5	2
59	9.57 326	32	9.60 605	36	0.39 395	9.96 722	5	1
60	9.57 358		9.60 641		0.39 359	9.96 717		**0**
′	L. Cos.	d.	L. Cot.	c.d.	L. Tan.	L. Sin.	d.	′

P. P.

″	**38**	**37**	**36**
1	0.6	0.6	0.6
2	1.3	1.2	1.2
3	1.9	1.8	1.8
4	2.5	2.5	2.4
5	3.2	3.1	3.0
6	3.8	3.7	3.6
7	4.4	4.3	4.2
8	5.1	4.9	4.8
9	5.7	5.6	5.4
10	6.3	6.2	6.0
20	12.7	12.3	12.0
30	19.0	18.5	18.0
40	25.3	24.7	24.0
50	31.7	30.8	30.0

″	**33**	**32**	**31**
1	0.6	0.5	0.5
2	1.1	1.1	1.0
3	1.6	1.6	1.6
4	2.2	2.1	2.1
5	2.8	2.7	2.6
6	3.3	3.2	3.1
7	3.8	3.7	3.6
8	4.4	4.3	4.1
9	5.0	4.8	4.6
10	5.5	5.3	5.2
20	11.0	10.7	10.3
30	16.5	16.0	15.5
40	22.0	21.3	20.7
50	27.5	26.7	25.8

″	**6**	**5**	**4**
1	0.1	0.1	0.1
2	0.2	0.2	0.1
3	0.3	0.2	0.2
4	0.4	0.3	0.3
5	0.5	0.4	0.3
6	0.6	0.5	0.4
7	0.7	0.6	0.5
8	0.8	0.7	0.5
9	0.9	0.8	0.6
10	1.0	0.8	0.7
20	2.0	1.7	1.3
30	3.0	2.5	2.0
40	4.0	3.3	2.7
50	5.0	4.2	3.3

	6/**37**	**5**/**38**	**5**/**37**
0			
	3.1	3.8	3.7
1			
	9.2	11.4	11.1
2			
	15.4	19.0	18.5
3			
	21.6	26.6	25.9
4			
	27.8	34.2	33.3
5			
	33.9	—	—
6			

	5/**36**	**4**/**38**	**4**/**37**
0			
	3.6	4.8	4.6
1			
	10.8	14.2	13.9
2			
	18.0	23.8	23.1
3			
	25.2	33.2	32.4
4			
	32.4	—	—
5			

P. P.

111° (291°) (248°) **68°**

22° (202°) (337°) **157°**

′	L. Sin.	d.	L. Tan.	c.d.	L. Cot.	L. Cos.	d.	′
0	9.57 358	31	9.60 641	36	0.39 359	9.96 717	6	**60**
1	9.57 389	31	9.60 677	37	0.39 323	9.96 711	5	59
2	9.57 420	31	9.60 714	36	0.39 286	9.96 706	5	58
3	9.57 451	31	9.60 750	36	0.39 250	9.96 701	5	57
4	9.57 482	32	9.60 786	37	0.39 214	9.96 696	5	56
5	9.57 514	31	9.60 823	36	0.39 177	9.96 691	5	55
6	9.57 545	31	9.60 859	36	0.39 141	9.96 686	5	54
7	9.57 576	31	9.60 895	36	0.39 105	9.96 681	5	53
8	9.57 607	31	9.60 931	36	0.39 069	9.96 676	6	52
9	9.57 638	31	9.60 967	37	0.39 033	9.96 670	5	51
10	9.57 669	31	9.61 004	36	0.38 996	9.96 665	5	**50**
11	9.57 700	31	9.61 040	36	0.38 960	9.96 660	5	49
12	9.57 731	31	9.61 076	36	0.38 924	9.96 655	5	48
13	9.57 762	31	9.61 112	36	0.38 888	9.96 650	5	47
14	9.57 793	31	9.61 148	36	0.38 852	9.96 645	5	46
15	9.57 824	31	9.61 184	36	0.38 816	9.96 640	6	45
16	9.57 855	30	9.61 220	36	0.38 780	9.96 634	5	44
17	9.57 885	31	9.61 256	36	0.38 744	9.96 629	5	43
18	9.57 916	31	9.61 292	36	0.38 708	9.96 624	5	42
19	9.57 947	31	9.61 328	36	0.38 672	9.96 619	5	41
20	9.57 978	30	9.61 364	36	0.38 636	9.96 614	6	**40**
21	9.58 008	31	9.61 400	36	0.38 600	9.96 608	5	39
22	9.58 039	31	9.61 436	36	0.38 564	9.96 603	5	38
23	9.58 070	31	9.61 472	36	0.38 528	9.96 598	5	37
24	9.58 101	30	9.61 508	36	0.38 492	9.96 593	5	36
25	9.58 131	31	9.61 544	35	0.38 456	9.96 588	6	35
26	9.58 162	30	9.61 579	36	0.38 421	9.96 582	5	34
27	9.58 192	31	9.61 615	36	0.38 385	9.96 577	5	33
28	9.58 223	30	9.61 651	36	0.38 349	9.96 572	5	32
29	9.58 253	31	9.61 687	35	0.38 313	9.96 567	5	31
30	9.58 284	30	9.61 722	36	0.38 278	9.96 562	6	**30**
31	9.58 314	31	9.61 758	36	0.38 242	9.96 556	5	29
32	9.58 345	30	9.61 794	36	0.38 206	9.96 551	5	28
33	9.58 375	31	9.61 830	35	0.38 170	9.96 546	5	27
34	9.58 406	30	9.61 865	36	0.38 135	9.96 541	6	26
35	9.58 436	31	9.61 901	35	0.38 099	9.96 535	5	25
36	9.58 467	30	9.61 936	36	0.38 064	9.96 530	5	24
37	9.58 497	30	9.61 972	36	0.38 028	9.96 525	5	23
38	9.58 527	30	9.62 008	35	0.37 992	9.96 520	6	22
39	9.58 557	31	9.62 043	36	0.37 957	9.96 514	5	21
40	9.58 588	30	9.62 079	35	0.37 921	9.96 509	5	**20**
41	9.58 618	30	9.62 114	36	0.37 886	9.96 504	6	19
42	9.58 648	30	9.62 150	35	0.37 850	9.96 498	5	18
43	9.58 678	31	9.62 185	36	0.37 815	9.96 493	5	17
44	9.58 709	30	9.62 221	35	0.37 779	9.96 488	5	16
45	9.58 739	30	9.62 256	36	0.37 744	9.96 483	6	15
46	9.58 769	30	9.62 292	35	0.37 708	9.96 477	5	14
47	9.58 799	30	9.62 327	35	0.37 673	9.96 472	5	13
48	9.58 829	30	9.62 362	36	0.37 638	9.96 467	6	12
49	9.58 859	30	9.62 398	35	0.37 602	9.96 461	5	11
50	9.58 889	30	9.62 433	35	0.37 567	9.96 456	5	**10**
51	9.58 919	30	9.62 468	36	0.37 532	9.96 451	6	9
52	9.58 949	30	9.62 504	35	0.37 496	9.96 445	5	8
53	9.58 979	30	9.62 539	35	0.37 461	9.96 440	5	7
54	9.59 009	30	9.62 574	35	0.37 426	9.96 435	6	6
55	9.59 039	30	9.62 609	36	0.37 391	9.96 429	5	5
56	9.59 069	29	9.62 645	35	0.37 355	9.96 424	5	4
57	9.59 098	30	9.62 680	35	0.37 320	9.96 419	6	3
58	9.59 128	30	9.62 715	35	0.37 285	9.96 413	5	2
59	9.59 158	30	9.62 750	35	0.37 250	9.96 408	5	1
60	9.59 188		9.62 785		0.37 215	9.96 403		**0**
′	L. Cos.	d.	L. Cot.	c.d.	L. Tan.	L. Sin.	d.	′

P. P.

″	**37**	**36**	**35**
1	0.6	0.6	0.6
2	1.2	1.2	1.2
3	1.8	1.8	1.8
4	2.5	2.4	2.3
5	3.1	3.0	2.9
6	3.7	3.6	3.5
7	4.3	4.2	4.1
8	4.9	4.8	4.7
9	5.6	5.4	5.2
10	6.2	6.0	5.8
20	12.3	12.0	11.7
30	18.5	18.0	17.5
40	24.7	24.0	23.3
50	30.8	30.0	29.2

″	**32**	**31**	**30**
1	0.5	0.5	0.5
2	1.1	1.0	1.0
3	1.6	1.6	1.5
4	2.1	2.1	2.0
5	2.7	2.6	2.5
6	3.2	3.1	3.0
7	3.7	3.6	3.5
8	4.3	4.1	4.0
9	4.8	4.6	4.5
10	5.3	5.2	5.0
20	10.7	10.3	10.0
30	16.0	15.5	15.0
40	21.3	20.7	20.0
50	26.7	25.8	25.0

″	**29**	**6**	**5**
1	0.5	0.1	0.1
2	1.0	0.2	0.2
3	1.4	0.3	0.2
4	1.9	0.4	0.3
5	2.4	0.5	0.4
6	2.9	0.6	0.5
7	3.4	0.7	0.6
8	3.9	0.8	0.7
9	4.4	0.9	0.8
10	4.8	1.0	0.8
20	9.7	2.0	1.7
30	14.5	3.0	2.5
40	19.3	4.0	3.3
50	24.2	5.0	4.2

	6 / **36**	**6** / **35**
0	3.0	2.9
1	9.0	8.8
2	15.0	14.6
3	21.0	20.4
4	27.0	26.2
5	33.0	32.1
6		

	5 / **37**	**5** / **36**	**5** / **35**
0	3.7	3.6	3.5
1	11.1	10.8	10.5
2	18.5	18.0	17.5
3	25.9	25.2	24.5
4	33.3	32.4	31.5
5			

P. P.

112° (292°) (247°) **67°**

23° (203°) (336°) **156°**

′	L. Sin.	d.	L. Tan.	c.d.	L. Cot.	L. Cos.	d.	′
0	9.59 188	30	9.62 785	35	0.37 215	9.96 403	6	**60**
1	9.59 218	29	9.62 820	35	0.37 180	9.96 397	5	59
2	9.59 247	30	9.62 855	35	0.37 145	9.96 392	5	58
3	9.59 277	30	9.62 890	36	0.37 110	9.96 387	6	57
4	9.59 307	29	9.62 926	35	0.37 074	9.96 381	5	56
5	9.59 336	30	9.62 961	35	0.37 039	9.96 376	6	55
6	9.59 366	30	9.62 996	35	0.37 004	9.96 370	5	54
7	9.59 396	29	9.63 031	35	0.36 969	9.96 365	5	53
8	9.59 425	30	9.63 066	35	0.36 934	9.96 360	6	52
9	9.59 455	29	9.63 101	34	0.36 899	9.96 354	5	51
10	9.59 484	30	9.63 135	35	0.36 865	9.96 349	6	**50**
11	9.59 514	29	9.63 170	35	0.36 830	9.96 343	5	49
12	9.59 543	30	9.63 205	35	0.36 795	9.96 338	5	48
13	9.59 573	29	9.63 240	35	0.36 760	9.96 333	6	47
14	9.59 602	30	9.63 275	35	0.36 725	9.96 327	5	46
15	9.59 632	29	9.63 310	35	0.36 690	9.96 322	6	45
16	9.59 661	29	9.63 345	34	0.36 655	9.96 316	5	44
17	9.59 690	30	9.63 379	35	0.36 621	9.96 311	6	43
18	9.59 720	29	9.63 414	35	0.36 586	9.96 305	5	42
19	9.59 749	29	9.63 449	35	0.36 551	9.96 300	6	41
20	9.59 778	30	9.63 484	35	0.36 516	9.96 294	5	**40**
21	9.59 808	29	9.63 519	34	0.36 481	9.96 289	5	39
22	9.59 837	29	9.63 553	35	0.36 447	9.96 284	6	38
23	9.59 866	29	9.63 588	35	0.36 412	9.96 278	5	37
24	9.59 895	29	9.63 623	34	0.36 377	9.96 273	6	36
25	9.59 924	30	9.63 657	35	0.36 343	9.96 267	5	35
26	9.59 954	29	9.63 692	34	0.36 308	9.96 262	6	34
27	9.59 983	29	9.63 726	35	0.36 274	9.96 256	5	33
28	9.60 012	29	9.63 761	35	0.36 239	9.96 251	6	32
29	9.60 041	29	9.63 796	34	0.36 204	9.96 245	5	31
30	9.60 070	29	9.63 830	35	0.36 170	9.96 240	6	**30**
31	9.60 099	29	9.63 865	34	0.36 135	9.96 234	5	29
32	9.60 128	29	9.63 899	35	0.36 101	9.96 229	6	28
33	9.60 157	29	9.63 934	34	0.36 066	9.96 223	5	27
34	9.60 186	29	9.63 968	35	0.36 032	9.96 218	6	26
35	9.60 215	29	9.64 003	34	0.35 997	9.96 212	5	25
36	9.60 244	29	9.64 037	35	0.35 963	9.96 207	6	24
37	9.60 273	29	9.64 072	34	0.35 928	9.96 201	5	23
38	9.60 302	29	9.64 106	34	0.35 894	9.96 196	6	22
39	9.60 331	28	9.64 140	35	0.35 860	9.96 190	5	21
40	9.60 359	29	9.64 175	34	0.35 825	9.96 185	6	**20**
41	9.60 388	29	9.64 209	34	0.35 791	9.96 179	5	19
42	9.60 417	29	9.64 243	35	0.35 757	9.96 174	6	18
43	9.60 446	28	9.64 278	34	0.35 722	9.96 168	6	17
44	9.60 474	29	9.64 312	34	0.35 688	9.96 162	5	16
45	9.60 503	29	9.64 346	35	0.35 654	9.96 157	6	15
46	9.60 532	29	9.64 381	34	0.35 619	9.96 151	5	14
47	9.60 561	28	9.64 415	34	0.35 585	9.96 146	6	13
48	9.60 589	29	9.64 449	34	0.35 551	9.96 140	5	12
49	9.60 618	28	9.64 483	34	0.35 517	9.96 135	6	11
50	9.60 646	29	9.64 517	35	0.35 483	9.96 129	6	**10**
51	9.60 675	29	9.64 552	34	0.35 448	9.96 123	5	9
52	9.60 704	28	9.64 586	34	0.35 414	9.96 118	6	8
53	9.60 732	29	9.64 620	34	0.35 380	9.96 112	5	7
54	9.60 761	28	9.64 654	34	0.35 346	9.96 107	6	6
55	9.60 789	29	9.64 688	34	0.35 312	9.96 101	6	5
56	9.60 818	28	9.64 722	34	0.35 278	9.96 095	5	4
57	9.60 846	29	9.64 756	34	0.35 244	9.96 090	6	3
58	9.60 875	28	9.64 790	34	0.35 210	9.96 084	5	2
59	9.60 903	28	9.64 824	34	0.35 176	9.96 079	6	1
60	9.60 931		9.64 858		0.35 142	9.96 073		**0**
′	L. Cos.	d.	L. Cot.	c.d.	L. Tan.	L. Sin.	d.	′

P. P.

″	36	35	34
1	0.6	0.6	0.6
2	1.2	1.2	1.1
3	1.8	1.8	1.7
4	2.4	2.3	2.3
5	3.0	2.9	2.8
6	3.6	3.5	3.4
7	4.2	4.1	4.0
8	4.8	4.7	4.5
9	5.4	5.2	5.1
10	6.0	5.8	5.7
20	12.0	11.7	11.3
30	18.0	17.5	17.0
40	24.0	23.3	22.7
50	30.0	29.2	28.3

″	30	29	28
1	0.5	0.5	0.5
2	1.0	1.0	0.9
3	1.5	1.4	1.4
4	2.0	1.9	1.9
5	2.5	2.4	2.3
6	3.0	2.9	2.8
7	3.5	3.4	3.3
8	4.0	3.9	3.7
9	4.5	4.4	4.2
10	5.0	4.8	4.7
20	10.0	9.7	9.3
30	15.0	14.5	14.0
40	20.0	19.3	18.7
50	25.0	24.2	23.3

″	6	5
1	0.1	0.1
2	0.2	0.2
3	0.3	0.2
4	0.4	0.3
5	0.5	0.4
6	0.6	0.5
7	0.7	0.6
8	0.8	0.7
9	0.9	0.8
10	1.0	0.8
20	2.0	1.7
30	3.0	2.5
40	4.0	3.3
50	5.0	4.2

	6/36	6/35	6/34
0	3.0	2.9	2.8
1	9.0	8.8	8.5
2	15.0	14.6	14.2
3	21.0	20.4	19.8
4	27.0	26.2	25.5
5	33.0	32.1	31.2
6			

	5/35	5/34
0	3.5	3.4
1	10.5	10.2
2	17.5	17.0
3	24.5	23.8
4	31.5	30.6
5		

P. P.

113° (293°) (246°) **66°**

24° (204°) (335°) **155°**

′	L. Sin.	d.	L. Tan.	c.d.	L. Cot.	L. Cos.	d.	′
0	9.60 931	29	9.64 858	34	0.35 142	9.96 073	6	**60**
1	9.60 960	28	9.64 892	34	0.35 108	9.96 067	5	59
2	9.60 988	28	9.64 926	34	0.35 074	9.96 062	6	58
3	9.61 016	29	9.64 960	34	0.35 040	9.96 056	6	57
4	9.61 045	28	9.64 994	34	0.35 006	9.96 050	5	56
5	9.61 073	28	9.65 028	34	0.34 972	9.96 045	6	55
6	9.61 101	28	9.65 062	34	0.34 938	9.96 039	5	54
7	9.61 129	29	9.65 096	34	0.34 904	9.96 034	6	53
8	9.61 158	28	9.65 130	34	0.34 870	9.96 028	6	52
9	9.61 186	28	9.65 164	33	0.34 836	9.96 022	5	51
10	9.61 214	28	9.65 197	34	0.34 803	9.96 017	6	**50**
11	9.61 242	28	9.65 231	34	0.34 769	9.96 011	6	49
12	9.61 270	28	9.65 265	34	0.34 735	9.96 005	5	48
13	9.61 298	28	9.65 299	34	0.34 701	9.96 000	6	47
14	9.61 326	28	9.65 333	33	0.34 667	9.95 994	6	46
15	9.61 354	28	9.65 366	34	0.34 634	9.95 988	6	45
16	9.61 382	29	9.65 400	34	0.34 600	9.95 982	5	44
17	9.61 411	27	9.65 434	33	0.34 566	9.95 977	6	43
18	9.61 438	28	9.65 467	34	0.34 533	9.95 971	6	42
19	9.61 466	28	9.65 501	34	0.34 499	9.95 965	5	41
20	9.61 494	28	9.65 535	33	0.34 465	9.95 960	6	**40**
21	9.61 522	28	9.65 568	34	0.34 432	9.95 954	6	39
22	9.61 550	28	9.65 602	34	0.34 398	9.95 948	6	38
23	9.61 578	28	9.65 636	33	0.34 364	9.95 942	5	37
24	9.61 606	28	9.65 669	34	0.34 331	9.95 937	6	36
25	9.61 634	28	9.65 703	33	0.34 297	9.95 931	6	35
26	9.61 662	27	9.65 736	34	0.34 264	9.95 925	5	34
27	9.61 689	28	9.65 770	33	0.34 230	9.95 920	6	33
28	9.61 717	28	9.65 803	34	0.34 197	9.95 914	6	32
29	9.61 745	28	9.65 837	33	0.34 163	9.95 908	6	31
30	9.61 773	27	9.65 870	34	0.34 130	9.95 902	5	**30**
31	9.61 800	28	9.65 904	33	0.34 096	9.95 897	6	29
32	9.61 828	28	9.65 937	34	0.34 063	9.95 891	6	28
33	9.61 856	27	9.65 971	33	0.34 029	9.95 885	6	27
34	9.61 883	28	9.66 004	34	0.33 996	9.95 879	6	26
35	9.61 911	28	9.66 038	33	0.33 962	9.95 873	5	25
36	9.61 939	27	9.66 071	33	0.33 929	9.95 868	6	24
37	9.61 966	28	9.66 104	34	0.33 896	9.95 862	6	23
38	9.61 994	27	9.66 138	33	0.33 862	9.95 856	6	22
39	9.62 021	28	9.66 171	33	0.33 829	9.95 850	6	21
40	9.62 049	27	9.66 204	34	0.33 796	9.95 844	5	**20**
41	9.62 076	28	9.66 238	33	0.33 762	9.95 839	6	19
42	9.62 104	27	9.66 271	33	0.33 729	9.95 833	6	18
43	9.62 131	28	9.66 304	33	0.33 696	9.95 827	6	17
44	9.62 159	27	9.66 337	34	0.33 663	9.95 821	6	16
45	9.62 186	28	9.66 371	33	0.33 629	9.95 815	5	15
46	9.62 214	27	9.66 404	33	0.33 596	9.95 810	6	14
47	9.62 241	27	9.66 437	33	0.33 563	9.95 804	6	13
48	9.62 268	28	9.66 470	33	0.33 530	9.95 798	6	12
49	9.62 296	27	9.66 503	34	0.33 497	9.95 792	6	11
50	9.62 323	27	9.66 537	33	0.33 463	9.95 786	6	**10**
51	9.62 350	27	9.66 570	33	0.33 430	9.95 780	5	9
52	9.62 377	28	9.66 603	33	0.33 397	9.95 775	6	8
53	9.62 405	27	9.66 636	33	0.33 364	9.95 769	6	7
54	9.62 432	27	9.66 669	33	0.33 331	9.95 763	6	6
55	9.62 459	27	9.66 702	33	0.33 298	9.95 757	6	5
56	9.62 486	27	9.66 735	33	0.33 265	9.95 751	6	4
57	9.62 513	28	9.66 768	33	0.33 232	9.95 745	6	3
58	9.62 541	27	9.66 801	33	0.33 199	9.95 739	6	2
59	9.62 568	27	9.66 834	33	0.33 166	9.95 733	5	1
60	9.62 595		9.66 867		0.33 133	9.95 728		**0**
′	L. Cos.	d.	L. Cot.	c.d.	L. Tan.	L. Sin.	d.	′

P. P.

″	**34**	**33**
1	0.6	0.6
2	1.1	1.1
3	1.7	1.6
4	2.3	2.2
5	2.8	2.8
6	3.4	3.3
7	4.0	3.8
8	4.5	4.4
9	5.1	5.0
10	5.7	5.5
20	11.3	11.0
30	17.0	16.5
40	22.7	22.0
50	28.3	27.5

″	**29**	**28**	**27**
1	0.5	0.5	0.4
2	1.0	0.9	0.9
3	1.4	1.4	1.4
4	1.9	1.9	1.8
5	2.4	2.3	2.2
6	2.9	2.8	2.7
7	3.4	3.3	3.2
8	3.9	3.7	3.6
9	4.4	4.2	4.0
10	4.8	4.7	4.5
20	9.7	9.3	9.0
30	14.5	14.0	13.5
40	19.3	18.7	18.0
50	24.2	23.3	22.5

″	**6**	**5**
1	0.1	0.1
2	0.2	0.2
3	0.3	0.2
4	0.4	0.3
5	0.5	0.4
6	0.6	0.5
7	0.7	0.6
8	0.8	0.7
9	0.9	0.8
10	1.0	0.8
20	2.0	1.7
30	3.0	2.5
40	4.0	3.3
50	5.0	4.2

	6/34	**6/33**	**5/34**
0	2.8	2.8	3.4
1	8.5	8.2	10.2
2	14.2	13.8	17.0
3	19.8	19.2	23.8
4	25.5	24.8	30.6
5	31.2	30.2	—
6			

P. P.

114° (294°) (245°) **65°**

25° (205°) (334°) **154°**

′	L. Sin.	d.	L. Tan.	c.d.	L. Cot.	L. Cos.	d.	′
0	9.62 595	27	9.66 867	33	0.33 133	9.95 728	6	**60**
1	9.62 622	27	9.66 900	33	0.33 100	9.95 722	6	59
2	9.62 649	27	9.66 933	33	0.33 067	9.95 716	6	58
3	9.62 676	27	9.66 966	33	0.33 034	9.95 710	6	57
4	9.62 703	27	9.66 999	33	0.33 001	9.95 704	6	56
5	9.62 730	27	9.67 032	33	0.32 968	9.95 698	6	55
6	9.62 757	27	9.67 065	33	0.32 935	9.95 692	6	54
7	9.62 784	27	9.67 098	33	0.32 902	9.95 686	6	53
8	9.62 811	27	9.67 131	32	0.32 869	9.95 680	6	52
9	9.62 838	27	9.67 163	33	0.32 837	9.95 674	6	51
10	9.62 865	27	9.67 196	33	0.32 804	9.95 668	5	**50**
11	9.62 892	26	9.67 229	33	0.32 771	9.95 663	6	49
12	9.62 918	27	9.67 262	33	0.32 738	9.95 657	6	48
13	9.62 945	27	9.67 295	32	0.32 705	9.95 651	6	47
14	9.62 972	27	9.67 327	33	0.32 673	9.95 645	6	46
15	9.62 999	27	9.67 360	33	0.32 640	9.95 639	6	45
16	9.63 026	26	9.67 393	33	0.32 607	9.95 633	6	44
17	9.63 052	27	9.67 426	32	0.32 574	9.95 627	6	43
18	9.63 079	27	9.67 458	33	0.32 542	9.95 621	6	42
19	9.63 106	27	9.67 491	33	0.32 509	9.95 615	6	41
20	9.63 133	26	9.67 524	32	0.32 476	9.95 609	6	**40**
21	9.63 159	27	9.67 556	33	0.32 444	9.95 603	6	39
22	9.63 186	27	9.67 589	33	0.32 411	9.95 597	6	38
23	9.63 213	26	9.67 622	32	0.32 378	9.95 591	6	37
24	9.63 239	27	9.67 654	33	0.32 346	9.95 585	6	36
25	9.63 266	26	9.67 687	32	0.32 313	9.95 579	6	35
26	9.63 292	27	9.67 719	33	0.32 281	9.95 573	6	34
27	9.63 319	26	9.67 752	33	0.32 248	9.95 567	6	33
28	9.63 345	27	9.67 785	32	0.32 215	9.95 561	6	32
29	9.63 372	26	9.67 817	33	0.32 183	9.95 555	6	31
30	9.63 398	27	9.67 850	32	0.32 150	9.95 549	6	**30**
31	9.63 425	26	9.67 882	33	0.32 118	9.95 543	6	29
32	9.63 451	27	9.67 915	32	0.32 085	9.95 537	6	28
33	9.63 478	26	9.67 947	33	0.32 053	9.95 531	6	27
34	9.63 504	27	9.67 980	32	0.32 020	9.95 525	6	26
35	9.63 531	26	9.68 012	32	0.31 988	9.95 519	6	25
36	9.63 557	26	9.68 044	33	0.31 956	9.95 513	6	24
37	9.63 583	27	9.68 077	32	0.31 923	9.95 507	7	23
38	9.63 610	26	9.68 109	33	0.31 891	9.95 500	6	22
39	9.63 636	26	9.68 142	32	0.31 858	9.95 494	6	21
40	9.63 662	27	9.68 174	32	0.31 826	9.95 488	6	**20**
41	9.63 689	26	9.68 206	33	0.31 794	9.95 482	6	19
42	9.63 715	26	9.68 239	32	0.31 761	9.95 476	6	18
43	9.63 741	26	9.68 271	32	0.31 729	9.95 470	6	17
44	9.63 767	27	9.68 303	33	0.31 697	9.95 464	6	16
45	9.63 794	26	9.68 336	32	0.31 664	9.95 458	6	15
46	9.63 820	26	9.68 368	32	0.31 632	9.95 452	6	14
47	9.63 846	26	9.68 400	32	0.31 600	9.95 446	6	13
48	9.63 872	26	9.68 432	33	0.31 568	9.95 440	6	12
49	9.63 898	26	9.68 465	32	0.31 535	9.95 434	7	11
50	9.63 924	26	9.68 497	32	0.31 503	9.95 427	6	**10**
51	9.63 950	26	9.68 529	32	0.31 471	9.95 421	6	9
52	9.63 976	26	9.68 561	32	0.31 439	9.95 415	6	8
53	9.64 002	26	9.68 593	33	0.31 407	9.95 409	6	7
54	9.64 028	26	9.68 626	32	0.31 374	9.95 403	6	6
55	9.64 054	26	9.68 658	32	0.31 342	9.95 397	6	5
56	9.64 080	26	9.68 690	32	0.31 310	9.95 391	7	4
57	9.64 106	26	9.68 722	32	0.31 278	9.95 384	6	3
58	9.64 132	26	9.68 754	32	0.31 246	9.95 378	6	2
59	9.64 158	26	9.68 786	32	0.31 214	9.95 372	6	1
60	9.64 184		9.68 818		0.31 182	9.95 366		**0**
′	L. Cos.	d.	L. Cot.	c.d.	L. Tan.	L. Sin.	d.	′

115° (295°) (244°) **64°**

P. P.

″	**33**	**32**
1	0.6	0.5
2	1.1	1.1
3	1.6	1.6
4	2.2	2.1
5	2.8	2.7
6	3.3	3.2
7	3.8	3.7
8	4.4	4.3
9	5.0	4.8
10	5.5	5.3
20	11.0	10.7
30	16.5	16.0
40	22.0	21.3
50	27.5	26.7

″	**27**	**26**
1	0.4	0.4
2	0.9	0.9
3	1.4	1.3
4	1.8	1.7
5	2.2	2.2
6	2.7	2.6
7	3.2	3.0
8	3.6	3.5
9	4.0	3.9
10	4.5	4.3
20	9.0	8.7
30	13.5	13.0
40	18.0	17.3
50	22.5	21.7

″	**7**	**6**	**5**
1	0.1	0.1	0.1
2	0.2	0.2	0.2
3	0.4	0.3	0.2
4	0.5	0.4	0.3
5	0.6	0.5	0.4
6	0.7	0.6	0.5
7	0.8	0.7	0.6
8	0.9	0.8	0.7
9	1.0	0.9	0.8
10	1.2	1.0	0.8
20	2.3	2.0	1.7
30	3.5	3.0	2.5
40	4.7	4.0	3.3
50	5.8	5.0	4.2

	7/**32**	**6**/**32**	**5**/**33**
0	2.3	2.7	3.3
1	6.9	8.0	9.9
2	11.4	13.3	16.5
3	16.0	18.7	23.1
4	20.6	24.0	29.7
5	25.1	29.3	—
6	29.7	—	—
7			

P. P.

26° (206°) (333°) **153°**

′	L. Sin.	d.	L. Tan.	c.d.	L. Cot.	L. Cos.	d.	′
0	9.64 184	26	9.68 818	32	0.31 182	9.95 366	6	**60**
1	9.64 210	26	9.68 850	32	0.31 150	9.95 360	6	59
2	9.64 236	26	9.68 882	32	0.31 118	9.95 354	6	58
3	9.64 262	26	9.68 914	32	0.31 086	9.95 348	7	57
4	9.64 288	25	9.68 946	32	0.31 054	9.95 341	6	56
5	9.64 313	26	9.68 978	32	0.31 022	9.95 335	6	55
6	9.64 339	26	9.69 010	32	0.30 990	9.95 329	6	54
7	9.64 365	26	9.69 042	32	0.30 958	9.95 323	6	53
8	9.64 391	26	9.69 074	32	0.30 926	9.95 317	7	52
9	9.64 417	25	9.69 106	32	0.30 894	9.95 310	6	51
10	9.64 442	26	9.69 138	32	0.30 862	9.95 304	6	**50**
11	9.64 468	26	9.69 170	32	0.30 830	9.95 298	6	49
12	9.64 494	25	9.69 202	32	0.30 798	9.95 292	6	48
13	9.64 519	26	9.69 234	32	0.30 766	9.95 286	7	47
14	9.64 545	26	9.69 266	32	0.30 734	9.95 279	6	46
15	9.64 571	25	9.69 298	31	0.30 702	9.95 273	6	45
16	9.64 596	26	9.69 329	32	0.30 671	9.95 267	6	44
17	9.64 622	25	9.69 361	32	0.30 639	9.95 261	7	43
18	9.64 647	26	9.69 393	32	0.30 607	9.95 254	6	42
19	9.64 673	25	9.69 425	32	0.30 575	9.95 248	6	41
20	9.64 698	26	9.69 457	31	0.30 543	9.95 242	6	**40**
21	9.64 724	25	9.69 488	32	0.30 512	9.95 236	7	39
22	9.64 749	26	9.69 520	32	0.30 480	9.95 229	6	38
23	9.64 775	25	9.69 552	32	0.30 448	9.95 223	6	37
24	9.64 800	26	9.69 584	31	0.30 416	9.95 217	6	36
25	9.64 826	25	9.69 615	32	0.30 385	9.95 211	7	35
26	9.64 851	26	9.69 647	32	0.30 353	9.95 204	6	34
27	9.64 877	25	9.69 679	31	0.30 321	9.95 198	6	33
28	9.64 902	25	9.69 710	32	0.30 290	9.95 192	7	32
29	9.64 927	26	9.69 742	32	0.30 258	9.95 185	6	31
30	9.64 953	25	9.69 774	31	0.30 226	9.95 179	6	**30**
31	9.64 978	25	9.69 805	32	0.30 195	9.95 173	6	29
32	9.65 003	26	9.69 837	31	0.30 163	9.95 167	7	28
33	9.65 029	25	9.69 868	32	0.30 132	9.95 160	6	27
34	9.65 054	25	9.69 900	32	0.30 100	9.95 154	6	26
35	9.65 079	25	9.69 932	31	0.30 068	9.95 148	7	25
36	9.65 104	26	9.69 963	32	0.30 037	9.95 141	6	24
37	9.65 130	25	9.69 995	31	0.30 005	9.95 135	6	23
38	9.65 155	25	9.70 026	32	0.29 974	9.95 129	7	22
39	9.65 180	25	9.70 058	31	0.29 942	9.95 122	6	21
40	9.65 205	25	9.70 089	32	0.29 911	9.95 116	6	**20**
41	9.65 230	25	9.70 121	31	0.29 879	9.95 110	7	19
42	9.65 255	26	9.70 152	32	0.29 848	9.95 103	6	18
43	9.65 281	25	9.70 184	31	0.29 816	9.95 097	7	17
44	9.65 306	25	9.70 215	32	0.29 785	9.95 090	6	16
45	9.65 331	25	9.70 247	31	0.29 753	9.95 084	6	15
46	9.65 356	25	9.70 278	31	0.29 722	9.95 078	7	14
47	9.65 381	25	9.70 309	32	0.29 691	9.95 071	6	13
48	9.65 406	25	9.70 341	31	0.29 659	9.95 065	6	12
49	9.65 431	25	9.70 372	32	0.29 628	9.95 059	7	11
50	9.65 456	25	9.70 404	31	0.29 596	9.95 052	6	**10**
51	9.65 481	25	9.70 435	31	0.29 565	9.95 046	7	9
52	9.65 506	25	9.70 466	32	0.29 534	9.95 039	6	8
53	9.65 531	25	9.70 498	31	0.29 502	9.95 033	6	7
54	9.65 556	24	9.70 529	31	0.29 471	9.95 027	7	6
55	9.65 580	25	9.70 560	32	0.29 440	9.95 020	6	5
56	9.65 605	25	9.70 592	31	0.29 408	9.95 014	7	4
57	9.65 630	25	9.70 623	31	0.29 377	9.95 007	6	3
58	9.65 655	25	9.70 654	31	0.29 346	9.95 001	6	2
59	9.65 680	25	9.70 685	32	0.29 315	9.94 995	7	1
60	9.65 705		9.70 717		0.29 283	9.94 988		**0**
′	L. Cos.	d.	L. Cot.	c.d.	L. Tan.	L. Sin.	d.	′

P. P.

″	32	31
1	0.5	0.5
2	1.1	1.0
3	1.6	1.6
4	2.1	2.1
5	2.7	2.6
6	3.2	3.1
7	3.7	3.6
8	4.3	4.1
9	4.8	4.6
10	5.3	5.2
20	10.7	10.3
30	16.0	15.5
40	21.3	20.7
50	26.7	25.8

″	26	25	24
1	0.4	0.4	0.4
2	0.9	0.8	0.8
3	1.3	1.2	1.2
4	1.7	1.7	1.6
5	2.2	2.1	2.0
6	2.6	2.5	2.4
7	3.0	2.9	2.8
8	3.5	3.3	3.2
9	3.9	3.8	3.6
10	4.3	4.2	4.0
20	8.7	8.3	8.0
30	13.0	12.5	12.0
40	17.3	16.7	16.0
50	21.7	20.8	20.0

″	7	6
1	0.1	0.1
2	0.2	0.2
3	0.4	0.3
4	0.5	0.4
5	0.6	0.5
6	0.7	0.6
7	0.8	0.7
8	0.9	0.8
9	1.0	0.9
10	1.2	1.0
20	2.3	2.0
30	3.5	3.0
40	4.7	4.0
50	5.8	5.0

	7/32	7/31	6/32
0	2.3	2.2	2.7
1	6.9	6.6	8.0
2	11.4	11.1	13.3
3	16.0	15.5	18.7
4	20.6	19.9	24.0
5	25.1	24.4	29.3
6	29.7	28.8	—
7			

P. P.

116° (296°) (243°) **63°**

27° (207°) (332°) **152°**

′	L. Sin.	d.	L. Tan.	c.d.	L. Cot.	L. Cos.	d.	′
0	9.65 705̄	24	9.70 717	31	0.29 283	9.94 988	6	**60**
1	9.65 729	25	9.70 748	31	0.29 252	9.94 982	7	59
2	9.65 754	25	9.70 779	31	0.29 221	9.94 975̇	6	58
3	9.65 779	25	9.70 810	31	0.29 190	9.94 969	7	57
4	9.65 804	24	9.70 841	32	0.29 159	9.94 962	6	56
5	9.65 828	25	9.70 873	31	0.29 127	9.94 956	7	55
6	9.65 853	25	9.70 904	31	0.29 096	9.94 949	6	54
7	9.65 878	24	9.70 935̄	31	0.29 065̇	9.94 943	7	53
8	9.65 902	25	9.70 966	31	0.29 034	9.94 936	6	52
9	9.65 927	25	9.70 997	31	0.29 003	9.94 930	7	51
10	9.65 952	24	9.71 028	31	0.28 972	9.94 923	6	**50**
11	9.65 976	25	9.71 059	31	0.28 941	9.94 917	6	49
12	9.66 001	24	9.71 090	31	0.28 910	9.94 911	7	48
13	9.66 025̇	25	9.71 121	32	0.28 879	9.94 904	6	47
14	9.66 050̇	25	9.71 153	31	0.28 847	9.94 898	7	46
15	9.66 075̄	24	9.71 184	31	0.28 816	9.94 891	6	45
16	9.66 099	25	9.71 215̄	31	0.28 785̇	9.94 885̄	7	44
17	9.66 124	24	9.71 246	31	0.28 754	9.94 878	7	43
18	9.66 148	25	9.71 277	31	0.28 723	9.94 871	6	42
19	9.66 173	24	9.71 308	31	0.28 692	9.94 865̄	7	41
20	9.66 197	24	9.71 339	31	0.28 661	9.94 858	6	**40**
21	9.66 221	25	9.71 370	31	0.28 630	9.94 852	7	39
22	9.66 246	24	9.71 401	30	0.28 599	9.94 845̇	6	38
23	9.66 270	25	9.71 431	31	0.28 569	9.94 839	7	37
24	9.66 295̄	24	9.71 462	31	0.28 538	9.94 832	6	36
25	9.66 319	24	9.71 493	31	0.28 507	9.94 826	7	35
26	9.66 343	25	9.71 524	31	0.28 476	9.94 819	6	34
27	9.66 368	24	9.71 555̇	31	0.28 445̄	9.94 813	7	33
28	9.66 392	24	9.71 586	31	0.28 414	9.94 806	7	32
29	9.66 416	25	9.71 617	31	0.28 383	9.94 799	6	31
30	9.66 441	24	9.71 648	31	0.28 352	9.94 793	7	**30**
31	9.66 465̄	24	9.71 679	30	0.28 321	9.94 786	6	29
32	9.66 489	24	9.71 709	31	0.28 291	9.94 780	7	28
33	9.66 513	24	9.71 740	31	0.28 260	9.94 773	6	27
34	9.66 537	25	9.71 771	31	0.28 229	9.94 767	7	26
35	9.66 562	24	9.71 802	31	0.28 198	9.94 760	7	25
36	9.66 586	24	9.71 833	30	0.28 167	9.94 753	6	24
37	9.66 610	24	9.71 863	31	0.28 137	9.94 747	7	23
38	9.66 634	24	9.71 894	31	0.28 106	9.94 740	6	22
39	9.66 658	24	9.71 925̄	30	0.28 075̇	9.94 734	7	21
40	9.66 682	24	9.71 955̇	31	0.28 045̄	9.94 727	7	**20**
41	9.66 706	25	9.71 986	31	0.28 014	9.94 720	6	19
42	9.66 731	24	9.72 017	31	0.27 983	9.94 714	7	18
43	9.66 755̄	24	9.72 048	30	0.27 952	9.94 707	7	17
44	9.66 779	24	9.72 078	31	0.27 922	9.94 700	6	16
45	9.66 803	24	9.72 109	31	0.27 891	9.94 694	7	15
46	9.66 827	24	9.72 140	30	0.27 860	9.94 687	7	14
47	9.66 851	24	9.72 170	31	0.27 830	9.94 680	6	13
48	9.66 875̄	24	9.72 201	30	0.27 799	9.94 674	7	12
49	9.66 899	23	9.72 231	31	0.27 769	9.94 667	7	11
50	9.66 922	24	9.72 262	31	0.27 738	9.94 660	6	**10**
51	9.66 946	24	9.72 293	30	0.27 707	9.94 654	7	9
52	9.66 970	24	9.72 323	31	0.27 677	9.94 647	7	8
53	9.66 994	24	9.72 354	30	0.27 646	9.94 640	6	7
54	9.67 018	24	9.72 384	31	0.27 616	9.94 634	7	6
55	9.67 042	24	9.72 415̄	30	0.27 585̇	9.94 627	7	5
56	9.67 066	24	9.72 445̇	31	0.27 555̄	9.94 620	6	4
57	9.67 090	23	9.72 476	30	0.27 524	9.94 614	7	3
58	9.67 113	24	9.72 506	31	0.27 494	9.94 607	7	2
59	9.67 137	24	9.72 537	30	0.27 463	9.94 600	7	1
60	9.67 161		9.72 567		0.27 433	9.94 593		**0**
′	L. Cos.	d.	L. Cot.	c.d.	L. Tan.	L. Sin.	d.	′

117° (297°) (242°) **62°**

P. P.

″	**32**	**31**	**30**
1	0.5̇	0.5̇	0.5
2	1.1	1.0	1.0
3	1.6	1.6	1.5
4	2.1	2.1	2.0
5	2.7	2.6	2.5
6	3.2	3.1	3.0
7	3.7	3.6	3.5
8	4.3	4.1	4.0
9	4.8	4.6	4.5
10	5.3	5.2	5.0
20	10.7	10.3	10.0
30	16.0	15.5	15.0
40	21.3	20.7	20.0
50	26.7	25.8	25.0

″	**25**	**24**	**23**
1	0.4	0.4	0.4
2	0.8	0.8	0.8
3	1.2	1.2	1.2
4	1.7	1.6	1.5̇
5	2.1	2.0	1.9
6	2.5	2.4	2.3
7	2.9	2.8	2.7
8	3.3	3.2	3.1
9	3.8	3.6	3.4
10	4.2	4.0	3.8
20	8.3	8.0	7.7
30	12.5	12.0	11.5
40	16.7	16.0	15.3
50	20.8	20.0	19.2

″	**7**	**6**
1	0.1	0.1
2	0.2	0.2
3	0.4	0.3
4	0.5̄	0.4
5	0.6	0.5
6	0.7	0.6
7	0.8	0.7
8	0.9	0.8
9	1.0	0.9
10	1.2	1.0
20	2.3	2.0
30	3.5	3.0
40	4.7	4.0
50	5.8	5.0

	7/30	**6/31**	**6/30**
0	2.1	2.6	2.5
1	6.4	7.8	7.5
2	10.7	12.9	12.5
3	15.0	18.1	17.5
4	19.3	23.2	22.5
5	23.6	28.4	27.5
6	27.9	—	—
7			

P. P.

28° (208°) (331°) **151°**

′	L. Sin.	d.	L. Tan.	c.d.	L. Cot.	L. Cos.	d.	′
0	9.67 161	24	9.72 567	31	0.27 433	9.94 593	6	**60**
1	9.67 185	23	9.72 598	30	0.27 402	9.94 587	7	59
2	9.67 208	24	9.72 628	31	0.27 372	9.94 580	7	58
3	9.67 232	24	9.72 659	30	0.27 341	9.94 573	6	57
4	9.67 256	24	9.72 689	31	0.27 311	9.94 567	7	56
5	9.67 280	23	9.72 720	30	0.27 280	9.94 560	7	55
6	9.67 303	24	9.72 750	30	0.27 250	9.94 553	7	54
7	9.67 327	23	9.72 780	31	0.27 220	9.94 546	6	53
8	9.67 350	24	9.72 811	30	0.27 189	9.94 540	7	52
9	9.67 374	24	9.72 841	31	0.27 159	9.94 533	7	51
10	9.67 398	23	9.72 872	30	0.27 128	9.94 526	7	**50**
11	9.67 421	24	9.72 902	30	0.27 098	9.94 519	6	49
12	9.67 445	23	9.72 932	31	0.27 068	9.94 513	7	48
13	9.67 468	24	9.72 963	30	0.27 037	9.94 506	7	47
14	9.67 492	23	9.72 993	30	0.27 007	9.94 499	7	46
15	9.67 515	24	9.73 023	31	0.26 977	9.94 492	7	45
16	9.67 539	23	9.73 054	30	0.26 946	9.94 485	6	44
17	9.67 562	24	9.73 084	30	0.26 916	9.94 479	7	43
18	9.67 586	23	9.73 114	30	0.26 886	9.94 472	7	42
19	9.67 609	24	9.73 144	31	0.26 856	9.94 465	7	41
20	9.67 633	23	9.73 175	30	0.26 825	9.94 458	7	**40**
21	9.67 656	24	9.73 205	30	0.26 795	9.94 451	6	39
22	9.67 680	23	9.73 235	30	0.26 765	9.94 445	7	38
23	9.67 703	23	9.73 265	30	0.26 735	9.94 438	7	37
24	9.67 726	24	9.73 295	31	0.26 705	9.94 431	7	36
25	9.67 750	23	9.73 326	30	0.26 674	9.94 424	7	35
26	9.67 773	23	9.73 356	30	0.26 644	9.94 417	7	34
27	9.67 796	24	9.73 386	30	0.26 614	9.94 410	6	33
28	9.67 820	23	9.73 416	30	0.26 584	9.94 404	7	32
29	9.67 843	23	9.73 446	30	0.26 554	9.94 397	7	31
30	9.67 866	24	9.73 476	31	0.26 524	9.94 390	7	**30**
31	9.67 890	23	9.73 507	30	0.26 493	9.94 383	7	29
32	9.67 913	23	9.73 537	30	0.26 463	9.94 376	7	28
33	9.67 936	23	9.73 567	30	0.26 433	9.94 369	7	27
34	9.67 959	23	9.73 597	30	0.26 403	9.94 362	7	26
35	9.67 982	24	9.73 627	30	0.26 373	9.94 355	6	25
36	9.68 006	23	9.73 657	30	0.26 343	9.94 349	7	24
37	9.68 029	23	9.73 687	30	0.26 313	9.94 342	7	23
38	9.68 052	23	9.73 717	30	0.26 283	9.94 335	7	22
39	9.68 075	23	9.73 747	30	0.26 253	9.94 328	7	21
40	9.68 098	23	9.73 777	30	0.26 223	9.94 321	7	**20**
41	9.68 121	23	9.73 807	30	0.26 193	9.94 314	7	19
42	9.68 144	23	9.73 837	30	0.26 163	9.94 307	7	18
43	9.68 167	23	9.73 867	30	0.26 133	9.94 300	7	17
44	9.68 190	23	9.73 897	30	0.26 103	9.94 293	7	16
45	9.68 213	24	9.73 927	30	0.26 073	9.94 286	7	15
46	9.68 237	23	9.73 957	30	0.26 043	9.94 279	6	14
47	9.68 260	23	9.73 987	30	0.26 013	9.94 273	7	13
48	9.68 283	22	9.74 017	30	0.25 983	9.94 266	7	12
49	9.68 305	23	9.74 047	30	0.25 953	9.94 259	7	11
50	9.68 328	23	9.74 077	30	0.25 923	9.94 252	7	**10**
51	9.68 351	23	9.74 107	30	0.25 893	9.94 245	7	9
52	9.68 374	23	9.74 137	29	0.25 863	9.94 238	7	8
53	9.68 397	23	9.74 166	30	0.25 834	9.94 231	7	7
54	9.68 420	23	9.74 196	30	0.25 804	9.94 224	7	6
55	9.68 443	23	9.74 226	30	0.25 774	9.94 217	7	5
56	9.68 466	23	9.74 256	30	0.25 744	9.94 210	7	4
57	9.68 489	23	9.74 286	30	0.25 714	9.94 203	7	3
58	9.68 512	22	9.74 316	29	0.25 684	9.94 196	7	2
59	9.68 534	23	9.74 345	30	0.25 655	9.94 189	7	1
60	9.68 557		9.74 375		0.25 625	9.94 182		**0**
′	L. Cos.	d.	L. Cot.	c.d.	L. Tan.	L. Sin.	d.	′

P. P.

″	**31**	**30**	**29**
1	0.5	0.5	0.5
2	1.0	1.0	1.0
3	1.6	1.5	1.4
4	2.1	2.0	1.9
5	2.6	2.5	2.4
6	3.1	3.0	2.9
7	3.6	3.5	3.4
8	4.1	4.0	3.9
9	4.6	4.5	4.4
10	5.2	5.0	4.8
20	10.3	10.0	9.7
30	15.5	15.0	14.5
40	20.7	20.0	19.3
50	25.8	25.0	24.2

″	**24**	**23**	**22**
1	0.4	0.4	0.4
2	0.8	0.8	0.7
3	1.2	1.2	1.1
4	1.6	1.5	1.5
5	2.0	1.9	1.8
6	2.4	2.3	2.2
7	2.8	2.7	2.6
8	3.2	3.1	2.9
9	3.6	3.4	3.3
10	4.0	3.8	3.7
20	8.0	7.7	7.3
30	12.0	11.5	11.0
40	16.0	15.3	14.7
50	20.0	19.2	18.3

″	**7**	**6**
1	0.1	0.1
2	0.2	0.2
3	0.4	0.3
4	0.5	0.4
5	0.6	0.5
6	0.7	0.6
7	0.8	0.7
8	0.9	0.8
9	1.0	0.9
10	1.2	1.0
20	2.3	2.0
30	3.5	3.0
40	4.7	4.0
50	5.8	5.0

	7/31	**6/31**	**6/30**
0	2.2	2.6	2.5
1	6.6	7.8	7.5
2	11.1	12.9	12.5
3	15.5	18.1	17.5
4	19.9	23.2	22.5
5	24.4	28.4	27.5
6	28.8	—	—
7			

P. P.

118° (298°) (241°) **61°**

29° (209°) (330°) **150°**

′	L. Sin.	d.	L. Tan.	c.d.	L. Cot.	L. Cos.	d.	′
0	9.68 557	23	9.74 375	30	0.25 625	9.94 182	7	**60**
1	9.68 580	23	9.74 405	30	0.25 595	9.94 175	7	59
2	9.68 603	22	9.74 435	30	0.25 565	9.94 168	7	58
3	9.68 625	23	9.74 465	29	0.25 535	9.94 161	7	57
4	9.68 648	23	9.74 494	30	0.25 506	9.94 154	7	56
5	9.68 671	23	9.74 524	30	0.25 476	9.94 147	7	55
6	9.68 694	22	9.74 554	29	0.25 446	9.94 140	7	54
7	9.68 716	23	9.74 583	30	0.25 417	9.94 133	7	53
8	9.68 739	23	9.74 613	30	0.25 387	9.94 126	7	52
9	9.68 762	22	9.74 643	30	0.25 357	9.94 119	7	51
10	9.68 784	23	9.74 673	29	0.25 327	9.94 112	7	**50**
11	9.68 807	22	9.74 702	30	0.25 298	9.94 105	7	49
12	9.68 829	23	9.74 732	30	0.25 268	9.94 098	8	48
13	9.68 852	23	9.74 762	29	0.25 238	9.94 090	7	47
14	9.68 875	22	9.74 791	30	0.25 209	9.94 083	7	46
15	9.68 897	23	9.74 821	30	0.25 179	9.94 076	7	45
16	9.68 920	22	9.74 851	29	0.25 149	9.94 069	7	44
17	9.68 942	23	9.74 880	30	0.25 120	9.94 062	7	43
18	9.68 965	22	9.74 910	29	0.25 090	9.94 055	7	42
19	9.68 987	23	9.74 939	30	0.25 061	9.94 048	7	41
20	9.69 010	22	9.74 969	29	0.25 031	9.94 041	7	**40**
21	9.69 032	23	9.74 998	30	0.25 002	9.94 034	7	39
22	9.69 055	22	9.75 028	30	0.24 972	9.94 027	7	38
23	9.69 077	23	9.75 058	29	0.24 942	9.94 020	8	37
24	9.69 100	22	9.75 087	30	0.24 913	9.94 012	7	36
25	9.69 122	22	9.75 117	29	0.24 883	9.94 005	7	35
26	9.69 144	23	9.75 146	30	0.24 854	9.93 998	7	34
27	9.69 167	22	9.75 176	29	0.24 824	9.93 991	7	33
28	9.69 189	23	9.75 205	30	0.24 795	9.93 984	7	32
29	9.69 212	22	9.75 235	29	0.24 765	9.93 977	7	31
30	9.69 234	22	9.75 264	30	0.24 736	9.93 970	7	**30**
31	9.69 256	23	9.75 294	29	0.24 706	9.93 963	8	29
32	9.69 279	22	9.75 323	30	0.24 677	9.93 955	7	28
33	9.69 301	22	9.75 353	29	0.24 647	9.93 948	7	27
34	9.69 323	22	9.75 382	29	0.24 618	9.93 941	7	26
35	9.69 345	23	9.75 411	30	0.24 589	9.93 934	7	25
36	9.69 368	22	9.75 441	29	0.24 559	9.93 927	7	24
37	9.69 390	22	9.75 470	30	0.24 530	9.93 920	8	23
38	9.69 412	22	9.75 500	29	0.24 500	9.93 912	7	22
39	9.69 434	22	9.75 529	29	0.24 471	9.93 905	7	21
40	9.69 456	23	9.75 558	30	0.24 442	9.93 898	7	**20**
41	9.69 479	22	9.75 588	29	0.24 412	9.93 891	7	19
42	9.69 501	22	9.75 617	30	0.24 383	9.93 884	8	18
43	9.69 523	22	9.75 647	29	0.24 353	9.93 876	7	17
44	9.69 545	22	9.75 676	29	0.24 324	9.93 869	7	16
45	9.69 567	22	9.75 705	30	0.24 295	9.93 862	7	15
46	9.69 589	22	9.75 735	29	0.24 265	9.93 855	8	14
47	9.69 611	22	9.75 764	29	0.24 236	9.93 847	7	13
48	9.69 633	22	9.75 793	29	0.24 207	9.93 840	7	12
49	9.69 655	22	9.75 822	30	0.24 178	9.93 833	7	11
50	9.69 677	22	9.75 852	29	0.24 148	9.93 826	7	**10**
51	9.69 699	22	9.75 881	29	0.24 119	9.93 819	8	9
52	9.69 721	22	9.75 910	29	0.24 090	9.93 811	7	8
53	9.69 743	22	9.75 939	30	0.24 061	9.93 804	7	7
54	9.69 765	22	9.75 969	29	0.24 031	9.93 797	8	6
55	9.69 787	22	9.75 998	29	0.24 002	9.93 789	7	5
56	9.69 809	22	9.76 027	29	0.23 973	9.93 782	7	4
57	9.69 831	22	9.76 056	30	0.23 944	9.93 775	7	3
58	9.69 853	22	9.76 086	29	0.23 914	9.93 768	8	2
59	9.69 875	22	9.76 115	29	0.23 885	9.93 760	7	1
60	9.69 897		9.76 144		0.23 856	9.93 753		**0**
′	L. Cos.	d.	L. Cot.	c.d.	L. Tan.	L. Sin.	d.	′

P. P.

″	**30**	**29**	**23**
1	0.5	0.5	0.4
2	1.0	1.0	0.8
3	1.5	1.4	1.2
4	2.0	1.9	1.5
5	2.5	2.4	1.9
6	3.0	2.9	2.3
7	3.5	3.4	2.7
8	4.0	3.9	3.1
9	4.5	4.4	3.4
10	5.0	4.8	3.8
20	10.0	9.7	7.7
30	15.0	14.5	11.5
40	20.0	19.3	15.3
50	25.0	24.2	19.2

″	**22**	**8**	**7**
1	0.4	0.1	0.1
2	0.7	0.3	0.2
3	1.1	0.4	0.4
4	1.5	0.5	0.5
5	1.8	0.7	0.6
6	2.2	0.8	0.7
7	2.6	0.9	0.8
8	2.9	1.1	0.9
9	3.3	1.2	1.0
10	3.7	1.3	1.2
20	7.3	2.7	2.3
30	11.0	4.0	3.5
40	14.7	5.3	4.7
50	18.3	6.7	5.8

	8/30	**8/29**
0		
1	1.9	1.8
2	5.6	5.4
3	9.4	9.1
4	13.1	12.7
5	16.9	16.3
6	20.6	19.9
7	24.4	23.6
8	28.1	27.2

	7/30	**7/29**
0		
1	2.1	2.1
2	6.4	6.2
3	10.7	10.4
4	15.0	14.5
5	19.3	18.6
6	23.6	22.8
7	27.9	26.9

P. P.

119° (299°) (240°) **60°**

30° (210°) (329°) **149°**

′	L. Sin.	d.	L. Tan.	c.d.	L. Cot.	L. Cos.	d.	′
0	9.69 897	22	9.76 144	29	0.23 856	9.93 753	7	**60**
1	9.69 919	22	9.76 173	29	0.23 827	9.93 746	8	59
2	9.69 941	22	9.76 202	29	0.23 798	9.93 738	7	58
3	9.69 963	21	9.76 231	30	0.23 769	9.93 731	7	57
4	9.69 984	22	9.76 261	29	0.23 739	9.93 724	7	56
5	9.70 006	22	9.76 290	29	0.23 710	9.93 717	8	55
6	9.70 028	22	9.76 319	29	0.23 681	9.93 709	7	54
7	9.70 050	22	9.76 348	29	0.23 652	9.93 702	7	53
8	9.70 072	21	9.76 377	29	0.23 623	9.93 695	8	52
9	9.70 093	22	9.76 406	29	0.23 594	9.93 687	7	51
10	9.70 115	22	9.76 435	29	0.23 565	9.93 680	7	**50**
11	9.70 137	22	9.76 464	29	0.23 536	9.93 673	8	49
12	9.70 159	21	9.76 493	29	0.23 507	9.93 665	7	48
13	9.70 180	22	9.76 522	29	0.23 478	9.93 658	8	47
14	9.70 202	22	9.76 551	29	0.23 449	9.93 650	7	46
15	9.70 224	21	9.76 580	29	0.23 420	9.93 643	7	45
16	9.70 245	22	9.76 609	30	0.23 391	9.93 636	8	44
17	9.70 267	21	9.76 639	29	0.23 361	9.93 628	7	43
18	9.70 288	22	9.76 668	29	0.23 332	9.93 621	7	42
19	9.70 310	22	9.76 697	28	0.23 303	9.93 614	8	41
20	9.70 332	21	9.76 725	29	0.23 275	9.93 606	7	**40**
21	9.70 353	22	9.76 754	29	0.23 246	9.93 599	8	39
22	9.70 375	21	9.76 783	29	0.23 217	9.93 591	7	38
23	9.70 396	22	9.76 812	29	0.23 188	9.93 584	7	37
24	9.70 418	21	9.76 841	29	0.23 159	9.93 577	8	36
25	9.70 439	22	9.76 870	29	0.23 130	9.93 569	7	35
26	9.70 461	21	9.76 899	29	0.23 101	9.93 562	8	34
27	9.70 482	22	9.76 928	29	0.23 072	9.93 554	7	33
28	9.70 504	21	9.76 957	29	0.23 043	9.93 547	8	32
29	9.70 525	22	9.76 986	29	0.23 014	9.93 539	7	31
30	9.70 547	21	9.77 015	29	0.22 985	9.93 532	7	**30**
31	9.70 568	22	9.77 044	29	0.22 956	9.93 525	8	29
32	9.70 590	21	9.77 073	28	0.22 927	9.93 517	7	28
33	9.70 611	22	9.77 101	29	0.22 899	9.93 510	8	27
34	9.70 633	21	9.77 130	29	0.22 870	9.93 502	7	26
35	9.70 654	21	9.77 159	29	0.22 841	9.93 495	8	25
36	9.70 675	22	9.77 188	29	0.22 812	9.93 487	7	24
37	9.70 697	21	9.77 217	29	0.22 783	9.93 480	8	23
38	9.70 718	21	9.77 246	28	0.22 754	9.93 472	7	22
39	9.70 739	22	9.77 274	29	0.22 726	9.93 465	8	21
40	9.70 761	21	9.77 303	29	0.22 697	9.93 457	7	**20**
41	9.70 782	21	9.77 332	29	0.22 668	9.93 450	8	19
42	9.70 803	21	9.77 361	29	0.22 639	9.93 442	7	18
43	9.70 824	22	9.77 390	28	0.22 610	9.93 435	8	17
44	9.70 846	21	9.77 418	29	0.22 582	9.93 427	7	16
45	9.70 867	21	9.77 447	29	0.22 553	9.93 420	8	15
46	9.70 888	21	9.77 476	29	0.22 524	9.93 412	7	14
47	9.70 909	22	9.77 505	28	0.22 495	9.93 405	8	13
48	9.70 931	21	9.77 533	29	0.22 467	9.93 397	7	12
49	9.70 952	21	9.77 562	29	0.22 438	9.93 390	8	11
50	9.70 973	21	9.77 591	28	0.22 409	9.93 382	7	**10**
51	9.70 994	21	9.77 619	29	0.22 381	9.93 375	8	9
52	9.71 015	21	9.77 648	29	0.22 352	9.93 367	7	8
53	9.71 036	22	9.77 677	29	0.22 323	9.93 360	8	7
54	9.71 058	21	9.77 706	28	0.22 294	9.93 352	8	6
55	9.71 079	21	9.77 734	29	0.22 266	9.93 344	7	5
56	9.71 100	21	9.77 763	28	0.22 237	9.93 337	8	4
57	9.71 121	21	9.77 791	29	0.22 209	9.93 329	7	3
58	9.71 142	21	9.77 820	29	0.22 180	9.93 322	8	2
59	9.71 163	21	9.77 849	28	0.22 151	9.93 314	7	1
60	9.71 184		9.77 877		0.22 123	9.93 307		**0**
′	L. Cos.	d.	L. Cot.	c.d.	L. Tan.	L. Sin.	d.	′

P. P.

″	30	29	28
1	0.5	0.5	0.5
2	1.0	1.0	0.9
3	1.5	1.4	1.4
4	2.0	1.9	1.9
5	2.5	2.4	2.3
6	3.0	2.9	2.8
7	3.5	3.4	3.3
8	4.0	3.9	3.7
9	4.5	4.4	4.2
10	5.0	4.8	4.7
20	10.0	9.7	9.3
30	15.0	14.5	14.0
40	20.0	19.3	18.7
50	25.0	24.2	23.3

″	22	21
1	0.4	0.4
2	0.7	0.7
3	1.1	1.0
4	1.5	1.4
5	1.8	1.8
6	2.2	2.1
7	2.6	2.4
8	2.9	2.8
9	3.3	3.2
10	3.7	3.5
20	7.3	7.0
30	11.0	10.5
40	14.7	14.0
50	18.3	17.5

″	8	7
1	0.1	0.1
2	0.3	0.2
3	0.4	0.4
4	0.5	0.5
5	0.7	0.6
6	0.8	0.7
7	0.9	0.8
8	1.1	0.9
9	1.2	1.0
10	1.3	1.2
20	2.7	2.3
30	4.0	3.5
40	5.3	4.7
50	6.7	5.8

	7/30	7/29	7/28
0	2.1	2.1	2.0
1	6.4	6.2	6.0
2	10.7	10.4	10.0
3	15.0	14.5	14.0
4	19.3	18.6	18.0
5	23.6	22.8	22.0
6	27.9	26.9	26.0
7			

P. P.

120° (300°) (239°) **59°**

31° (211°) (328°) **148°**

′	L. Sin.	d.	L. Tan.	c.d.	L. Cot.	L. Cos.	d.	′
0	9.71 184	21	9.77 877	29	0.22 123	9.93 307	8	**60**
1	9.71 205̄	21	9.77 906	29	0.22 094	9.93 299	8	59
2	9.71 226	21	9.77 935̄	28	0.22 065̇	9.93 291	7	58
3	9.71 247	21	9.77 963	29	0.22 037	9.93 284	8	57
4	9.71 268	21	9.77 992	28	0.22 008	9.93 276	7	56
5	9.71 289	21	9.78 020	29	0.21 980	9.93 269	8	55
6	9.71 310	21	9.78 049	28	0.21 951	9.93 261	8	54
7	9.71 331	21	9.78 077	29	0.21 923	9.93 253	7	53
8	9.71 352	21	9.78 106	29	0.21 894	9.93 246	8	52
9	9.71 373	20	9.78 135̄	28	0.21 865̇	9.93 238	8	51
10	9.71 393	21	9.78 163	29	0.21 837	9.93 230	7	**50**
11	9.71 414	21	9.78 192	28	0.21 808	9.93 223	8	49
12	9.71 435̇	21	9.78 220	29	0.21 780	9.93 215̇	8	48
13	9.71 456	21	9.78 249	28	0.21 751	9.93 207	7	47
14	9.71 477	21	9.78 277	29	0.21 723	9.93 200	8	46
15	9.71 498	21	9.78 306	28	0.21 694	9.93 192	8	45
16	9.71 519	20	9.78 334	29	0.21 666	9.93 184	7	44
17	9.71 539	21	9.78 363	28	0.21 637	9.93 177	8	43
18	9.71 560	21	9.78 391	28	0.21 609	9.93 169	8	42
19	9.71 581	21	9.78 419	29	0.21 581	9.93 161	7	41
20	9.71 602	20	9.78 448	28	0.21 552	9.93 154	8	**40**
21	9.71 622	21	9.78 476	29	0.21 524	9.93 146	8	39
22	9.71 643	21	9.78 505̄	28	0.21 495̇	9.93 138	7	38
23	9.71 664	21	9.78 533	29	0.21 467	9.93 131	8	37
24	9.71 685̄	20	9.78 562	28	0.21 438	9.93 123	8	36
25	9.71 705̇	21	9.78 590	28	0.21 410	9.93 115̇	7	35
26	9.71 726	21	9.78 618	29	0.21 382	9.93 108	8	34
27	9.71 747	20	9.78 647	28	0.21 353	9.93 100	8	33
28	9.71 767	21	9.78 675̇	29	0.21 325̄	9.93 092	8	32
29	9.71 788	21	9.78 704	28	0.21 296	9.93 084	7	31
30	9.71 809	20	9.78 732	28	0.21 268	9.93 077	8	**30**
31	9.71 829	21	9.78 760	29	0.21 240	9.93 069	8	29
32	9.71 850̄	20	9.78 789	28	0.21 211	9.93 061	8	28
33	9.71 870	21	9.78 817	28	0.21 183	9.93 053	7	27
34	9.71 891	20	9.78 845̇	29	0.21 155̄	9.93 046	8	26
35	9.71 911	21	9.78 874	28	0.21 126	9.93 038	8	25
36	9.71 932	20	9.78 902	28	0.21 098	9.93 030	8	24
37	9.71 952	21	9.78 930	29	0.21 070	9.93 022	8	23
38	9.71 973	21	9.78 959	28	0.21 041	9.93 014	7	22
39	9.71 994	20	9.78 987	28	0.21 013	9.93 007	8	21
40	9.72 014	20	9.79 015̇	28	0.20 985̄	9.92 999	8	**20**
41	9.72 034	21	9.79 043	29	0.20 957	9.92 991	8	19
42	9.72 055̄	20	9.79 072	28	0.20 928	9.92 983	7	18
43	9.72 075̇	21	9.79 100	28	0.20 900	9.92 976	8	17
44	9.72 096	20	9.79 128	28	0.20 872	9.92 968	8	16
45	9.72 116	21	9.79 156	29	0.20 844	9.92 960	8	15
46	9.72 137	20	9.79 185̄	28	0.20 815̇	9.92 952	8	14
47	9.72 157	20	9.79 213	28	0.20 787	9.92 944	8	13
48	9.72 177	21	9.79 241	28	0.20 759	9.92 936	7	12
49	9.72 198	20	9.79 269	28	0.20 731	9.92 929	8	11
50	9.72 218	20	9.79 297	29	0.20 703	9.92 921	8	**10**
51	9.72 238	21	9.79 326	28	0.20 674	9.92 913	8	9
52	9.72 259	20	9.79 354	28	0.20 646	9.92 905̇	8	8
53	9.72 279	20	9.79 382	28	0.20 618	9.92 897	8	7
54	9.72 299	21	9.79 410	28	0.20 590	9.92 889	8	6
55	9.72 320	20	9.79 438	28	0.20 562	9.92 881	7	5
56	9.72 340	20	9.79 466	29	0.20 534	9.92 874	8	4
57	9.72 360	21	9.79 495̄	28	0.20 505̇	9.92 866	8	3
58	9.72 381	20	9.79 523	28	0.20 477	9.92 858	8	2
59	9.72 401	20	9.79 551	28	0.20 449	9.92 850̄	8	1
60	9.72 421		9.79 579		0.20 421	9.92 842		**0**
′	L. Cos.	d.	L. Cot.	c.d.	L. Tan.	L.Sin.	d.	′

P. P.

″	29	28
1	0.5̄	0.5̄
2	1.0	0.9
3	1.4	1.4
4	1.9	1.9
5	2.4	2.3
6	2.9	2.8
7	3.4	3.3
8	3.9	3.7
9	4.4	4.2
10	4.8	4.7
20	9.7	9.3
30	14.5	14.0
40	19.3	18.7
50	24.2	23.3

″	21	20
1	0.4	0.3
2	0.7	0.7
3	1.0	1.0
4	1.4	1.3
5	1.8	1.7
6	2.1	2.0
7	2.4	2.3
8	2.8	2.7
9	3.2	3.0
10	3.5	3.3
20	7.0	6.7
30	10.5	10.0
40	14.0	13.3
50	17.5	16.7

″	8	7
1	0.1	0.1
2	0.3	0.2
3	0.4	0.4
4	0.5̇	0.5̄
5	0.7	0.6
6	0.8	0.7
7	0.9	0.8
8	1.1	0.9
9	1.2	1.0
10	1.3	1.2
20	2.7	2.3
30	4.0	3.5
40	5.3	4.7
50	6.7	5.8

	8/30	8/29	8/28
0	1.9	1.8	1.8
1	5.6	5.4	5.2
2	9.4	9.1	8.8
3	13.1	12.7	12.2
4	16.9	16.3	15.8
5	20.6	19.9	19.2
6	24.4	23.6	22.8
7	28.1	27.2	26.2
8			

P. P.

121° (301°) (238°) **58°**

32° (212°) (327°) **147°**

′	L. Sin.	d.	L. Tan.	c.d.	L. Cot.	L. Cos.	d.	′
0	9.72 421	20	9.79 579	28	0.20 421	9.92 842	8	**60**
1	9.72 441	20	9.79 607	28	0.20 393	9.92 834	8	59
2	9.72 461	21	9.79 635	28	0.20 365	9.92 826	8	58
3	9.72 482	20	9.79 663	28	0.20 337	9.92 818	8	57
4	9.72 502	20	9.79 691	28	0.20 309	9.92 810	7	56
5	9.72 522	20	9.79 719	28	0.20 281	9.92 803	8	55
6	9.72 542	20	9.79 747	29	0.20 253	9.92 795	8	54
7	9.72 562	20	9.79 776	28	0.20 224	9.92 787	8	53
8	9.72 582	20	9.79 804	28	0.20 196	9.92 779	8	52
9	9.72 602	20	9.79 832	28	0.20 168	9.92 771	8	51
10	9.72 622	21	9.79 860	28	0.20 140	9.92 763	8	**50**
11	9.72 643	20	9.79 888	28	0.20 112	9.92 755	8	49
12	9.72 663	20	9.79 916	28	0.20 084	9.92 747	8	48
13	9.72 683	20	9.79 944	28	0.20 056	9.92 739	8	47
14	9.72 703	20	9.79 972	28	0.20 028	9.92 731	8	46
15	9.72 723	20	9.80 000	28	0.20 000	9.92 723	8	45
16	9.72 743	20	9.80 028	28	0.19 972	9.92 715	8	44
17	9.72 763	20	9.80 056	28	0.19 944	9.92 707	8	43
18	9.72 783	20	9.80 084	28	0.19 916	9.92 699	8	42
19	9.72 803	20	9.80 112	28	0.19 888	9.92 691	8	41
20	9.72 823	20	9.80 140	28	0.19 860	9.92 683	8	**40**
21	9.72 843	20	9.80 168	27	0.19 832	9.92 675	8	39
22	9.72 863	20	9.80 195	28	0.19 805	9.92 667	8	38
23	9.72 883	19	9.80 223	28	0.19 777	9.92 659	8	37
24	9.72 902	20	9.80 251	28	0.19 749	9.92 651	8	36
25	9.72 922	20	9.80 279	28	0.19 721	9.92 643	8	35
26	9.72 942	20	9.80 307	28	0.19 693	9.92 635	8	34
27	9.72 962	20	9.80 335	28	0.19 665	9.92 627	8	33
28	9.72 982	20	9.80 363	28	0.19 637	9.92 619	8	32
29	9.73 002	20	9.80 391	28	0.19 609	9.92 611	8	31
30	9.73 022	19	9.80 419	28	0.19 581	9.92 603	8	**30**
31	9.73 041	20	9.80 447	27	0.19 553	9.92 595	8	29
32	9.73 061	20	9.80 474	28	0.19 526	9.92 587	8	28
33	9.73 081	20	9.80 502	28	0.19 498	9.92 579	8	27
34	9.73 101	20	9.80 530	28	0.19 470	9.92 571	8	26
35	9.73 121	19	9.80 558	28	0.19 442	9.92 563	8	25
36	9.73 140	20	9.80 586	28	0.19 414	9.92 555	9	24
37	9.73 160	20	9.80 614	28	0.19 386	9.92 546	8	23
38	9.73 180	20	9.80 642	27	0.19 358	9.92 538	8	22
39	9.73 200	19	9.80 669	28	0.19 331	9.92 530	8	21
40	9.73 219	20	9.80 697	28	0.19 303	9.92 522	8	**20**
41	9.73 239	20	9.80 725	28	0.19 275	9.92 514	8	19
42	9.73 259	19	9.80 753	28	0.19 247	9.92 506	8	18
43	9.73 278	20	9.80 781	27	0.19 219	9.92 498	8	17
44	9.73 298	20	9.80 808	28	0.19 192	9.92 490	8	16
45	9.73 318	19	9.80 836	28	0.19 164	9.92 482	9	15
46	9.73 337	20	9.80 864	28	0.19 136	9.92 473	8	14
47	9.73 357	20	9.80 892	27	0.19 108	9.92 465	8	13
48	9.73 377	19	9.80 919	28	0.19 081	9.92 457	8	12
49	9.73 396	20	9.80 947	28	0.19 053	9.92 449	8	11
50	9.73 416	19	9.80 975	28	0.19 025	9.92 441	8	**10**
51	9.73 435	20	9.81 003	27	0.18 997	9.92 433	8	9
52	9.73 455	19	9.81 030	28	0.18 970	9.92 425	9	8
53	9.73 474	20	9.81 058	28	0.18 942	9.92 416	8	7
54	9.73 494	19	9.81 086	27	0.18 914	9.92 408	8	6
55	9.73 513	20	9.81 113	28	0.18 887	9.92 400	8	5
56	9.73 533	19	9.81 141	28	0.18 859	9.92 392	8	4
57	9.73 552	20	9.81 169	27	0.18 831	9.92 384	8	3
58	9.73 572	19	9.81 196	28	0.18 804	9.92 376	9	2
59	9.73 591	20	9.81 224	28	0.18 776	9.92 367	8	1
60	9.73 611		9.81 252		0.18 748	9.92 359		**0**
′	L. Cos.	d.	L. Cot.	c.d.	L. Tan.	L. Sin.	d.	′

P. P.

″	**29**	**28**	**27**
1	0.5	0.5	0.4
2	1.0	0.9	0.9
3	1.4	1.4	1.4
4	1.9	1.9	1.8
5	2.4	2.3	2.2
6	2.9	2.8	2.7
7	3.4	3.3	3.2
8	3.9	3.7	3.6
9	4.4	4.2	4.0
10	4.8	4.7	4.5
20	9.7	9.3	9.0
30	14.5	14.0	13.5
40	19.3	18.7	18.0
50	24.2	23.3	22.5

″	**21**	**20**	**19**
1	0.4	0.3	0.3
2	0.7	0.7	0.6
3	1.0	1.0	1.0
4	1.4	1.3	1.3
5	1.8	1.7	1.6
6	2.1	2.0	1.9
7	2.4	2.3	2.2
8	2.8	2.7	2.5
9	3.2	3.0	2.8
10	3.5	3.3	3.2
20	7.0	6.7	6.3
30	10.5	10.0	9.5
40	14.0	13.3	12.7
50	17.5	16.7	15.8

″	**9**	**8**	**7**
1	0.2	0.1	0.1
2	0.3	0.3	0.2
3	0.4	0.4	0.4
4	0.6	0.5	0.5
5	0.8	0.7	0.6
6	0.9	0.8	0.7
7	1.0	0.9	0.8
8	1.2	1.1	0.9
9	1.4	1.2	1.0
10	1.5	1.3	1.2
20	3.0	2.7	2.3
30	4.5	4.0	3.5
40	6.0	5.3	4.7
50	7.5	6.7	5.8

	8/29	**8/28**	**7/28**
0	1.8	1.8	2.0
1	5.4	5.2	6.0
2	9.1	8.8	10.0
3	12.7	12.2	14.0
4	16.3	15.8	18.0
5	19.9	19.2	22.0
6	23.6	22.8	26.0
7	27.2	26.2	—
8			

P. P.

122° (302°) (237°) **57°**

33° (213°) | (326°) **146°**

′	L. Sin.	d.	L. Tan.	c.d.	L. Cot.	L. Cos.	d.	′
0	9.73 611	19	9.81 252	27	0.18 748	9.92 359	8	**60**
1	9.73 630	20	9.81 279	28	0.18 721	9.92 351	8	59
2	9.73 650	19	9.81 307	28	0.18 693	9.92 343	8	58
3	9.73 669	20	9.81 335	27	0.18 665	9.92 335	9	57
4	9.73 689	19	9.81 362	28	0.18 638	9.92 326	8	56
5	9.73 708	19	9.81 390	28	0.18 610	9.92 318	8	55
6	9.73 727	20	9.81 418	27	0.18 582	9.92 310	8	54
7	9.73 747	19	9.81 445	28	0.18 555	9.92 302	9	53
8	9.73 766	19	9.81 473	27	0.18 527	9.92 293	8	52
9	9.73 785	20	9.81 500	28	0.18 500	9.92 285	8	51
10	9.73 805	19	9.81 528	28	0.18 472	9.92 277	8	**50**
11	9.73 824	19	9.81 556	27	0.18 444	9.92 269	9	49
12	9.73 843	20	9.81 583	28	0.18 417	9.92 260	8	48
13	9.73 863	19	9.81 611	27	0.18 389	9.92 252	8	47
14	9.73 882	19	9.81 638	28	0.18 362	9.92 244	9	46
15	9.73 901	20	9.81 666	27	0.18 334	9.92 235	8	45
16	9.73 921	19	9.81 693	28	0.18 307	9.92 227	8	44
17	9.73 940	19	9.81 721	27	0.18 279	9.92 219	8	43
18	9.73 959	19	9.81 748	28	0.18 252	9.92 211	9	42
19	9.73 978	19	9.81 776	27	0.18 224	9.92 202	8	41
20	9.73 997	20	9.81 803	28	0.18 197	9.92 194	8	**40**
21	9.74 017	19	9.81 831	27	0.18 169	9.92 186	9	39
22	9.74 036	19	9.81 858	28	0.18 142	9.92 177	8	38
23	9.74 055	19	9.81 886	27	0.18 114	9.92 169	8	37
24	9.74 074	19	9.81 913	28	0.18 087	9.92 161	9	36
25	9.74 093	20	9.81 941	27	0.18 059	9.92 152	8	35
26	9.74 113	19	9.81 968	28	0.18 032	9.92 144	8	34
27	9.74 132	19	9.81 996	27	0.18 004	9.92 136	9	33
28	9.74 151	19	9.82 023	28	0.17 977	9.92 127	8	32
29	9.74 170	19	9.82 051	27	0.17 949	9.92 119	8	31
30	9.74 189	19	9.82 078	28	0.17 922	9.92 111	9	**30**
31	9.74 208	19	9.82 106	27	0.17 894	9.92 102	8	29
32	9.74 227	19	9.82 133	28	0.17 867	9.92 094	8	28
33	9.74 246	19	9.82 161	27	0.17 839	9.92 086	9	27
34	9.74 265	19	9.82 188	27	0.17 812	9.92 077	8	26
35	9.74 284	19	9.82 215	28	0.17 785	9.92 069	9	25
36	9.74 303	19	9.82 243	27	0.17 757	9.92 060	8	24
37	9.74 322	19	9.82 270	28	0.17 730	9.92 052	8	23
38	9.74 341	19	9.82 298	27	0.17 702	9.92 044	9	22
39	9.74 360	19	9.82 325	27	0.17 675	9.92 035	8	21
40	9.74 379	19	9.82 352	28	0.17 648	9.92 027	9	**20**
41	9.74 398	19	9.82 380	27	0.17 620	9.92 018	8	19
42	9.74 417	19	9.82 407	28	0.17 593	9.92 010	8	18
43	9.74 436	19	9.82 435	27	0.17 565	9.92 002	9	17
44	9.74 455	19	9.82 462	27	0.17 538	9.91 993	8	16
45	9.74 474	19	9.82 489	28	0.17 511	9.91 985	9	15
46	9.74 493	19	9.82 517	27	0.17 483	9.91 976	8	14
47	9.74 512	19	9.82 544	27	0.17 456	9.91 968	9	13
48	9.74 531	18	9.82 571	28	0.17 429	9.91 959	8	12
49	9.74 549	19	9.82 599	27	0.17 401	9.91 951	9	11
50	9.74 568	19	9.82 626	27	0.17 374	9.91 942	8	**10**
51	9.74 587	19	9.82 653	28	0.17 347	9.91 934	9	9
52	9.74 606	19	9.82 681	27	0.17 319	9.91 925	8	8
53	9.74 625	19	9.82 708	27	0.17 292	9.91 917	9	7
54	9.74 644	18	9.82 735	27	0.17 265	9.91 908	8	6
55	9.74 662	19	9.82 762	28	0.17 238	9.91 900	9	5
56	9.74 681	19	9.82 790	27	0.17 210	9.91 891	8	4
57	9.74 700	19	9.82 817	27	0.17 183	9.91 883	9	3
58	9.74 719	18	9.82 844	27	0.17 156	9.91 874	8	2
59	9.74 737	19	9.82 871	28	0.17 129	9.91 866	9	1
60	9.74 756		9.82 899		0.17 101	9.91 857		**0**
′	L. Cos.	d.	L. Cot.	c.d.	L. Tan.	L. Sin.	d.	′

P. P.

″	**28**	**27**
1	0.5	0.4
2	0.9	0.9
3	1.4	1.4
4	1.9	1.8
5	2.3	2.2
6	2.8	2.7
7	3.3	3.2
8	3.7	3.6
9	4.2	4.0
10	4.7	4.5
20	9.3	9.0
30	14.0	13.5
40	18.7	18.0
50	23.3	22.5

″	**20**	**19**	**18**
1	0.3	0.3	0.3
2	0.7	0.6	0.6
3	1.0	1.0	0.9
4	1.3	1.3	1.2
5	1.7	1.6	1.5
6	2.0	1.9	1.8
7	2.3	2.2	2.1
8	2.7	2.5	2.4
9	3.0	2.8	2.7
10	3.3	3.2	3.0
20	6.7	6.3	6.0
30	10.0	9.5	9.0
40	13.3	12.7	12.0
50	16.7	15.8	15.0

″	**9**	**8**
1	0.2	0.1
2	0.3	0.3
3	0.4	0.4
4	0.6	0.5
5	0.8	0.7
6	0.9	0.8
7	1.0	0.9
8	1.2	1.1
9	1.4	1.2
10	1.5	1.3
20	3.0	2.7
30	4.5	4.0
40	6.0	5.3
50	7.5	6.7

	9 / **28**	**9** / **27**	**8** / **27**
0	1.6	1.5	1.7
1	4.7	4.5	5.1
2	7.8	7.5	8.4
3	10.9	10.5	11.8
4	14.0	13.5	15.2
5	17.1	16.5	18.6
6	20.2	19.5	21.9
7	23.3	22.5	25.3
8	26.4	25.5	—
9			

P. P.

123° (303°) | (236°) **56°**

34° (214°) (325°) **145°**

′	L. Sin.	d.	L. Tan.	c.d.	L. Cot.	L. Cos.	d.	′
0	9.74 756	19	9.82 899	27	0.17 101	9.91 857	8	**60**
1	9.74 775	19	9.82 926	27	0.17 074	9.91 849	9	59
2	9.74 794	18	9.82 953	27	0.17 047	9.91 840	8	58
3	9.74 812	19	9.82 980	28	0.17 020	9.91 832	9	57
4	9.74 831	19	9.83 008	27	0.16 992	9.91 823	8	56
5	9.74 850	18	9.83 035	27	0.16 965	9.91 815	9	55
6	9.74 868	19	9.83 062	27	0.16 938	9.91 806	8	54
7	9.74 887	19	9.83 089	28	0.16 911	9.91 798	9	53
8	9.74 906	18	9.83 117	27	0.16 883	9.91 789	8	52
9	9.74 924	19	9.83 144	27	0.16 856	9.91 781	9	51
10	9.74 943	18	9.83 171	27	0.16 829	9.91 772	9	**50**
11	9.74 961	19	9.83 198	27	0.16 802	9.91 763	8	49
12	9.74 980	19	9.83 225	27	0.16 775	9.91 755	9	48
13	9.74 999	18	9.83 252	28	0.16 748	9.91 746	8	47
14	9.75 017	19	9.83 280	27	0.16 720	9.91 738	9	46
15	9.75 036	18	9.83 307	27	0.16 693	9.91 729	9	45
16	9.75 054	19	9.83 334	27	0.16 666	9.91 720	8	44
17	9.75 073	18	9.83 361	27	0.16 639	9.91 712	9	43
18	9.75 091	19	9.83 388	27	0.16 612	9.91 703	8	42
19	9.75 110	18	9.83 415	27	0.16 585	9.91 695	9	41
20	9.75 128	19	9.83 442	28	0.16 558	9.91 686	9	**40**
21	9.75 147	18	9.83 470	27	0.16 530	9.91 677	8	39
22	9.75 165	19	9.83 497	27	0.16 503	9.91 669	9	38
23	9.75 184	18	9.83 524	27	0.16 476	9.91 660	9	37
24	9.75 202	19	9.83 551	27	0.16 449	9.91 651	8	36
25	9.75 221	18	9.83 578	27	0.16 422	9.91 643	9	35
26	9.75 239	19	9.83 605	27	0.16 395	9.91 634	9	34
27	9.75 258	18	9.83 632	27	0.16 368	9.91 625	8	33
28	9.75 276	18	9.83 659	27	0.16 341	9.91 617	9	32
29	9.75 294	19	9.83 686	27	0.16 314	9.91 608	9	31
30	9.75 313	18	9.83 713	27	0.16 287	9.91 599	8	**30**
31	9.75 331	19	9.83 740	28	0.16 260	9.91 591	9	29
32	9.75 350	18	9.83 768	27	0.16 232	9.91 582	9	28
33	9.75 368	18	9.83 795	27	0.16 205	9.91 573	8	27
34	9.75 386	19	9.83 822	27	0.16 178	9.91 565	9	26
35	9.75 405	18	9.83 849	27	0.16 151	9.91 556	9	25
36	9.75 423	18	9.83 876	27	0.16 124	9.91 547	9	24
37	9.75 441	18	9.83 903	27	0.16 097	9.91 538	8	23
38	9.75 459	19	9.83 930	27	0.16 070	9.91 530	9	22
39	9.75 478	18	9.83 957	27	0.16 043	9.91 521	9	21
40	9.75 496	18	9.83 984	27	0.16 016	9.91 512	8	**20**
41	9.75 514	19	9.84 011	27	0.15 989	9.91 504	9	19
42	9.75 533	18	9.84 038	27	0.15 962	9.91 495	9	18
43	9.75 551	18	9.84 065	27	0.15 935	9.91 486	9	17
44	9.75 569	18	9.84 092	27	0.15 908	9.91 477	8	16
45	9.75 587	18	9.84 119	27	0.15 881	9.91 469	9	15
46	9.75 605	19	9.84 146	27	0.15 854	9.91 460	9	14
47	9.75 624	18	9.84 173	27	0.15 827	9.91 451	9	13
48	9.75 642	18	9.84 200	27	0.15 800	9.91 442	9	12
49	9.75 660	18	9.84 227	27	0.15 773	9.91 433	8	11
50	9.75 678	18	9.84 254	26	0.15 746	9.91 425	9	**10**
51	9.75 696	18	9.84 280	27	0.15 720	9.91 416	9	9
52	9.75 714	19	9.84 307	27	0.15 693	9.91 407	9	8
53	9.75 733	18	9.84 334	27	0.15 666	9.91 398	9	7
54	9.75 751	18	9.84 361	27	0.15 639	9.91 389	8	6
55	9.75 769	18	9.84 388	27	0.15 612	9.91 381	9	5
56	9.75 787	18	9.84 415	27	0.15 585	9.91 372	9	4
57	9.75 805	18	9.84 442	27	0.15 558	9.91 363	9	3
58	9.75 823	18	9.84 469	27	0.15 531	9.91 354	9	2
59	9.75 841	18	9.84 496	27	0.15 504	9.91 345	9	1
60	9.75 859		9.84 523		0.15 477	9.91 336		**0**
′	L. Cos.	d.	L. Cot.	c.d.	L. Tan.	L. Sin.	d.	′

P. P.

″	28	27	26
1	0.5	0.4	0.4
2	0.9	0.9	0.9
3	1.4	1.4	1.3
4	1.9	1.8	1.7
5	2.3	2.2	2.2
6	2.8	2.7	2.6
7	3.3	3.2	3.0
8	3.7	3.6	3.5
9	4.2	4.0	3.9
10	4.7	4.5	4.3
20	9.3	9.0	8.7
30	14.0	13.5	13.0
40	18.7	18.0	17.3
50	23.3	22.5	21.7

″	19	18
1	0.3	0.3
2	0.6	0.6
3	1.0	0.9
4	1.3	1.2
5	1.6	1.5
6	1.9	1.8
7	2.2	2.1
8	2.5	2.4
9	2.8	2.7
10	3.2	3.0
20	6.3	6.0
30	9.5	9.0
40	12.7	12.0
50	15.8	15.0

″	9	8
1	0.2	0.1
2	0.3	0.3
3	0.4	0.4
4	0.6	0.5
5	0.8	0.7
6	0.9	0.8
7	1.0	0.9
8	1.2	1.1
9	1.4	1.2
10	1.5	1.3
20	3.0	2.7
30	4.5	4.0
40	6.0	5.3
50	7.5	6.7

	9/28	8/28	8/27
0	1.6	1.8	1.7
1	4.7	5.2	5.1
2	7.8	8.8	8.4
3	10.9	12.2	11.8
4	14.0	15.8	15.2
5	17.1	19.2	18.6
6	20.2	22.8	21.9
7	23.3	26.2	25.3
8	26.4	—	—
9			

P. P.

124° (304°) (235°) **55°**

′	L. Sin.	d.	L. Tan.	c.d.	L. Cot.	L. Cos.	d.	′
0	9.75 859	18	9.84 523	27	0.15 477	9.91 336	8	**60**
1	9.75 877	18	9.84 550	26	0.15 450	9.91 328	9	59
2	9.75 895	18	9.84 576	27	0.15 424	9.91 319	9	58
3	9.75 913	18	9.84 603	27	0.15 397	9.91 310	9	57
4	9.75 931	18	9.84 630	27	0.15 370	9.91 301	9	56
5	9.75 949	18	9.84 657	27	0.15 343	9.91 292	9	55
6	9.75 967	18	9.84 684	27	0.15 316	9.91 283	9	54
7	9.75 985	18	9.84 711	27	0.15 289	9.91 274	8	53
8	9.76 003	18	9.84 738	26	0.15 262	9.91 266	9	52
9	9.76 021	18	9.84 764	27	0.15 236	9.91 257	9	51
10	9.76 039	18	9.84 791	27	0.15 209	9.91 248	9	**50**
11	9.76 057	18	9.84 818	27	0.15 182	9.91 239	9	49
12	9.76 075	18	9.84 845	27	0.15 155	9.91 230	9	48
13	9.76 093	18	9.84 872	27	0.15 128	9.91 221	9	47
14	9.76 111	18	9.84 899	26	0.15 101	9.91 212	9	46
15	9.76 129	17	9.84 925	27	0.15 075	9.91 203	9	45
16	9.76 146	18	9.84 952	27	0.15 048	9.91 194	9	44
17	9.76 164	18	9.84 979	27	0.15 021	9.91 185	9	43
18	9.76 182	18	9.85 006	27	0.14 994	9.91 176	9	42
19	9.76 200	18	9.85 033	26	0.14 967	9.91 167	9	41
20	9.76 218	18	9.85 059	27	0.14 941	9.91 158	9	**40**
21	9.76 236	17	9.85 086	27	0.14 914	9.91 149	8	39
22	9.76 253	18	9.85 113	27	0.14 887	9.91 141	9	38
23	9.76 271	18	9.85 140	26	0.14 860	9.91 132	9	37
24	9.76 289	18	9.85 166	27	0.14 834	9.91 123	9	36
25	9.76 307	17	9.85 193	27	0.14 807	9.91 114	9	35
26	9.76 324	18	9.85 220	27	0.14 780	9.91 105	9	34
27	9.76 342	18	9.85 247	26	0.14 753	9.91 096	9	33
28	9.76 360	18	9.85 273	27	0.14 727	9.91 087	9	32
29	9.76 378	17	9.85 300	27	0.14 700	9.91 078	9	31
30	9.76 395	18	9.85 327	27	0.14 673	9.91 069	9	**30**
31	9.76 413	18	9.85 354	26	0.14 646	9.91 060	9	29
32	9.76 431	17	9.85 380	27	0.14 620	9.91 051	9	28
33	9.76 448	18	9.85 407	27	0.14 593	9.91 042	9	27
34	9.76 466	18	9.85 434	26	0.14 566	9.91 033	10	26
35	9.76 484	17	9.85 460	27	0.14 540	9.91 023	9	25
36	9.76 501	18	9.85 487	27	0.14 513	9.91 014	9	24
37	9.76 519	18	9.85 514	26	0.14 486	9.91 005	9	23
38	9.76 537	17	9.85 540	27	0.14 460	9.90 996	9	22
39	9.76 554	18	9.85 567	27	0.14 433	9.90 987	9	21
40	9.76 572	18	9.85 594	26	0.14 406	9.90 978	9	**20**
41	9.76 590	17	9.85 620	27	0.14 380	9.90 969	9	19
42	9.76 607	18	9.85 647	27	0.14 353	9.90 960	9	18
43	9.76 625	17	9.85 674	26	0.14 326	9.90 951	9	17
44	9.76 642	18	9.85 700	27	0.14 300	9.90 942	9	16
45	9.76 660	17	9.85 727	27	0.14 273	9.90 933	9	15
46	9.76 677	18	9.85 754	26	0.14 246	9.90 924	9	14
47	9.76 695	17	9.85 780	27	0.14 220	9.90 915	9	13
48	9.76 712	18	9.85 807	27	0.14 193	9.90 906	10	12
49	9.76 730	17	9.85 834	26	0.14 166	9.90 896	9	11
50	9.76 747	18	9.85 860	27	0.14 140	9.90 887	9	**10**
51	9.76 765	17	9.85 887	26	0.14 113	9.90 878	9	9
52	9.76 782	18	9.85 913	27	0.14 087	9.90 869	9	8
53	9.76 800	17	9.85 940	27	0.14 060	9.90 860	9	7
54	9.76 817	18	9.85 967	26	0.14 033	9.90 851	9	6
55	9.76 835	17	9.85 993	27	0.14 007	9.90 842	10	5
56	9.76 852	18	9.86 020	26	0.13 980	9.90 832	9	4
57	9.76 870	17	9.86 046	27	0.13 954	9.90 823	9	3
58	9.76 887	17	9.86 073	27	0.13 927	9.90 814	9	2
59	9.76 904	18	9.86 100	26	0.13 900	9.90 805	9	1
60	9.76 922		9.86 126		0.13 874	9.90 796		**0**
′	L. Cos.	d.	L. Cot.	c.d.	L. Tan.	L. Sin.	d.	′

P. P.

″	**27**	**26**	**18**
1	0.4	0.4	0.3
2	0.9	0.9	0.6
3	1.4	1.3	0.9
4	1.8	1.7	1.2
5	2.2	2.2	1.5
6	2.7	2.6	1.8
7	3.2	3.0	2.1
8	3.6	3.5	2.4
9	4.0	3.9	2.7
10	4.5	4.3	3.0
20	9.0	8.7	6.0
30	13.5	13.0	9.0
40	18.0	17.3	12.0
50	22.5	21.7	15.0

″	**17**	**10**	**9**	**8**
1	0.3	0.2	0.2	0.1
2	0.6	0.3	0.3	0.3
3	0.8	0.5	0.4	0.4
4	1.1	0.7	0.6	0.5
5	1.4	0.8	0.8	0.7
6	1.7	1.0	0.9	0.8
7	2.0	1.2	1.0	0.9
8	2.3	1.3	1.2	1.1
9	2.6	1.5	1.4	1.2
10	2.8	1.7	1.5	1.3
20	5.7	3.3	3.0	2.7
30	8.5	5.0	4.5	4.0
40	11.3	6.7	6.0	5.3
50	14.2	8.3	7.5	6.7

	10/27	**10/26**
0	1.4	1.3
1	4.1	3.9
2	6.8	6.5
3	9.4	9.1
4	12.2	11.7
5	14.8	14.3
6	17.6	16.9
7	20.2	19.5
8	22.9	22.1
9	25.6	24.7
10		

	9/27	**9/26**
0	1.5	1.4
1	4.5	4.3
2	7.5	7.2
3	10.5	10.1
4	13.5	13.0
5	16.5	15.9
6	19.5	18.8
7	22.5	21.7
8	25.5	24.6
9		

P. P.

36° (216°) (323°) **143°**

′	L. Sin.	d.	L. Tan.	c.d.	L. Cot.	L. Cos.	d.	′
0	9.76 922	17	9.86 126	27	0.13 874	9.90 796	9	**60**
1	9.76 939	18	9.86 153	26	0.13 847	9.90 787	10	59
2	9.76 957	17	9.86 179	27	0.13 821	9.90 777	9	58
3	9.76 974	17	9.86 206	26	0.13 794	9.90 768	9	57
4	9.76 991	18	9.86 232	27	0.13 768	9.90 759	9	56
5	9.77 009	17	9.86 259	26	0.13 741	9.90 75̄0	9	55
6	9.77 026	17	9.86 285	27	0.13 715̄	9.90 741	10	54
7	9.77 043	18	9.86 312	26	0.13 688	9.90 731	9	53
8	9.77 061	17	9.86 338	27	0.13 662	9.90 722	9	52
9	9.77 078	17	9.86 365	27	0.13 635̄	9.90 713	9	51
10	9.77 095	17	9.86 392	26	0.13 608	9.90 704	10	**50**
11	9.77 112	18	9.86 418	27	0.13 582	9.90 694	9	49
12	9.77 130	17	9.86 445̄	26	0.13 555	9.90 685	9	48
13	9.77 147	17	9.86 471	27	0.13 529	9.90 676	9	47
14	9.77 164	17	9.86 498	26	0.13 502	9.90 667	10	46
15	9.77 181	18	9.86 524	27	0.13 476	9.90 657	9	45
16	9.77 199	17	9.86 551	26	0.13 449	9.90 648	9	44
17	9.77 216	17	9.86 577	26	0.13 423	9.90 639	9	43
18	9.77 233	17	9.86 603	27	0.13 397	9.90 630	10	42
19	9.77 250	18	9.86 630	26	0.13 370	9.90 620	9	41
20	9.77 268	17	9.86 656	27	0.13 344	9.90 611	9	**40**
21	9.77 285̄	17	9.86 683	26	0.13 317	9.90 602	10	39
22	9.77 302	17	9.86 709	27	0.13 291	9.90 592	9	38
23	9.77 319	17	9.86 736	26	0.13 264	9.90 583	9	37
24	9.77 336	17	9.86 762	27	0.13 238	9.90 574	9	36
25	9.77 353	17	9.86 789	26	0.13 211	9.90 565̄	10	35
26	9.77 370	17	9.86 815	27	0.13 185̄	9.90 555	9	34
27	9.77 387	18	9.86 842	26	0.13 158	9.90 546	9	33
28	9.77 405̄	17	9.86 868	26	0.13 132	9.90 537	10	32
29	9.77 422	17	9.86 894	27	0.13 106	9.90 527	9	31
30	9.77 439	17	9.86 921	26	0.13 079	9.90 518	9	**30**
31	9.77 456	17	9.86 947	27	0.13 053	9.90 509	10	29
32	9.77 473	17	9.86 974	26	0.13 026	9.90 499	9	28
33	9.77 490	17	9.87 000	27	0.13 000	9.90 490	10	27
34	9.77 507	17	9.87 027	26	0.12 973	9.90 480	9	26
35	9.77 524	17	9.87 053	26	0.12 947	9.90 471	9	25
36	9.77 541	17	9.87 079	27	0.12 921	9.90 462	10	24
37	9.77 558	17	9.87 106	26	0.12 894	9.90 452	9	23
38	9.77 575	17	9.87 132	26	0.12 868	9.90 443	9	22
39	9.77 592	17	9.87 158	27	0.12 842	9.90 434	10	21
40	9.77 609	17	9.87 185̄	26	0.12 815	9.90 424	9	**20**
41	9.77 626	17	9.87 211	27	0.12 789	9.90 415̄	10	19
42	9.77 643	17	9.87 238	26	0.12 762	9.90 405	9	18
43	9.77 660	17	9.87 264	26	0.12 736	9.90 396	10	17
44	9.77 677	17	9.87 290	27	0.12 710	9.90 386	9	16
45	9.77 694	17	9.87 317	26	0.12 683	9.90 377	9	15
46	9.77 711	17	9.87 343	26	0.12 657	9.90 368	10	14
47	9.77 728	16	9.87 369	27	0.12 631	9.90 358	9	13
48	9.77 744	17	9.87 396	26	0.12 604	9.90 349	10	12
49	9.77 761	17	9.87 422	26	0.12 578	9.90 339	9	11
50	9.77 778	17	9.87 448	27	0.12 552	9.90 330	10	**10**
51	9.77 795	17	9.87 475̄	26	0.12 525	9.90 320	9	9
52	9.77 812	17	9.87 501	26	0.12 499	9.90 311	10	8
53	9.77 829	17	9.87 527	27	0.12 473	9.90 301	9	7
54	9.77 846	16	9.87 554	26	0.12 446	9.90 292	10	6
55	9.77 862	17	9.87 580	26	0.12 420	9.90 282	9	5
56	9.77 879	17	9.87 606	27	0.12 394	9.90 273	10	4
57	9.77 896	17	9.87 633	26	0.12 367	9.90 263	9	3
58	9.77 913	17	9.87 659	26	0.12 341	9.90 254	10	2
59	9.77 930	16	9.87 685	26	0.12 315̄	9.90 244	9	1
60	9.77 946		9.87 711		0.12 289	9.90 235̄		**0**
′	L. Cos.	d.	L. Cot.	c.d.	L. Tan.	L. Sin.	d.	′

126° (306°) (233°) **53°**

P. P.

″	**27**	**26**
1	0.4	0.4
2	0.9	0.9
3	1.4	1.3
4	1.8	1.7
5	2.2	2.2
6	2.7	2.6
7	3.2	3.0
8	3.6	3.5̄
9	4.0	3.9
10	4.5	4.3
20	9.0	8.7
30	13.5	13.0
40	18.0	17.3
50	22.5	21.7

″	**18**	**17**	**16**
1	0.3	0.3	0.3
2	0.6	0.6	0.5
3	0.9	0.8	0.8
4	1.2	1.1	1.1
5	1.5	1.4	1.3
6	1.8	1.7	1.6
7	2.1	2.0	1.9
8	2.4	2.3	2.1
9	2.7	2.6	2.4
10	3.0	2.8	2.7
20	6.0	5.7	5.3
30	9.0	8.5	8.0
40	12.0	11.3	10.7
50	15.0	14.2	13.3

″	**10**	**9**
1	0.2	0.2
2	0.3	0.3
3	0.5	0.4
4	0.7	0.6
5	0.8	0.8
6	1.0	0.9
7	1.2	1.0
8	1.3	1.2
9	1.5	1.4
10	1.7	1.5
20	3.3	3.0
30	5.0	4.5
40	6.7	6.0
50	8.3	7.5

	9/27	**9/26**
0	1.5	1.4
1	4.5	4.3
2	7.5	7.2
3	10.5	10.1
4	13.5	13.0
5	16.5	15.9
6	19.5	18.8
7	22.5	21.7
8	25.5	24.6
9		

P. P.

37° (217°) (322°) **142°**

′	L. Sin.	d.	L. Tan.	c.d.	L. Cot.	L. Cos.	d.	′
0	9.77 946	17	9.87 711	27	0.12 289	9.90 235̄	10	**60**
1	9.77 963	17	9.87 738	26	0.12 262	9.90 225̄	9	59
2	9.77 980	17	9.87 764	26	0.12 236	9.90 216	10	58
3	9.77 997	16	9.87 790	27	0.12 210	9.90 206	9	57
4	9.78 013	17	9.87 817	26	0.12 183	9.90 197	10	56
5	9.78 030	17	9.87 843	26	0.12 157	9.90 187	9	55
6	9.78 047	16	9.87 869	26	0.12 131	9.90 178	10	54
7	9.78 063	17	9.87 895̄	27	0.12 105̄	9.90 168	9	53
8	9.78 080	17	9.87 922	26	0.12 078	9.90 159	10	52
9	9.78 097	16	9.87 948	26	0.12 052	9.90 149	10	51
10	9.78 113	17	9.87 974	26	0.12 026	9.90 139	9	**50**
11	9.78 130	17	9.88 000	27	0.12 000	9.90 130	10	49
12	9.78 147	16	9.88 027	26	0.11 973	9.90 120	9	48
13	9.78 163	17	9.88 053	26	0.11 947	9.90 111	10	47
14	9.78 180	17	9.88 079	26	0.11 921	9.90 101	10	46
15	9.78 197	16	9.88 105̄	26	0.11 895̄	9.90 091	9	45
16	9.78 213	17	9.88 131	27	0.11 869	9.90 082	10	44
17	9.78 230	16	9.88 158	26	0.11 842	9.90 072	9	43
18	9.78 246	17	9.88 184	26	0.11 816	9.90 063	10	42
19	9.78 263	17	9.88 210	26	0.11 790	9.90 053	10	41
20	9.78 280	16	9.88 236	26	0.11 764	9.90 043	9	**40**
21	9.78 296	17	9.88 262	27	0.11 738	9.90 034	10	39
22	9.78 313	16	9.88 289	26	0.11 711	9.90 024	10	38
23	9.78 329	17	9.88 315̄	26	0.11 685̄	9.90 014	9	37
24	9.78 346	16	9.88 341	26	0.11 659	9.90 005̄	10	36
25	9.78 362	17	9.88 367	26	0.11 633	9.89 995̄	10	35
26	9.78 379	16	9.88 393	27	0.11 607	9.89 985̄	9	34
27	9.78 395̄	17	9.88 420	26	0.11 580	9.89 976	10	33
28	9.78 412	16	9.88 446	26	0.11 554	9.89 966	10	32
29	9.78 428	17	9.88 472	26	0.11 528	9.89 956	9	31
30	9.78 445̄	16	9.88 498	26	0.11 502	9.89 947	10	**30**
31	9.78 461	17	9.88 524	26	0.11 476	9.89 937	10	29
32	9.78 478	16	9.88 550	27	0.11 450	9.89 927	9	28
33	9.78 494	16	9.88 577	26	0.11 423	9.89 918	10	27
34	9.78 510	17	9.88 603	26	0.11 397	9.89 908	10	26
35	9.78 527	16	9.88 629	26	0.11 371	9.89 898	10	25
36	9.78 543	17	9.88 655̄	26	0.11 345̄	9.89 888	9	24
37	9.78 560	16	9.88 681	26	0.11 319	9.89 879	10	23
38	9.78 576	16	9.88 707	26	0.11 293	9.89 869	10	22
39	9.78 592	17	9.88 733	26	0.11 267	9.89 859	10	21
40	9.78 609	16	9.88 759	27	0.11 241	9.89 849	9	**20**
41	9.78 625̄	17	9.88 786	26	0.11 214	9.89 840	10	19
42	9.78 642	16	9.88 812	26	0.11 188	9.89 830	10	18
43	9.78 658	16	9.88 838	26	0.11 162	9.89 820	10	17
44	9.78 674	17	9.88 864	26	0.11 136	9.89 810	9	16
45	9.78 691	16	9.88 890	26	0.11 110	9.89 801	10	15
46	9.78 707	16	9.88 916	26	0.11 084	9.89 791	10	14
47	9.78 723	16	9.88 942	26	0.11 058	9.89 781	10	13
48	9.78 739	17	9.88 968	26	0.11 032	9.89 771	10	12
49	9.78 756	16	9.88 994	26	0.11 006	9.89 761	9	11
50	9.78 772	16	9.89 020	26	0.10 980	9.89 752	10	**10**
51	9.78 788	17	9.89 046	27	0.10 954	9.89 742	10	9
52	9.78 805̄	16	9.89 073	26	0.10 927	9.89 732	10	8
53	9.78 821	16	9.89 099	26	0.10 901	9.89 722	10	7
54	9.78 837	16	9.89 125̄	26	0.10 875̄	9.89 712	10	6
55	9.78 853	16	9.89 151	26	0.10 849	9.89 702	9	5
56	9.78 869	17	9.89 177	26	0.10 823	9.89 693	10	4
57	9.78 886	16	9.89 203	26	0.10 797	9.89 683	10	3
58	9.78 902	16	9.89 229	26	0.10 771	9.89 673	10	2
59	9.78 918	16	9.89 255̄	26	0.10 745̄	9.89 663	10	1
60	9.78 934		9.89 281		0.10 719	9.89 653		**0**
′	L. Cos.	d.	L. Cot.	c.d.	L. Tan.	L. Sin.	d.	′

P. P.

″	**27**	**26**
1	0.4	0.4
2	0.9	0.9
3	1.4	1.3
4	1.8	1.7
5	2.2	2.2
6	2.7	2.6
7	3.2	3.0
8	3.6	3.5̄
9	4.0	3.9
10	4.5	4.3
20	9.0	8.7
30	13.5	13.0
40	18.0	17.3
50	22.5	21.7

″	**17**	**16**
1	0.3	0.3
2	0.6	0.5̄
3	0.8	0.8
4	1.1	1.1
5	1.4	1.3
6	1.7	1.6
7	2.0	1.9
8	2.3	2.1
9	2.6	2.4
10	2.8	2.7
20	5.7	5.3
30	8.5	8.0
40	11.3	10.7
50	14.2	13.3

″	**10**	**9**
1	0.2	0.2
2	0.3	0.3
3	0.5	0.4
4	0.7	0.6
5	0.8	0.8
6	1.0	0.9
7	1.2	1.0
8	1.3	1.2
9	1.5	1.4
10	1.7	1.5
20	3.3	3.0
30	5.0	4.5
40	6.7	6.0
50	8.3	7.5

	10/27	**10/26**
0		
1	1.4	1.3
2	4.1	3.9
3	6.8	6.5
4	9.4	9.1
5	12.2	11.7
6	14.8	14.3
7	17.6	16.9
8	20.2	19.5
9	22.9	22.1
10	25.6	24.7

P. P.

127° (307°) (232°) **52°**

38° (218°) | (321°) **141°**

′	L. Sin.	d.	L. Tan.	c.d.	L. Cot.	L. Cos.	d.	′
0	9.78 934	16	9.89 281	26	0.10 719	9.89 653	10	**60**
1	9.78 950	17	9.89 307	26	0.10 693	9.89 643	10	59
2	9.78 967	16	9.89 333	26	0.10 667	9.89 633	9	58
3	9.78 983	16	9.89 359	26	0.10 641	9.89 624	10	57
4	9.78 999	16	9.89 385	26	0.10 615	9.89 614	10	56
5	9.79 015	16	9.89 411	26	0.10 589	9.89 604	10	55
6	9.79 031	16	9.89 437	26	0.10 563	9.89 594	10	54
7	9.79 047	16	9.89 463	26	0.10 537	9.89 584	10	53
8	9.79 063	16	9.89 489	26	0.10 511	9.89 574	10	52
9	9.79 079	16	9.89 515	26	0.10 485	9.89 564	10	51
10	9.79 095	16	9.89 541	26	0.10 459	9.89 554	10	**50**
11	9.79 111	17	9.89 567	26	0.10 433	9.89 544	10	49
12	9.79 128	16	9.89 593	26	0.10 407	9.89 534	10	48
13	9.79 144	16	9.89 619	26	0.10 381	9.89 524	10	47
14	9.79 160	16	9.89 645	26	0.10 355	9.89 514	10	46
15	9.79 176	16	9.89 671	26	0.10 329	9.89 504	9	45
16	9.79 192	16	9.89 697	26	0.10 303	9.89 495	10	44
17	9.79 208	16	9.89 723	26	0.10 277	9.89 485	10	43
18	9.79 224	16	9.89 749	26	0.10 251	9.89 475	10	42
19	9.79 240	16	9.89 775	26	0.10 225	9.89 465	10	41
20	9.79 256	16	9.89 801	26	0.10 199	9.89 455	10	**40**
21	9.79 272	16	9.89 827	26	0.10 173	9.89 445	10	39
22	9.79 288	16	9.89 853	26	0.10 147	9.89 435	10	38
23	9.79 304	15	9.89 879	26	0.10 121	9.89 425	10	37
24	9.79 319	16	9.89 905	26	0.10 095	9.89 415	10	36
25	9.79 335	16	9.89 931	26	0.10 069	9.89 405	10	35
26	9.79 351	16	9.89 957	26	0.10 043	9.89 395	10	34
27	9.79 367	16	9.89 983	26	0.10 017	9.89 385	10	33
28	9.79 383	16	9.90 009	26	0.09 991	9.89 375	11	32
29	9.79 399	16	9.90 035	26	0.09 965	9.89 364	10	31
30	9.79 415	16	9.90 061	25	0.09 939	9.89 354	10	**30**
31	9.79 431	16	9.90 086	26	0.09 914	9.89 344	10	29
32	9.79 447	16	9.90 112	26	0.09 888	9.89 334	10	28
33	9.79 463	15	9.90 138	26	0.09 862	9.89 324	10	27
34	9.79 478	16	9.90 164	26	0.09 836	9.89 314	10	26
35	9.79 494	16	9.90 190	26	0.09 810	9.89 304	10	25
36	9.79 510	16	9.90 216	26	0.09 784	9.89 294	10	24
37	9.79 526	16	9.90 242	26	0.09 758	9.89 284	10	23
38	9.79 542	16	9.90 268	26	0.09 732	9.89 274	10	22
39	9.79 558	15	9.90 294	26	0.09 706	9.89 264	10	21
40	9.79 573	16	9.90 320	26	0.09 680	9.89 254	10	**20**
41	9.79 589	16	9.90 346	25	0.09 654	9.89 244	11	19
42	9.79 605	16	9.90 371	26	0.09 629	9.89 233	10	18
43	9.79 621	15	9.90 397	26	0.09 603	9.89 223	10	17
44	9.79 636	16	9.90 423	26	0.09 577	9.89 213	10	16
45	9.79 652	16	9.90 449	26	0.09 551	9.89 203	10	15
46	9.79 668	16	9.90 475	26	0.09 525	9.89 193	10	14
47	9.79 684	15	9.90 501	26	0.09 499	9.89 183	10	13
48	9.79 699	16	9.90 527	26	0.09 473	9.89 173	11	12
49	9.79 715	16	9.90 553	25	0.09 447	9.89 162	10	11
50	9.79 731	15	9.90 578	26	0.09 422	9.89 152	10	**10**
51	9.79 746	16	9.90 604	26	0.09 396	9.89 142	10	9
52	9.79 762	16	9.90 630	26	0.09 370	9.89 132	10	8
53	9.79 778	15	9.90 656	26	0.09 344	9.89 122	10	7
54	9.79 793	16	9.90 682	26	0.09 318	9.89 112	11	6
55	9.79 809	16	9.90 708	26	0.09 292	9.89 101	10	5
56	9.79 825	15	9.90 734	25	0.09 266	9.89 091	10	4
57	9.79 840	16	9.90 759	26	0.09 241	9.89 081	10	3
58	9.79 856	16	9.90 785	26	0.09 215	9.89 071	11	2
59	9.79 872	15	9.90 811	26	0.09 189	9.89 060	10	1
60	9.79 887		9.90 837		0.09 163	9.89 050		**0**
′	L. Cos.	d.	L. Cot.	c.d.	L. Tan.	L. Sin.	d.	′

P. P.

″	26	25
1	0.4	0.4
2	0.9	0.8
3	1.3	1.2
4	1.7	1.7
5	2.2	2.1
6	2.6	2.5
7	3.0	2.9
8	3.5	3.3
9	3.9	3.8
10	4.3	4.2
20	8.7	8.3
30	13.0	12.5
40	17.3	16.7
50	21.7	20.8

″	17	16	15
1	0.3	0.3	0.2
2	0.6	0.5	0.5
3	0.8	0.8	0.8
4	1.1	1.1	1.0
5	1.4	1.3	1.2
6	1.7	1.6	1.5
7	2.0	1.9	1.8
8	2.3	2.1	2.0
9	2.6	2.4	2.2
10	2.8	2.7	2.5
20	5.7	5.3	5.0
30	8.5	8.0	7.5
40	11.3	10.7	10.0
50	14.2	13.3	12.5

″	11	10	9
1	0.2	0.2	0.2
2	0.4	0.3	0.3
3	0.6	0.5	0.4
4	0.7	0.7	0.6
5	0.9	0.8	0.8
6	1.1	1.0	0.9
7	1.3	1.2	1.0
8	1.5	1.3	1.2
9	1.6	1.5	1.4
10	1.8	1.7	1.5
20	3.7	3.3	3.0
30	5.5	5.0	4.5
40	7.3	6.7	6.0
50	9.2	8.3	7.5

	10/26	10/25	9/26
0	1.3	1.2	1.4
1	3.9	3.8	4.3
2	6.5	6.2	7.2
3	9.1	8.8	10.1
4	11.7	11.2	13.0
5	14.3	13.8	15.9
6	16.9	16.2	18.8
7	19.5	18.8	21.7
8	22.1	21.2	24.6
9	24.7	23.8	—
10			

P. P.

128° (308°) | (231°) **51°**

39° (219°) (320°) **140°**

′	L. Sin.	d.	L. Tan.	c.d.	L. Cot.	L. Cos.	d.	′
0	9.79 887	16	9.90 837	26	0.09 163	9.89 050	10	**60**
1	9.79 903	15	9.90 863	26	0.09 137	9.89 040	10	59
2	9.79 918	16	9.90 889	25	0.09 111	9.89 030	10	58
3	9.79 934	16	9.90 914	26	0.09 086	9.89 020	11	57
4	9.79 950	15	9.90 940	26	0.09 060	9.89 009	10	56
5	9.79 965	16	9.90 966	26	0.09 034	9.88 999	10	55
6	9.79 981	15	9.90 992	26	0.09 008	9.88 989	11	54
7	9.79 996	16	9.91 018	25	0.08 982	9.88 978	10	53
8	9.80 012	15	9.91 043	26	0.08 957	9.88 968	10	52
9	9.80 027	16	9.91 069	26	0.08 931	9.88 958	10	51
10	9.80 043	15	9.91 095	26	0.08 905	9.88 948	11	**50**
11	9.80 058	16	9.91 121	26	0.08 879	9.88 937	10	49
12	9.80 074	15	9.91 147	25	0.08 853	9.88 927	10	48
13	9.80 089	16	9.91 172	26	0.08 828	9.88 917	11	47
14	9.80 105	15	9.91 198	26	0.08 802	9.88 906	10	46
15	9.80 120	16	9.91 224	26	0.08 776	9.88 896	10	45
16	9.80 136	15	9.91 250	26	0.08 750	9.88 886	11	44
17	9.80 151	15	9.91 276	25	0.08 724	9.88 875	10	43
18	9.80 166	16	9.91 301	26	0.08 699	9.88 865	10	42
19	9.80 182	15	9.91 327	26	0.08 673	9.88 855	11	41
20	9.80 197	16	9.91 353	26	0.08 647	9.88 844	10	**40**
21	9.80 213	15	9.91 379	25	0.08 621	9.88 834	10	39
22	9.80 228	16	9.91 404	26	0.08 596	9.88 824	11	38
23	9.80 244	15	9.91 430	26	0.08 570	9.88 813	10	37
24	9.80 259	15	9.91 456	26	0.08 544	9.88 803	10	36
25	9.80 274	16	9.91 482	25	0.08 518	9.88 793	11	35
26	9.80 290	15	9.91 507	26	0.08 493	9.88 782	10	34
27	9.80 305	15	9.91 533	26	0.08 467	9.88 772	11	33
28	9.80 320	16	9.91 559	26	0.08 441	9.88 761	10	32
29	9.80 336	15	9.91 585	25	0.08 415	9.88 751	10	31
30	9.80 351	15	9.91 610	26	0.08 390	9.88 741	11	**30**
31	9.80 366	16	9.91 636	26	0.08 364	9.88 730	10	29
32	9.80 382	15	9.91 662	26	0.08 338	9.88 720	11	28
33	9.80 397	15	9.91 688	25	0.08 312	9.88 709	10	27
34	9.80 412	16	9.91 713	26	0.08 287	9.88 699	11	26
35	9.80 428	15	9.91 739	26	0.08 261	9.88 688	10	25
36	9.80 443	15	9.91 765	26	0.08 235	9.88 678	10	24
37	9.80 458	15	9.91 791	25	0.08 209	9.88 668	11	23
38	9.80 473	16	9.91 816	26	0.08 184	9.88 657	10	22
39	9.80 489	15	9.91 842	26	0.08 158	9.88 647	11	21
40	9.80 504	15	9.91 868	25	0.08 132	9.88 636	10	**20**
41	9.80 519	15	9.91 893	26	0.08 107	9.88 626	11	19
42	9.80 534	16	9.91 919	26	0.08 081	9.88 615	10	18
43	9.80 550	15	9.91 945	26	0.08 055	9.88 605	11	17
44	9.80 565	15	9.91 971	25	0.08 029	9.88 594	10	16
45	9.80 580	15	9.91 996	26	0.08 004	9.88 584	11	15
46	9.80 595	15	9.92 022	26	0.07 978	9.88 573	10	14
47	9.80 610	15	9.92 048	25	0.07 952	9.88 563	11	13
48	9.80 625	16	9.92 073	26	0.07 927	9.88 552	10	12
49	9.80 641	15	9.92 099	26	0.07 901	9.88 542	11	11
50	9.80 656	15	9.92 125	25	0.07 875	9.88 531	10	**10**
51	9.80 671	15	9.92 150	26	0.07 850	9.88 521	11	9
52	9.80 686	15	9.92 176	26	0.07 824	9.88 510	11	8
53	9.80 701	15	9.92 202	25	0.07 798	9.88 499	10	7
54	9.80 716	15	9.92 227	26	0.07 773	9.88 489	11	6
55	9.80 731	15	9.92 253	26	0.07 747	9.88 478	10	5
56	9.80 746	16	9.92 279	25	0.07 721	9.88 468	11	4
57	9.80 762	15	9.92 304	26	0.07 696	9.88 457	10	3
58	9.80 777	15	9.92 330	26	0.07 670	9.88 447	11	2
59	9.80 792	15	9.92 356	25	0.07 644	9.88 436	11	1
60	9.80 807		9.92 381		0.07 619	9.88 425		**0**
′	L. Cos.	d.	L. Cot.	c.d.	L. Tan.	L. Sin.	d.	′

P. P.

″	**26**	**25**
1	0.4	0.4
2	0.9	0.8
3	1.3	1.2
4	1.7	1.7
5	2.2	2.1
6	2.6	2.5
7	3.0	2.9
8	3.5	3.3
9	3.9	3.8
10	4.3	4.2
20	8.7	8.3
30	13.0	12.5
40	17.3	16.7
50	21.7	20.8

″	**16**	**15**
1	0.3	0.2
2	0.5	0.5
3	0.8	0.8
4	1.1	1.0
5	1.3	1.2
6	1.6	1.5
7	1.9	1.8
8	2.1	2.0
9	2.4	2.2
10	2.7	2.5
20	5.3	5.0
30	8.0	7.5
40	10.7	10.0
50	13.3	12.5

″	**11**	**10**
1	0.2	0.2
2	0.4	0.3
3	0.6	0.5
4	0.7	0.7
5	0.9	0.8
6	1.1	1.0
7	1.3	1.2
8	1.5	1.3
9	1.6	1.5
10	1.8	1.7
20	3.7	3.3
30	5.5	5.0
40	7.3	6.7
50	9.2	8.3

	11/26	**11/25**
0	1.2	1.1
1	3.5	3.4
2	5.9	5.7
3	8.3	7.9
4	10.6	10.2
5	13.0	12.5
6	15.4	14.8
7	17.7	17.1
8	20.1	19.3
9	22.5	21.6
10	24.8	23.9
11		

P. P.

129° (309°) (230°) **50°**

40° (220°) (319°) **139°**

′	L. Sin.	d.	L. Tan.	c.d.	L. Cot.	L. Cos.	d.	′
0	9.80 807	15	9.92 381	26	0.07 619	9.88 425	10	**60**
1	9.80 822	15	9.92 407	26	0.07 593	9.88 415	11	59
2	9.80 837	15	9.92 433	25	0.07 567	9.88 404	10	58
3	9.80 852	15	9.92 458	26	0.07 542	9.88 394	11	57
4	9.80 867	15	9.92 484	26	0.07 516	9.88 383	11	56
5	9.80 882	15	9.92 510	25	0.07 490	9.88 372	10	55
6	9.80 897	15	9.92 535	26	0.07 465	9.88 362	11	54
7	9.80 912	15	9.92 561	26	0.07 439	9.88 351	11	53
8	9.80 927	15	9.92 587	25	0.07 413	9.88 340	10	52
9	9.80 942	15	9.92 612	26	0.07 388	9.88 330	11	51
10	9.80 957	15	9.92 638	25	0.07 362	9.88 319	11	**50**
11	9.80 972	15	9.92 663	26	0.07 337	9.88 308	10	49
12	9.80 987	15	9.92 689	26	0.07 311	9.88 298	11	48
13	9.81 002	15	9.92 715	25	0.07 285	9.88 287	11	47
14	9.81 017	15	9.92 740	26	0.07 260	9.88 276	10	46
15	9.81 032	15	9.92 766	26	0.07 234	9.88 266	11	45
16	9.81 047	14	9.92 792	25	0.07 208	9.88 255	11	44
17	9.81 061	15	9.92 817	26	0.07 183	9.88 244	10	43
18	9.81 076	15	9.92 843	25	0.07 157	9.88 234	11	42
19	9.81 091	15	9.92 868	26	0.07 132	9.88 223	11	41
20	9.81 106	15	9.92 894	26	0.07 106	9.88 212	11	**40**
21	9.81 121	15	9.92 920	25	0.07 080	9.88 201	10	39
22	9.81 136	15	9.92 945	26	0.07 055	9.88 191	11	38
23	9.81 151	15	9.92 971	25	0.07 029	9.88 180	11	37
24	9.81 166	14	9.92 996	26	0.07 004	9.88 169	11	36
25	9.81 180	15	9.93 022	26	0.06 978	9.88 158	10	35
26	9.81 195	15	9.93 048	25	0.06 952	9.88 148	11	34
27	9.81 210	15	9.93 073	26	0.06 927	9.88 137	11	33
28	9.81 225	15	9.93 099	25	0.06 901	9.88 126	11	32
29	9.81 240	14	9.93 124	26	0.06 876	9.88 115	10	31
30	9.81 254	15	9.93 150	25	0.06 850	9.88 105	11	**30**
31	9.81 269	15	9.93 175	26	0.06 825	9.88 094	11	29
32	9.81 284	15	9.93 201	26	0.06 799	9.88 083	11	28
33	9.81 299	15	9.93 227	25	0.06 773	9.88 072	11	27
34	9.81 314	14	9.93 252	26	0.06 748	9.88 061	10	26
35	9.81 328	15	9.93 278	25	0.06 722	9.88 051	11	25
36	9.81 343	15	9.93 303	26	0.06 697	9.88 040	11	24
37	9.81 358	14	9.93 329	25	0.06 671	9.88 029	11	23
38	9.81 372	15	9.93 354	26	0.06 646	9.88 018	11	22
39	9.81 387	15	9.93 380	26	0.06 620	9.88 007	11	21
40	9.81 402	15	9.93 406	25	0.06 594	9.87 996	11	**20**
41	9.81 417	14	9.93 431	26	0.06 569	9.87 985	10	19
42	9.81 431	15	9.93 457	25	0.06 543	9.87 975	11	18
43	9.81 446	15	9.93 482	26	0.06 518	9.87 964	11	17
44	9.81 461	14	9.93 508	25	0.06 492	9.87 953	11	16
45	9.81 475	15	9.93 533	26	0.06 467	9.87 942	11	15
46	9.81 490	15	9.93 559	25	0.06 441	9.87 931	11	14
47	9.81 505	14	9.93 584	26	0.06 416	9.87 920	11	13
48	9.81 519	15	9.93 610	26	0.06 390	9.87 909	11	12
49	9.81 534	15	9.93 636	25	0.06 364	9.87 898	11	11
50	9.81 549	14	9.93 661	26	0.06 339	9.87 887	10	**10**
51	9.81 563	15	9.93 687	25	0.06 313	9.87 877	11	9
52	9.81 578	14	9.93 712	26	0.06 288	9.87 866	11	8
53	9.81 592	15	9.93 738	25	0.06 262	9.87 855	11	7
54	9.81 607	15	9.93 763	26	0.06 237	9.87 844	11	6
55	9.81 622	14	9.93 789	25	0.06 211	9.87 833	11	5
56	9.81 636	15	9.93 814	26	0.06 186	9.87 822	11	4
57	9.81 651	14	9.93 840	25	0.06 160	9.87 811	11	3
58	9.81 665	15	9.93 865	26	0.06 135	9.87 800	11	2
59	9.81 680	14	9.93 891	25	0.06 109	9.87 789	11	1
60	9.81 694		9.93 916		0.06 084	9.87 778		**0**
′	L. Cos.	d.	L. Cot.	c.d.	L. Tan.	L. Sin.	d.	′

P. P.

″	26	25
1	0.4	0.4
2	0.9	0.8
3	1.3	1.2
4	1.7	1.7
5	2.2	2.1
6	2.6	2.5
7	3.0	2.9
8	3.5	3.3
9	3.9	3.8
10	4.3	4.2
20	8.7	8.3
30	13.0	12.5
40	17.3	16.7
50	21.7	20.8

″	15	14
1	0.2	0.2
2	0.5	0.5
3	0.8	0.7
4	1.0	0.9
5	1.2	1.2
6	1.5	1.4
7	1.8	1.6
8	2.0	1.9
9	2.2	2.1
10	2.5	2.3
20	5.0	4.7
30	7.5	7.0
40	10.0	9.3
50	12.5	11.7

″	11	10
1	0.2	0.2
2	0.4	0.3
3	0.6	0.5
4	0.7	0.7
5	0.9	0.8
6	1.1	1.0
7	1.3	1.2
8	1.5	1.3
9	1.6	1.5
10	1.8	1.7
20	3.7	3.3
30	5.5	5.0
40	7.3	6.7
50	9.2	8.3

	11/26	10/26	10/25
0	1.2	1.3	1.2
1	3.5	3.9	3.8
2	5.9	6.5	6.2
3	8.3	9.1	8.8
4	10.6	11.7	11.2
5	13.0	14.3	13.8
6	15.4	16.9	16.2
7	17.7	19.5	18.8
8	20.1	22.1	21.2
9	22.5	24.7	23.8
10	24.8	—	—
11			

P. P.

130° (310°) (229°) **49°**

41° (221°) (318°) **138°**

′	L. Sin.	d.	L. Tan.	c.d.	L. Cot.	L. Cos.	d.	′
0	9.81 694	15	9.93 916	26	0.06 084	9.87 778	11	**60**
1	9.81 709	14	9.93 942	25	0.06 058	9.87 767	11	59
2	9.81 723	15	9.93 967	26	0.06 033	9.87 756	11	58
3	9.81 738	14	9.93 993	25	0.06 007	9.87 745̄	11	57
4	9.81 752	15	9.94 018	26	0.05 982	9.87 734	11	56
5	9.81 767	14	9.94 044	25	0.05 956	9.87 723	11	55
6	9.81 781	15	9.94 069	26	0.05 931	9.87 712	11	54
7	9.81 796	14	9.94 095̄	25	0.05 905̄	9.87 701	11	53
8	9.81 810	15	9.94 120	26	0.05 880	9.87 690	11	52
9	9.81 825̄	14	9.94 146	25	0.05 854	9.87 679	11	51
10	9.81 839	15	9.94 171	26	0.05 829	9.87 668	11	**50**
11	9.81 854	14	9.94 197	25	0.05 803	9.87 657	11	49
12	9.81 868	14	9.94 222	26	0.05 778	9.87 646	11	48
13	9.81 882	15	9.94 248	25	0.05 752	9.87 635̄	11	47
14	9.81 897	14	9.94 273	26	0.05 727	9.87 624	11	46
15	9.81 911	15	9.94 299	25	0.05 701	9.87 613	12	45
16	9.81 926	14	9.94 324	26	0.05 676	9.87 601	11	44
17	9.81 940	15	9.94 350	25	0.05 650	9.87 590	11	43
18	9.81 955̄	14	9.94 375̄	26	0.05 625̄	9.87 579	11	42
19	9.81 969	14	9.94 401	25	0.05 599	9.87 568	11	41
20	9.81 983	15	9.94 426	26	0.05 574	9.87 557	11	**40**
21	9.81 998	14	9.94 452	25	0.05 548	9.87 546	11	39
22	9.82 012	14	9.94 477	26	0.05 523	9.87 535̄	11	38
23	9.82 026	15	9.94 503	25	0.05 497	9.87 524	11	37
24	9.82 041	14	9.94 528	26	0.05 472	9.87 513	12	36
25	9.82 055̄	14	9.94 554	25	0.05 446	9.87 501	11	35
26	9.82 069	15	9.94 579	25	0.05 421	9.87 490	11	34
27	9.82 084	14	9.94 604	26	0.05 396	9.87 479	11	33
28	9.82 098	14	9.94 630	25	0.05 370	9.87 468	11	32
29	9.82 112	14	9.94 655̄	26	0.05 345̄	9.87 457	11	31
30	9.82 126	15	9.94 681	25	0.05 319	9.87 446	12	**30**
31	9.82 141	14	9.94 706	26	0.05 294	9.87 434	11	29
32	9.82 155̄	14	9.94 732	25	0.05 268	9.87 423	11	28
33	9.82 169	15	9.94 757	26	0.05 243	9.87 412	11	27
34	9.82 184	14	9.94 783	25	0.05 217	9.87 401	11	26
35	9.82 198	14	9.94 808	26	0.05 192	9.87 390	12	25
36	9.82 212	14	9.94 834	25	0.05 166	9.87 378	11	24
37	9.82 226	14	9.94 859	25	0.05 141	9.87 367	11	23
38	9.82 240	15	9.94 884	26	0.05 116	9.87 356	11	22
39	9.82 255̄	14	9.94 910	25	0.05 090	9.87 345̄	11	21
40	9.82 269	14	9.94 935̄	26	0.05 065̄	9.87 334	12	**20**
41	9.82 283	14	9.94 961	25	0.05 039	9.87 322	11	19
42	9.82 297	14	9.94 986	26	0.05 014	9.87 311	11	18
43	9.82 311	15	9.95 012	25	0.04 988	9.87 300	12	17
44	9.82 326	14	9.95 037	25	0.04 963	9.87 288	11	16
45	9.82 340	14	9.95 062	26	0.04 938	9.87 277	11	15
46	9.82 354	14	9.95 088	25	0.04 912	9.87 266	11	14
47	9.82 368	14	9.95 113	26	0.04 887	9.87 255̄	12	13
48	9.82 382	14	9.95 139	25	0.04 861	9.87 243	11	12
49	9.82 396	14	9.95 164	26	0.04 836	9.87 232	11	11
50	9.82 410	14	9.95 190	25	0.04 810	9.87 221	12	**10**
51	9.82 424	15	9.95 215̄	25	0.04 785̄	9.87 209	11	9
52	9.82 439	14	9.95 240	26	0.04 760	9.87 198	11	8
53	9.82 453	14	9.95 266	25	0.04 734	9.87 187	12	7
54	9.82 467	14	9.95 291	26	0.04 709	9.87 175̄	11	6
55	9.82 481	14	9.95 317	25	0.04 683	9.87 164	11	5
56	9.82 495̄	14	9.95 342	26	0.04 658	9.87 153	12	4
57	9.82 509	14	9.95 368	25	0.04 632	9.87 141	11	3
58	9.82 523	14	9.95 393	25	0.04 607	9.87 130	11	2
59	9.82 537	14	9.95 418	26	0.04 582	9.87 119	12	1
60	9.82 551		9.95 444		0.04 556	9.87 107		**0**
′	L. Cos.	d.	L. Cot.	c.d.	L. Tan.	L. Sin.	d.	′

P. P.

″	**26**	**25**
1	0.4	0.4
2	0.9	0.8
3	1.3	1.2
4	1.7	1.7
5	2.2	2.1
6	2.6	2.5
7	3.0	2.9
8	3.5̄	3.3
9	3.9	3.8
10	4.3	4.2
20	8.7	8.3
30	13.0	12.5
40	17.3	16.7
50	21.7	20.8

″	**15**	**14**
1	0.2	0.2
2	0.5	0.5̄
3	0.8	0.7
4	1.0	0.9
5	1.2	1.2
6	1.5	1.4
7	1.8	1.6
8	2.0	1.9
9	2.2	2.1
10	2.5	2.3
20	5.0	4.7
30	7.5	7.0
40	10.0	9.3
50	12.5	11.7

″	**12**	**11**
1	0.2	0.2
2	0.4	0.4
3	0.6	0.6
4	0.8	0.7
5	1.0	0.9
6	1.2	1.1
7	1.4	1.3
8	1.6	1.5̄
9	1.8	1.6
10	2.0	1.8
20	4.0	3.7
30	6.0	5.5
40	8.0	7.3
50	10.0	9.2

	12/26	**12/25**	**11/25**
0			
1	1.1	1.1	1.1
2	3.2	3.1	3.4
3	5.4	5.2	5.7
4	7.6	7.3	7.9
5	9.8	9.4	10.2
6	11.9	11.5̄	12.5
7	14.1	13.5̄	14.8
8	16.2	15.6	17.1
9	18.4	17.7	19.3
10	20.6	19.8	21.6
11	22.8	21.9	23.9
12	24.9	23.9	—

P. P.

131° (311°) (228°) **48°**

42° (222°) (317°) **137°**

′	L. Sin.	d.	L. Tan.	c.d.	L. Cot.	L. Cos.	d.	′
0	9.82 551	14	9.95 444	25	0.04 556	9.87 107	11	**60**
1	9.82 565	14	9.95 469	26	0.04 531	9.87 096	11	59
2	9.82 579	14	9.95 495	25	0.04 505	9.87 085	12	58
3	9.82 593	14	9.95 520	25	0.04 480	9.87 073	11	57
4	9.82 607	14	9.95 545	26	0.04 455	9.87 062	12	56
5	9.82 621	14	9.95 571	25	0.04 429	9.87 050	11	55
6	9.82 635	14	9.95 596	26	0.04 404	9.87 039	11	54
7	9.82 649	14	9.95 622	25	0.04 378	9.87 028	12	53
8	9.82 663	14	9.95 647	25	0.04 353	9.87 016	11	52
9	9.82 677	14	9.95 672	26	0.04 328	9.87 005	12	51
10	9.82 691	14	9.95 698	25	0.04 302	9.86 993	11	**50**
11	9.82 705	14	9.95 723	25	0.04 277	9.86 982	12	49
12	9.82 719	14	9.95 748	26	0.04 252	9.86 970	11	48
13	9.82 733	14	9.95 774	25	0.04 226	9.86 959	12	47
14	9.82 747	14	9.95 799	26	0.04 201	9.86 947	11	46
15	9.82 761	14	9.95 825	25	0.04 175	9.86 936	12	45
16	9.82 775	13	9.95 850	25	0.04 150	9.86 924	11	44
17	9.82 788	14	9.95 875	26	0.04 125	9.86 913	11	43
18	9.82 802	14	9.95 901	25	0.04 099	9.86 902	12	42
19	9.82 816	14	9.95 926	26	0.04 074	9.86 890	11	41
20	9.82 830	14	9.95 952	25	0.04 048	9.86 879	12	**40**
21	9.82 844	14	9.95 977	25	0.04 023	9.86 867	12	39
22	9.82 858	14	9.96 002	26	0.03 998	9.86 855	11	38
23	9.82 872	13	9.96 028	25	0.03 972	9.86 844	12	37
24	9.82 885	14	9.96 053	25	0.03 947	9.86 832	11	36
25	9.82 899	14	9.96 078	26	0.03 922	9.86 821	12	35
26	9.82 913	14	9.96 104	25	0.03 896	9.86 809	11	34
27	9.82 927	14	9.96 129	26	0.03 871	9.86 798	12	33
28	9.82 941	14	9.96 155	25	0.03 845	9.86 786	11	32
29	9.82 955	13	9.96 180	25	0.03 820	9.86 775	12	31
30	9.82 968	14	9.96 205	26	0.03 795	9.86 763	11	**30**
31	9.82 982	14	9.96 231	25	0.03 769	9.86 752	12	29
32	9.82 996	14	9.96 256	25	0.03 744	9.86 740	12	28
33	9.83 010	13	9.96 281	26	0.03 719	9.86 728	11	27
34	9.83 023	14	9.96 307	25	0.03 693	9.86 717	12	26
35	9.83 037	14	9.96 332	25	0.03 668	9.86 705	11	25
36	9.83 051	14	9.96 357	26	0.03 643	9.86 694	12	24
37	9.83 065	13	9.96 383	25	0.03 617	9.86 682	12	23
38	9.83 078	14	9.96 408	25	0.03 592	9.86 670	11	22
39	9.83 092	14	9.96 433	26	0.03 567	9.86 659	12	21
40	9.83 106	14	9.96 459	25	0.03 541	9.86 647	12	**20**
41	9.83 120	13	9.96 484	26	0.03 516	9.86 635	11	19
42	9.83 133	14	9.96 510	25	0.03 490	9.86 624	12	18
43	9.83 147	14	9.96 535	25	0.03 465	9.86 612	12	17
44	9.83 161	13	9.96 560	26	0.03 440	9.86 600	11	16
45	9.83 174	14	9.96 586	25	0.03 414	9.86 589	12	15
46	9.83 188	14	9.96 611	25	0.03 389	9.86 577	12	14
47	9.83 202	13	9.96 636	26	0.03 364	9.86 565	11	13
48	9.83 215	14	9.96 662	25	0.03 338	9.86 554	12	12
49	9.83 229	13	9.96 687	25	0.03 313	9.86 542	12	11
50	9.83 242	14	9.96 712	26	0.03 288	9.86 530	12	**10**
51	9.83 256	14	9.96 738	25	0.03 262	9.86 518	11	9
52	9.83 270	13	9.96 763	25	0.03 237	9.86 507	12	8
53	9.83 283	14	9.96 788	26	0.03 212	9.86 495	12	7
54	9.83 297	13	9.96 814	25	0.03 186	9.86 483	11	6
55	9.83 310	14	9.96 839	25	0.03 161	9.86 472	12	5
56	9.83 324	14	9.96 864	26	0.03 136	9.86 460	12	4
57	9.83 338	13	9.96 890	25	0.03 110	9.86 448	12	3
58	9.83 351	14	9.96 915	25	0.03 085	9.86 436	11	2
59	9.83 365	13	9.96 940	26	0.03 060	9.86 425	12	1
60	9.83 378		9.96 966		0.03 034	9.86 413		**0**
′	L. Cos.	d.	L. Cot.	c.d.	L. Tan.	L. Sin.	d.	′

P. P.

″	**26**	**25**
1	0.4	0.4
2	0.9	0.8
3	1.3	1.2
4	1.7	1.7
5	2.2	2.1
6	2.6	2.5
7	3.0	2.9
8	3.5	3.3
9	3.9	3.8
10	4.3	4.2
20	8.7	8.3
30	13.0	12.5
40	17.3	16.7
50	21.7	20.8

″	**14**	**13**
1	0.2	0.2
2	0.5	0.4
3	0.7	0.6
4	0.9	0.9
5	1.2	1.1
6	1.4	1.3
7	1.6	1.5
8	1.9	1.7
9	2.1	2.0
10	2.3	2.2
20	4.7	4.3
30	7.0	6.5
40	9.3	8.7
50	11.7	10.8

″	**12**	**11**
1	0.2	0.2
2	0.4	0.4
3	0.6	0.6
4	0.8	0.7
5	1.0	0.9
6	1.2	1.1
7	1.4	1.3
8	1.6	1.5
9	1.8	1.6
10	2.0	1.8
20	4.0	3.7
30	6.0	5.5
40	8.0	7.3
50	10.0	9.2

	12/26	**11/26**	**11/25**
0			
1	1.1	1.2	1.1
2	3.2	3.5	3.4
3	5.4	5.9	5.7
4	7.6	8.3	7.9
5	9.8	10.6	10.2
6	11.9	13.0	12.5
7	14.1	15.4	14.8
8	16.2	17.7	17.1
9	18.4	20.1	19.3
10	20.6	22.5	21.6
11	22.8	24.8	23.9
12	24.9	—	—

P. P.

132° (312°) (227°) **47°**

43° (223°) (316°) **136°**

′	L. Sin.	d.	L. Tan.	c.d.	L. Cot.	L. Cos.	d.	′
0	9.83 378	14	9.96 966	25	0.03 034	9.86 413	12	**60**
1	9.83 392	13	9.96 991	25	0.03 009	9.86 401	12	59
2	9.83 405	14	9.97 016	26	0.02 984	9.86 389	12	58
3	9.83 419	13	9.97 042	25	0.02 958	9.86 377	11	57
4	9.83 432	14	9.97 067	25	0.02 933	9.86 366	12	56
5	9.83 446	13	9.97 092	26	0.02 908	9.86 354	12	55
6	9.83 459	14	9.97 118	25	0.02 882	9.86 342	12	54
7	9.83 473	13	9.97 143	25	0.02 857	9.86 330	12	53
8	9.83 486	14	9.97 168	25	0.02 832	9.86 318	12	52
9	9.83 500	13	9.97 193	26	0.02 807	9.86 306	11	51
10	9.83 513	14	9.97 219	25	0.02 781	9.86 295	12	**50**
11	9.83 527	13	9.97 244	25	0.02 756	9.86 283	12	49
12	9.83 540	14	9.97 269	26	0.02 731	9.86 271	12	48
13	9.83 554	13	9.97 295	25	0.02 705	9.86 259	12	47
14	9.83 567	14	9.97 320	25	0.02 680	9.86 247	12	46
15	9.83 581	13	9.97 345	26	0.02 655	9.86 235	12	45
16	9.83 594	14	9.97 371	25	0.02 629	9.86 223	12	44
17	9.83 608	13	9.97 396	25	0.02 604	9.86 211	11	43
18	9.83 621	13	9.97 421	26	0.02 579	9.86 200	12	42
19	9.83 634	14	9.97 447	25	0.02 553	9.86 188	12	41
20	9.83 648	13	9.97 472	25	0.02 528	9.86 176	12	**40**
21	9.83 661	13	9.97 497	26	0.02 503	9.86 164	12	39
22	9.83 674	14	9.97 523	25	0.02 477	9.86 152	12	38
23	9.83 688	13	9.97 548	25	0.02 452	9.86 140	12	37
24	9.83 701	14	9.97 573	25	0.02 427	9.86 128	12	36
25	9.83 715	13	9.97 598	26	0.02 402	9.86 116	12	35
26	9.83 728	13	9.97 624	25	0.02 376	9.86 104	12	34
27	9.83 741	14	9.97 649	25	0.02 351	9.86 092	12	33
28	9.83 755	13	9.97 674	26	0.02 326	9.86 080	12	32
29	9.83 768	13	9.97 700	25	0.02 300	9.86 068	12	31
30	9.83 781	14	9.97 725	25	0.02 275	9.86 056	12	**30**
31	9.83 795	13	9.97 750	26	0.02 250	9.86 044	12	29
32	9.83 808	13	9.97 776	25	0.02 224	9.86 032	12	28
33	9.83 821	13	9.97 801	25	0.02 199	9.86 020	12	27
34	9.83 834	14	9.97 826	25	0.02 174	9.86 008	12	26
35	9.83 848	13	9.97 851	26	0.02 149	9.85 996	12	25
36	9.83 861	13	9.97 877	25	0.02 123	9.85 984	12	24
37	9.83 874	13	9.97 902	25	0.02 098	9.85 972	12	23
38	9.83 887	14	9.97 927	26	0.02 073	9.85 960	12	22
39	9.83 901	13	9.97 953	25	0.02 047	9.85 948	12	21
40	9.83 914	13	9.97 978	25	0.02 022	9.85 936	12	**20**
41	9.83 927	13	9.98 003	26	0.01 997	9.85 924	12	19
42	9.83 940	14	9.98 029	25	0.01 971	9.85 912	12	18
43	9.83 954	13	9.98 054	25	0.01 946	9.85 900	12	17
44	9.83 967	13	9.98 079	25	0.01 921	9.85 888	12	16
45	9.83 980	13	9.98 104	26	0.01 896	9.85 876	12	15
46	9.83 993	13	9.98 130	25	0.01 870	9.85 864	13	14
47	9.84 006	14	9.98 155	25	0.01 845	9.85 851	12	13
48	9.84 020	13	9.98 180	26	0.01 820	9.85 839	12	12
49	9.84 033	13	9.98 206	25	0.01 794	9.85 827	12	11
50	9.84 046	13	9.98 231	25	0.01 769	9.85 815	12	**10**
51	9.84 059	13	9.98 256	25	0.01 744	9.85 803	12	9
52	9.84 072	13	9.98 281	26	0.01 719	9.85 791	12	8
53	9.84 085	13	9.98 307	25	0.01 693	9.85 779	13	7
54	9.84 098	14	9.98 332	25	0.01 668	9.85 766	12	6
55	9.84 112	13	9.98 357	26	0.01 643	9.85 754	12	5
56	9.84 125	13	9.98 383	25	0.01 617	9.85 742	12	4
57	9.84 138	13	9.98 408	25	0.01 592	9.85 730	12	3
58	9.84 151	13	9.98 433	25	0.01 567	9.85 718	12	2
59	9.84 164	13	9.98 458	26	0.01 542	9.85 706	13	1
60	9.84 177		9.98 484		0.01 516	9.85 693		**0**
′	L. Cos.	d.	L. Cot.	c.d.	L. Tan.	L. Sin.	d.	′

P. P.

″	**26**	**25**
1	0.4	0.4
2	0.9	0.8
3	1.3	1.2
4	1.7	1.7
5	2.2	2.1
6	2.6	2.5
7	3.0	2.9
8	3.5	3.3
9	3.9	3.8
10	4.3	4.2
20	8.7	8.3
30	13.0	12.5
40	17.3	16.7
50	21.7	20.8

″	**14**	**13**
1	0.2	0.2
2	0.5	0.4
3	0.7	0.6
4	0.9	0.9
5	1.2	1.1
6	1.4	1.3
7	1.6	1.5
8	1.9	1.7
9	2.1	2.0
10	2.3	2.2
20	4.7	4.3
30	7.0	6.5
40	9.3	8.7
50	11.7	10.8

″	**12**	**11**
1	0.2	0.2
2	0.4	0.4
3	0.6	0.6
4	0.8	0.7
5	1.0	0.9
6	1.2	1.1
7	1.4	1.3
8	1.6	1.5
9	1.8	1.6
10	2.0	1.8
20	4.0	3.7
30	6.0	5.5
40	8.0	7.3
50	10.0	9.2

	13 / **26**	**13** / **25**	**12** / **25**
0	1.0	0.9	1.1
1	3.0	2.9	3.1
2	5.0	4.8	5.2
3	7.0	6.7	7.3
4	9.0	8.7	9.4
5	11.0	10.6	11.5
6	13.0	12.5	13.5
7	15.0	14.4	15.6
8	17.0	16.3	17.7
9	19.0	18.3	19.8
10	21.0	20.2	21.9
11	23.0	22.1	23.9
12	25.0	24.1	—
13			

P. P.

133° (313°) (226°) **46°**

44° (224°) (315°) **135°**

′	L. Sin.	d.	L. Tan.	c.d.	L. Cot.	L. Cos.	d.	′
0	9.84 177	13	9.98 484	25	0.01 516	9.85 693	12	**60**
1	9.84 190	13	9.98 509	25	0.01 491	9.85 681	12	59
2	9.84 203	13	9.98 534	26	0.01 466	9.85 669	12	58
3	9.84 216	13	9.98 560	25	0.01 440	9.85 657	12	57
4	9.84 229	13	9.98 585	25	0.01 415	9.85 645	13	56
5	9.84 242	13	9.98 610	25	0.01 390	9.85 632	12	55
6	9.84 255	14	9.98 635	26	0.01 365	9.85 620	12	54
7	9.84 269	13	9.98 661	25	0.01 339	9.85 608	12	53
8	9.84 282	13	9.98 686	25	0.01 314	9.85 596	13	52
9	9.84 295	13	9.98 711	26	0.01 289	9.85 583	12	51
10	9.84 308	13	9.98 737	25	0.01 263	9.85 571	12	**50**
11	9.84 321	13	9.98 762	25	0.01 238	9.85 559	12	49
12	9.84 334	13	9.98 787	25	0.01 213	9.85 547	13	48
13	9.84 347	13	9.98 812	26	0.01 188	9.85 534	12	47
14	9.84 360	13	9.98 838	25	0.01 162	9.85 522	12	46
15	9.84 373	12	9.98 863	25	0.01 137	9.85 510	13	45
16	9.84 385	13	9.98 888	25	0.01 112	9.85 497	12	44
17	9.84 398	13	9.98 913	26	0.01 087	9.85 485	12	43
18	9.84 411	13	9.98 939	25	0.01 061	9.85 473	13	42
19	9.84 424	13	9.98 964	25	0.01 036	9.85 460	12	41
20	9.84 437	13	9.98 989	26	0.01 011	9.85 448	12	**40**
21	9.84 450	13	9.99 015	25	0.00 985	9.85 436	13	39
22	9.84 463	13	9.99 040	25	0.00 960	9.85 423	12	38
23	9.84 476	13	9.99 065	25	0.00 935	9.85 411	12	37
24	9.84 489	13	9.99 090	26	0.00 910	9.85 399	13	36
25	9.84 502	13	9.99 116	25	0.00 884	9.85 386	12	35
26	9.84 515	13	9.99 141	25	0.00 859	9.85 374	13	34
27	9.84 528	12	9.99 166	25	0.00 834	9.85 361	12	33
28	9.84 540	13	9.99 191	26	0.00 809	9.85 349	12	32
29	9.84 553	13	9.99 217	25	0.00 783	9.85 337	13	31
30	9.84 566	13	9.99 242	25	0.00 758	9.85 324	12	**30**
31	9.84 579	13	9.99 267	26	0.00 733	9.85 312	13	29
32	9.84 592	13	9.99 293	25	0.00 707	9.85 299	12	28
33	9.84 605	13	9.99 318	25	0.00 682	9.85 287	13	27
34	9.84 618	12	9.99 343	25	0.00 657	9.85 274	12	26
35	9.84 630	13	9.99 368	26	0.00 632	9.85 262	12	25
36	9.84 643	13	9.99 394	25	0.00 606	9.85 250	13	24
37	9.84 656	13	9.99 419	25	0.00 581	9.85 237	12	23
38	9.84 669	13	9.99 444	25	0.00 556	9.85 225	13	22
39	9.84 682	12	9.99 469	26	0.00 531	9.85 212	12	21
40	9.84 694	13	9.99 495	25	0.00 505	9.85 200	13	**20**
41	9.84 707	13	9.99 520	25	0.00 480	9.85 187	12	19
42	9 84 720	13	9.99 545	25	0.00 455	9.85 175	13	18
43	9.84 733	12	9.99 570	26	0.00 430	9.85 162	12	17
44	9.84 745	13	9.99 596	25	0.00 404	9.85 150	13	16
45	9.84 758	13	9.99 621	25	0.00 379	9.85 137	12	15
46	9.84 771	13	9.99 646	26	0.00 354	9.85 125	13	14
47	9.84 784	12	9.99 672	25	0.00 328	9.85 112	12	13
48	9.84 796	13	9.99 697	25	0.00 303	9.85 100	13	12
49	9.84 809	13	9.99 722	25	0.00 278	9.85 087	13	11
50	9.84 822	13	9.99 747	26	0.00 253	9.85 074	12	**10**
51	9.84 835	12	9.99 773	25	0.00 227	9.85 062	13	9
52	9.84 847	13	9.99 798	25	0.00 202	9.85 049	12	8
53	9.84 860	13	9.99 823	25	0.00 177	9.85 037	13	7
54	9.84 873	12	9.99 848	26	0.00 152	9.85 024	12	6
55	9.84 885	13	9.99 874	25	0.00 126	9.85 012	13	5
56	9.84 898	13	9.99 899	25	0.00 101	9.84 999	13	4
57	9.84 911	12	9.99 924	25	0.00 076	9.84 986	12	3
58	9.84 923	13	9.99 949	26	0.00 051	9.84 974	13	2
59	9.84 936	13	9.99 975	25	0.00 025	9.84 961	12	1
60	9.84 949		0.00 000		0.00 000	9.84 949		**0**
′	L. Cos.	d.	L. Cot.	c.d.	L. Tan.	L. Sin.	d.	′

134° (314°) (225°) **45°**

P. P.

″	26	25
1	0.4	0.4
2	0.9	0.8
3	1.3	1.2
4	1.7	1.7
5	2.2	2.1
6	2.6	2.5
7	3.0	2.9
8	3.5	3.3
9	3.9	3.8
10	4.3	4.2
20	8.7	8.3
30	13.0	12.5
40	17.3	16.7
50	21.7	20.8

″	14	13	12
1	0.2	0.2	0.2
2	0.5	0.4	0.4
3	0.7	0.6	0.6
4	0.9	0.9	0.8
5	1.2	1.1	1.0
6	1.4	1.3	1.2
7	1.6	1.5	1.4
8	1.9	1.7	1.6
9	2.1	2.0	1.8
10	2.3	2.2	2.0
20	4.7	4.3	4.0
30	7.0	6.5	6.0
40	9.3	8.7	8.0
50	11.7	10.8	10.0

	13/26	13/25
0	1.0	0.9
1	3.0	2.9
2	5.0	4.8
3	7.0	6.7
4	9.0	8.7
5	11.0	10.6
6	13.0	12.5
7	15.0	14.4
8	17.0	16.3
9	19.0	18.3
10	21.0	20.2
11	23.0	22.1
12	25.0	24.1
13		

	12/26	12/25
0	1.1	1.1
1	3.2	3.1
2	5.4	5.2
3	7.6	7.3
4	9.8	9.4
5	11.9	11.5
6	14.1	13.5
7	16.2	15.6
8	18.4	17.7
9	20.6	19.8
10	22.8	21.9
11	24.9	23.9
12		

P. P.

NATURAL TRIGONOMETRIC FUNCTIONS

Values of the trigonometric functions of angles for each minute from 0–360°.

For degrees indicated at the top of the page use the column headings at the top. For degrees indicated at the bottom use the column indications at the bottom.

With degrees at the left of each block (top or bottom), use the minute column at the left and with degrees at the right of each block use the minute column at the right.

0° (180°) (359°) **179°**

′	Sin	Tan	Cot	Cos	′
0	.00000	.00000		1.0000	**60**
1	.00029	.00029	3437.7	1.0000	59
2	.00058	.00058	1718.9	1.0000	58
3	.00087	.00087	1145.9	1.0000	57
4	.00116	.00116	859.44	1.0000	56
5	.00145	.00145	687.55	1.0000	**55**
6	.00175	.00175	572.96	1.0000	54
7	.00204	.00204	491.11	1.0000	53
8	.00233	.00233	429.72	1.0000	52
9	.00262	.00262	381.97	1.0000	51
10	.00291	.00291	343.77	1.0000	**50**
11	.00320	.00320	312.52	.99999	49
12	.00349	.00349	286.48	.99999	48
13	.00378	.00378	264.44	.99999	47
14	.00407	.00407	245.55	.99999	46
15	.00436	.00436	229.18	.99999	**45**
16	.00465	.00465	214.86	.99999	44
17	.00495	.00495	202.22	.99999	43
18	.00524	.00524	190.98	.99999	42
19	.00553	.00553	180.93	.99998	41
20	.00582	.00582	171.89	.99998	**40**
21	.00611	.00611	163.70	.99998	39
22	.00640	.00640	156.26	.99998	38
23	.00669	.00669	149.47	.99998	37
24	.00698	.00698	143.24	.99998	36
25	.00727	.00727	137.51	.99997	**35**
26	.00756	.00756	132.22	.99997	34
27	.00785	.00785	127.32	.99997	33
28	.00814	.00815	122.77	.99997	32
29	.00844	.00844	118.54	.99996	31
30	.00873	.00873	114.59	.99996	**30**
31	.00902	.00902	110.89	.99996	29
32	.00931	.00931	107.43	.99996	28
33	.00960	.00960	104.17	.99995	27
34	.00989	.00989	101.11	.99995	26
35	.01018	.01018	98.218	.99995	**25**
36	.01047	.01047	95.489	.99995	24
37	.01076	.01076	92.908	.99994	23
38	.01105	.01105	90.463	.99994	22
39	.01134	.01135	88.144	.99994	21
40	.01164	.01164	85.940	.99993	**20**
41	.01193	.01193	83.844	.99993	19
42	.01222	.01222	81.847	.99993	18
43	.01251	.01251	79.943	.99992	17
44	.01280	.01280	78.126	.99992	16
45	.01309	.01309	76.390	.99991	**15**
46	.01338	.01338	74.729	.99991	14
47	.01367	.01367	73.139	.99991	13
48	.01396	.01396	71.615	.99990	12
49	.01425	.01425	70.153	.99990	11
50	.01454	.01455	68.750	.99989	**10**
51	.01483	.01484	67.402	.99989	9
52	.01513	.01513	66.105	.99989	8
53	.01542	.01542	64.858	.99988	7
54	.01571	.01571	63.657	.99988	6
55	.01600	.01600	62.499	.99987	**5**
56	.01629	.01629	61.383	.99987	4
57	.01658	.01658	60.306	.99986	3
58	.01687	.01687	59.266	.99986	2
59	.01716	.01716	58.261	.99985	1
60	.01745	.01746	57.290	.99985	**0**
′	Cos	Cot	Tan	Sin	′

90° (270°) (269°) **89°**

1° (181°) (358°) **178°**

′	Sin	Tan	Cot	Cos	′
0	.01745	.01746	57.290	.99985	**60**
1	.01774	.01775	56.351	.99984	59
2	.01803	.01804	55.442	.99984	58
3	.01832	.01833	54.561	.99983	57
4	.01862	.01862	53.709	.99983	56
5	.01891	.01891	52.882	.99982	**55**
6	.01920	.01920	52.081	.99982	54
7	.01949	.01949	51.303	.99981	53
8	.01978	.01978	50.549	.99980	52
9	.02007	.02007	49.816	.99980	51
10	.02036	.02036	49.104	.99979	**50**
11	.02065	.02066	48.412	.99979	49
12	.02094	.02095	47.740	.99978	48
13	.02123	.02124	47.085	.99977	47
14	.02152	.02153	46.449	.99977	46
15	.02181	.02182	45.829	.99976	**45**
16	.02211	.02211	45.226	.99976	44
17	.02240	.02240	44.639	.99975	43
18	.02269	.02269	44.066	.99974	42
19	.02298	.02298	43.508	.99974	41
20	.02327	.02328	42.964	.99973	**40**
21	.02356	.02357	42.433	.99972	39
22	.02385	.02386	41.916	.99972	38
23	.02414	.02415	41.411	.99971	37
24	.02443	.02444	40.917	.99970	36
25	.02472	.02473	40.436	.99969	**35**
26	.02501	.02502	39.965	.99969	34
27	.02530	.02531	39.506	.99968	33
28	.02560	.02560	39.057	.99967	32
29	.02589	.02589	38.618	.99966	31
30	.02618	.02619	38.188	.99966	**30**
31	.02647	.02648	37.769	.99965	29
32	.02676	.02677	37.358	.99964	28
33	.02705	.02706	36.956	.99963	27
34	.02734	.02735	36.563	.99963	26
35	.02763	.02764	36.178	.99962	**25**
36	.02792	.02793	35.801	.99961	24
37	.02821	.02822	35.431	.99960	23
38	.02850	.02851	35.070	.99959	22
39	.02879	.02881	34.715	.99959	21
40	.02908	.02910	34.368	.99958	**20**
41	.02938	.02939	34.027	.99957	19
42	.02967	.02968	33.694	.99956	18
43	.02996	.02997	33.366	.99955	17
44	.03025	.03026	33.045	.99954	16
45	.03054	.03055	32.730	.99953	**15**
46	.03083	.03084	32.421	.99952	14
47	.03112	.03114	32.118	.99952	13
48	.03141	.03143	31.821	.99951	12
49	.03170	.03172	31.528	.99950	11
50	.03199	.03201	31.242	.99949	**10**
51	.03228	.03230	30.960	.99948	9
52	.03257	.03259	30.683	.99947	8
53	.03286	.03288	30.412	.99946	7
54	.03316	.03317	30.145	.99945	6
55	.03345	.03346	29.882	.99944	**5**
56	.03374	.03376	29.624	.99943	4
57	.03403	.03405	29.371	.99942	3
58	.03432	.03434	29.122	.99941	2
59	.03461	.03463	28.877	.99940	1
60	.03490	.03492	28.636	.99939	**0**
′	Cos	Cot	Tan	Sin	′

91° (271°) (268°) **88°**

2° (182°) (357°) **177°**

′	Sin	Tan	Cot	Cos	′
0	.03490	.03492	28.636	.99939	**60**
1	.03519	.03521	28.399	.99938	59
2	.03548	.03550	28.166	.99937	58
3	.03577	.03579	27.937	.99936	57
4	.03606	.03609	27.712	.99935	56
5	.03635	.03638	27.490	.99934	**55**
6	.03664	.03667	27.271	.99933	54
7	.03693	.03696	27.057	.99932	53
8	.03723	.03725	26.845	.99931	52
9	.03752	.03754	26.637	.99930	51
10	.03781	.03783	26.432	.99929	**50**
11	.03810	.03812	26.230	.99927	49
12	.03839	.03842	26.031	.99926	48
13	.03868	.03871	25.835	.99925	47
14	.03897	.03900	25.642	.99924	46
15	.03926	.03929	25.452	.99923	**45**
16	.03955	.03958	25.264	.99922	44
17	.03984	.03987	25.080	.99921	43
18	.04013	.04016	24.898	.99919	42
19	.04042	.04046	24.719	.99918	41
20	.04071	.04075	24.542	.99917	**40**
21	.04100	.04104	24.368	.99916	39
22	.04129	.04133	24.196	.99915	38
23	.04159	.04162	24.026	.99913	37
24	.04188	.04191	23.859	.99912	36
25	.04217	.04220	23.695	.99911	**35**
26	.04246	.04250	23.532	.99910	34
27	.04275	.04279	23.372	.99909	33
28	.04304	.04308	23.214	.99907	32
29	.04333	.04337	23.058	.99906	31
30	.04362	.04366	22.904	.99905	**30**
31	.04391	.04395	22.752	.99904	29
32	.04420	.04424	22.602	.99902	28
33	.04449	.04454	22.454	.99901	27
34	.04478	.04483	22.308	.99900	26
35	.04507	.04512	22.164	.99898	**25**
36	.04536	.04541	22.022	.99897	24
37	.04565	.04570	21.881	.99896	23
38	.04594	.04599	21.743	.99894	22
39	.04623	.04628	21.606	.99893	21
40	.04653	.04658	21.470	.99892	**20**
41	.04682	.04687	21.337	.99890	19
42	.04711	.04716	21.205	.99889	18
43	.04740	.04745	21.075	.99888	17
44	.04769	.04774	20.946	.99886	16
45	.04798	.04803	20.819	.99885	**15**
46	.04827	.04833	20.693	.99883	14
47	.04856	.04862	20.569	.99882	13
48	.04885	.04891	20.446	.99881	12
49	.04914	.04920	20.325	.99879	11
50	.04943	.04949	20.206	.99878	**10**
51	.04972	.04978	20.087	.99876	9
52	.05001	.05007	19.970	.99875	8
53	.05030	.05037	19.855	.99873	7
54	.05059	.05066	19.740	.99872	6
55	.05088	.05095	19.627	.99870	**5**
56	.05117	.05124	19.516	.99869	4
57	.05146	.05153	19.405	.99867	3
58	.05175	.05182	19.296	.99866	2
59	.05205	.05212	19.188	.99864	1
60	.05234	.05241	19.081	.99863	**0**
′	Cos	Cot	Tan	Sin	′

92° (272°) (267°) **87°**

3° (183°) (356°) **176°**

′	Sin	Tan	Cot	Cos	′
0	.05234	.05241	19.081	.99863	**60**
1	.05263	.05270	18.976	.99861	59
2	.05292	.05299	18.871	.99860	58
3	.05321	.05328	18.768	.99858	57
4	.05350	.05357	18.666	.99857	56
5	.05379	.05387	18.564	.99855	**55**
6	.05408	.05416	18.464	.99854	54
7	.05437	.05445	18.366	.99852	53
8	.05466	.05474	18.268	.99851	52
9	.05495	.05503	18.171	.99849	51
10	.05524	.05533	18.075	.99847	**50**
11	.05553	.05562	17.980	.99846	49
12	.05582	.05591	17.886	.99844	48
13	.05611	.05620	17.793	.99842	47
14	.05640	.05649	17.702	.99841	46
15	.05669	.05678	17.611	.99839	**45**
16	.05698	.05708	17.521	.99838	44
17	.05727	.05737	17.431	.99836	43
18	.05756	.05766	17.343	.99834	42
19	.05785	.05795	17.256	.99833	41
20	.05814	.05824	17.169	.99831	**40**
21	.05844	.05854	17.084	.99829	39
22	.05873	.05883	16.999	.99827	38
23	.05902	.05912	16.915	.99826	37
24	.05931	.05941	16.832	.99824	36
25	.05960	.05970	16.750	.99822	**35**
26	.05989	.05999	16.668	.99821	34
27	.06018	.06029	16.587	.99819	33
28	.06047	.06058	16.507	.99817	32
29	.06076	.06087	16.428	.99815	31
30	.06105	.06116	16.350	.99813	**30**
31	.06134	.06145	16.272	.99812	29
32	.06163	.06175	16.195	.99810	28
33	.06192	.06204	16.119	.99808	27
34	.06221	.06233	16.043	.99806	26
35	.06250	.06262	15.969	.99804	**25**
36	.06279	.06291	15.895	.99803	24
37	.06308	.06321	15.821	.99801	23
38	.06337	.06350	15.748	.99799	22
39	.06366	.06379	15.676	.99797	21
40	.06395	.06408	15.605	.99795	**20**
41	.06424	.06438	15.534	.99793	19
42	.06453	.06467	15.464	.99792	18
43	.06482	.06496	15.394	.99790	17
44	.06511	.06525	15.325	.99788	16
45	.06540	.06554	15.257	.99786	**15**
46	.06569	.06584	15.189	.99784	14
47	.06598	.06613	15.122	.99782	13
48	.06627	.06642	15.056	.99780	12
49	.06656	.06671	14.990	.99778	11
50	.06685	.06700	14.924	.99776	**10**
51	.06714	.06730	14.860	.99774	9
52	.06743	.06759	14.795	.99772	8
53	.06773	.06788	14.732	.99770	7
54	.06802	.06817	14.669	.99768	6
55	.06831	.06847	14.606	.99766	**5**
56	.06860	.06876	14.544	.99764	4
57	.06889	.06905	14.482	.99762	3
58	.06918	.06934	14.421	.99760	2
59	.06947	.06963	14.361	.99758	1
60	.06976	.06993	14.301	.99756	**0**
′	Cos	Cot	Tan	Sin	′

93° (273°) (266°) **86°**

4° (184°) (355°) **175°**

′	Sin	Tan	Cot	Cos	′
0	.06976	.06993	14.301	.99756	**60**
1	.07005	.07022	14.241	.99754	59
2	.07034	.07051	14.182	.99752	58
3	.07063	.07080	14.124	.99750	57
4	.07092	.07110	14.065	.99748	56
5	.07121	.07139	14.008	.99746	**55**
6	.07150	.07168	13.951	.99744	54
7	.07179	.07197	13.894	.99742	53
8	.07208	.07227	13.838	.99740	52
9	.07237	.07256	13.782	.99738	51
10	.07266	.07285	13.727	.99736	**50**
11	.07295	.07314	13.672	.99734	49
12	.07324	.07344	13.617	.99731	48
13	.07353	.07373	13.563	.99729	47
14	.07382	.07402	13.510	.99727	46
15	.07411	.07431	13.457	.99725	**45**
16	.07440	.07461	13.404	.99723	44
17	.07469	.07490	13.352	.99721	43
18	.07498	.07519	13.300	.99719	42
19	.07527	.07548	13.248	.99716	41
20	.07556	.07578	13.197	.99714	**40**
21	.07585	.07607	13.146	.99712	39
22	.07614	.07636	13.096	.99710	38
23	.07643	.07665	13.046	.99708	37
24	.07672	.07695	12.996	.99705	36
25	.07701	.07724	12.947	.99703	**35**
26	.07730	.07753	12.898	.99701	34
27	.07759	.07782	12.850	.99699	33
28	.07788	.07812	12.801	.99696	32
29	.07817	.07841	12.754	.99694	31
30	.07846	.07870	12.706	.99692	**30**
31	.07875	.07899	12.659	.99689	29
32	.07904	.07929	12.612	.99687	28
33	.07933	.07958	12.566	.99685	27
34	.07962	.07987	12.520	.99683	26
35	.07991	.08017	12.474	.99680	**25**
36	.08020	.08046	12.429	.99678	24
37	.08049	.08075	12.384	.99676	23
38	.08078	.08104	12.339	.99673	22
39	.08107	.08134	12.295	.99671	21
40	.08136	.08163	12.251	.99668	**20**
41	.08165	.08192	12.207	.99666	19
42	.08194	.08221	12.163	.99664	18
43	.08223	.08251	12.120	.99661	17
44	.08252	.08280	12.077	.99659	16
45	.08281	.08309	12.035	.99657	**15**
46	.08310	.08339	11.992	.99654	14
47	.08339	.08368	11.950	.99652	13
48	.08368	.08397	11.909	.99649	12
49	.08397	.08427	11.867	.99647	11
50	.08426	.08456	11.826	.99644	**10**
51	.08455	.08485	11.785	.99642	9
52	.08484	.08514	11.745	.99639	8
53	.08513	.08544	11.705	.99637	7
54	.08542	.08573	11.664	.99635	6
55	.08571	.08602	11.625	.99632	**5**
56	.08600	.08632	11.585	.99630	4
57	.08629	.08661	11.546	.99627	3
58	.08658	.08690	11.507	.99625	2
59	.08687	.08720	11.468	.99622	1
60	.08716	.08749	11.430	.99619	**0**
′	Cos	Cot	Tan	Sin	′

94° (274°) (265°) **85°**

5° (185°) (354°) **174°**

′	Sin	Tan	Cot	Cos	′
0	.08716	.08749	11.430	.99619	**60**
1	.08745	.08778	11.392	.99617	59
2	.08774	.08807	11.354	.99614	58
3	.08803	.08837	11.316	.99612	57
4	.08831	.08866	11.279	.99609	56
5	.08860	.08895	11.242	.99607	**55**
6	.08889	.08925	11.205	.99604	54
7	.08918	.08954	11.168	.99602	53
8	.08947	.08983	11.132	.99599	52
9	.08976	.09013	11.095	.99596	51
10	.09005	.09042	11.059	.99594	**50**
11	.09034	.09071	11.024	.99591	49
12	.09063	.09101	10.988	.99588	48
13	.09092	.09130	10.953	.99586	47
14	.09121	.09159	10.918	.99583	46
15	.09150	.09189	10.883	.99580	**45**
16	.09179	.09218	10.848	.99578	44
17	.09208	.09247	10.814	.99575	43
18	.09237	.09277	10.780	.99572	42
19	.09266	.09306	10.746	.99570	41
20	.09295	.09335	10.712	.99567	**40**
21	.09324	.09365	10.678	.99564	39
22	.09353	.09394	10.645	.99562	38
23	.09382	.09423	10.612	.99559	37
24	.09411	.09453	10.579	.99556	36
25	.09440	.09482	10.546	.99553	**35**
26	.09469	.09511	10.514	.99551	34
27	.09498	.09541	10.481	.99548	33
28	.09527	.09570	10.449	.99545	32
29	.09556	.09600	10.417	.99542	31
30	.09585	.09629	10.385	.99540	**30**
31	.09614	.09658	10.354	.99537	29
32	.09642	.09688	10.322	.99534	28
33	.09671	.09717	10.291	.99531	27
34	.09700	.09746	10.260	.99528	26
35	.09729	.09776	10.229	.99526	**25**
36	.09758	.09805	10.199	.99523	24
37	.09787	.09834	10.168	.99520	23
38	.09816	.09864	10.138	.99517	22
39	.09845	.09893	10.108	.99514	21
40	.09874	.09923	10.078	.99511	**20**
41	.09903	.09952	10.048	.99508	19
42	.09932	.09981	10.019	.99506	18
43	.09961	.10011	9.9893	.99503	17
44	.09990	.10040	9.9601	.99500	16
45	.10019	.10069	9.9310	.99497	**15**
46	.10048	.10099	9.9021	.99494	14
47	.10077	.10128	9.8734	.99491	13
48	.10106	.10158	9.8448	.99488	12
49	.10135	.10187	9.8164	.99485	11
50	.10164	.10216	9.7882	.99482	**10**
51	.10192	.10246	9.7601	.99479	9
52	.10221	.10275	9.7322	.99476	8
53	.10250	.10305	9.7044	.99473	7
54	.10279	.10334	9.6768	.99470	6
55	.10308	.10363	9.6493	.99467	**5**
56	.10337	.10393	9.6220	.99464	4
57	.10366	.10422	9.5949	.99461	3
58	.10395	.10452	9.5679	.99458	2
59	.10424	.10481	9.5411	.99455	1
60	.10453	.10510	9.5144	.99452	**0**
′	Cos	Cot	Tan	Sin	′

95° (275°) (264°) **84°**

6° (186°) (353°) **173°**

′	Sin	Tan	Cot	Cos	′
0	.10453	.10510	9.5144	.99452	**60**
1	.10482	.10540	9.4878	.99449	59
2	.10511	.10569	9.4614	.99446	58
3	.10540	.10599	9.4352	.99443	57
4	.10569	.10628	9.4090	.99440	56
5	.10597	.10657	9.3831	.99437	**55**
6	.10626	.10687	9.3572	.99434	54
7	.10655	.10716	9.3315	.99431	53
8	.10684	.10746	9.3060	.99428	52
9	.10713	.10775	9.2806	.99424	51
10	.10742	.10805	9.2553	.99421	**50**
11	.10771	.10834	9.2302	.99418	49
12	.10800	.10863	9.2052	.99415	48
13	.10829	.10893	9.1803	.99412	47
14	.10858	.10922	9.1555	.99409	46
15	.10887	.10952	9.1309	.99406	**45**
16	.10916	.10981	9.1065	.99402	44
17	.10945	.11011	9.0821	.99399	43
18	.10973	.11040	9.0579	.99396	42
19	.11002	.11070	9.0338	.99393	41
20	.11031	.11099	9.0098	.99390	**40**
21	.11060	.11128	8.9860	.99386	39
22	.11089	.11158	8.9623	.99383	38
23	.11118	.11187	8.9387	.99380	37
24	.11147	.11217	8.9152	.99377	36
25	.11176	.11246	8.8919	.99374	**35**
26	.11205	.11276	8.8686	.99370	34
27	.11234	.11305	8.8455	.99367	33
28	.11263	.11335	8.8225	.99364	32
29	.11291	.11364	8.7996	.99360	31
30	.11320	.11394	8.7769	.99357	**30**
31	.11349	.11423	8.7542	.99354	29
32	.11378	.11452	8.7317	.99351	28
33	.11407	.11482	8.7093	.99347	27
34	.11436	.11511	8.6870	.99344	26
35	.11465	.11541	8.6648	.99341	**25**
36	.11494	.11570	8.6427	.99337	24
37	.11523	.11600	8.6208	.99334	23
38	.11552	.11629	8.5989	.99331	22
39	.11580	.11659	8.5772	.99327	21
40	.11609	.11688	8.5555	.99324	**20**
41	.11638	.11718	8.5340	.99320	19
42	.11667	.11747	8.5126	.99317	18
43	.11696	.11777	8.4913	.99314	17
44	.11725	.11806	8.4701	.99310	16
45	.11754	.11836	8.4490	.99307	**15**
46	.11783	.11865	8.4280	.99303	14
47	.11812	.11895	8.4071	.99300	13
48	.11840	.11924	8.3863	.99297	12
49	.11869	.11954	8.3656	.99293	11
50	.11898	.11983	8.3450	.99290	**10**
51	.11927	.12013	8.3245	.99286	9
52	.11956	.12042	8.3041	.99283	8
53	.11985	.12072	8.2838	.99279	7
54	.12014	.12101	8.2636	.99276	6
55	.12043	.12131	8.2434	.99272	**5**
56	.12071	.12160	8.2234	.99269	4
57	.12100	.12190	8.2035	.99265	3
58	.12129	.12219	8.1837	.99262	2
59	.12158	.12249	8.1640	.99258	1
60	.12187	.12278	8.1443	.99255	**0**
′	Cos	Cot	Tan	Sin	′

96° (276°) (263°) **83°**

7° (187°) (352°) **172°**

′	Sin	Tan	Cot	Cos	′
0	.12187	.12278	8.1443	.99255	**60**
1	.12216	.12308	8.1248	.99251	59
2	.12245	.12338	8.1054	.99248	58
3	.12274	.12367	8.0860	.99244	57
4	.12302	.12397	8.0667	.99240	56
5	.12331	.12426	8.0476	.99237	**55**
6	.12360	.12456	8.0285	.99233	54
7	.12389	.12485	8.0095	.99230	53
8	.12418	.12515	7.9906	.99226	52
9	.12447	.12544	7.9718	.99222	51
10	.12476	.12574	7.9530	.99219	**50**
11	.12504	.12603	7.9344	.99215	49
12	.12533	.12633	7.9158	.99211	48
13	.12562	.12662	7.8973	.99208	47
14	.12591	.12692	7.8789	.99204	46
15	.12620	.12722	7.8606	.99200	**45**
16	.12649	.12751	7.8424	.99197	44
17	.12678	.12781	7.8243	.99193	43
18	.12706	.12810	7.8062	.99189	42
19	.12735	.12840	7.7882	.99186	41
20	.12764	.12869	7.7704	.99182	**40**
21	.12793	.12899	7.7525	.99178	39
22	.12822	.12929	7.7348	.99175	38
23	.12851	.12958	7.7171	.99171	37
24	.12880	.12988	7.6996	.99167	36
25	.12908	.13017	7.6821	.99163	**35**
26	.12937	.13047	7.6647	.99160	34
27	.12966	.13076	7.6473	.99156	33
28	.12995	.13106	7.6301	.99152	32
29	.13024	.13136	7.6129	.99148	31
30	.13053	.13165	7.5958	.99144	**30**
31	.13081	.13195	7.5787	.99141	29
32	.13110	.13224	7.5618	.99137	28
33	.13139	.13254	7.5449	.99133	27
34	.13168	.13284	7.5281	.99129	26
35	.13197	.13313	7.5113	.99125	**25**
36	.13226	.13343	7.4947	.99122	24
37	.13254	.13372	7.4781	.99118	23
38	.13283	.13402	7.4615	.99114	22
39	.13312	.13432	7.4451	.99110	21
40	.13341	.13461	7.4287	.99106	**20**
41	.13370	.13491	7.4124	.99102	19
42	.13399	.13521	7.3962	.99098	18
43	.13427	.13550	7.3800	.99094	17
44	.13456	.13580	7.3639	.99091	16
45	.13485	.13609	7.3479	.99087	**15**
46	.13514	.13639	7.3319	.99083	14
47	.13543	.13669	7.3160	.99079	13
48	.13572	.13698	7.3002	.99075	12
49	.13600	.13728	7.2844	.99071	11
50	.13629	.13758	7.2687	.99067	**10**
51	.13658	.13787	7.2531	.99063	9
52	.13687	.13817	7.2375	.99059	8
53	.13716	.13846	7.2220	.99055	7
54	.13744	.13876	7.2066	.99051	6
55	.13773	.13906	7.1912	.99047	**5**
56	.13802	.13935	7.1759	.99043	4
57	.13831	.13965	7.1607	.99039	3
58	.13860	.13995	7.1455	.99035	2
59	.13889	.14024	7.1304	.99031	1
60	.13917	.14054	7.1154	.99027	**0**
′	Cos	Cot	Tan	Sin	′

97° (277°) (262°) **82°**

8° (188°) (351°) **171°**

′	Sin	Tan	Cot	Cos	′
0	.13917	.14054	7.1154	.99027	**60**
1	.13946	.14084	7.1004	.99023	59
2	.13975	.14113	7.0855	.99019	58
3	.14004	.14143	7.0706	.99015	57
4	.14033	.14173	7.0558	.99011	56
5	.14061	.14202	7.0410	.99006	**55**
6	.14090	.14232	7.0264	.99002	54
7	.14119	.14262	7.0117	.98998	53
8	.14148	.14291	6.9972	.98994	52
9	.14177	.14321	6.9827	.98990	51
10	.14205	.14351	6.9682	.98986	**50**
11	.14234	.14381	6.9538	.98982	49
12	.14263	.14410	6.9395	.98978	48
13	.14292	.14440	6.9252	.98973	47
14	.14320	.14470	6.9110	.98969	46
15	.14349	.14499	6.8969	.98965	**45**
16	.14378	.14529	6.8828	.98961	44
17	.14407	.14559	6.8687	.98957	43
18	.14436	.14588	6.8548	.98953	42
19	.14464	.14618	6.8408	.98948	41
20	.14493	.14648	6.8269	.98944	**40**
21	.14522	.14678	6.8131	.98940	39
22	.14551	.14707	6.7994	.98936	38
23	.14580	.14737	6.7856	.98931	37
24	.14608	.14767	6.7720	.98927	36
25	.14637	.14796	6.7584	.98923	**35**
26	.14666	.14826	6.7448	.98919	34
27	.14695	.14856	6.7313	.98914	33
28	.14723	.14886	6.7179	.98910	32
29	.14752	.14915	6.7045	.98906	31
30	.14781	.14945	6.6912	.98902	**30**
31	.14810	.14975	6.6779	.98897	29
32	.14838	.15005	6.6646	.98893	28
33	.14867	.15034	6.6514	.98889	27
34	.14896	.15064	6.6383	.98884	26
35	.14925	.15094	6.6252	.98880	**25**
36	.14954	.15124	6.6122	.98876	24
37	.14982	.15153	6.5992	.98871	23
38	.15011	.15183	6.5863	.98867	22
39	.15040	.15213	6.5734	.98863	21
40	.15069	.15243	6.5606	.98858	**20**
41	.15097	.15272	6.5478	.98854	19
42	.15126	.15302	6.5350	.98849	18
43	.15155	.15332	6.5223	.98845	17
44	.15184	.15362	6.5097	.98841	16
45	.15212	.15391	6.4971	.98836	**15**
46	.15241	.15421	6.4846	.98832	14
47	.15270	.15451	6.4721	.98827	13
48	.15299	.15481	6.4596	.98823	12
49	.15327	.15511	6.4472	.98818	11
50	.15356	.15540	6.4348	.98814	**10**
51	.15385	.15570	6.4225	.98809	9
52	.15414	.15600	6.4103	.98805	8
53	.15442	.15630	6.3980	.98800	7
54	.15471	.15660	6.3859	.98796	6
55	.15500	.15689	6.3737	.98791	**5**
56	.15529	.15719	6.3617	.98787	4
57	.15557	.15749	6.3496	.98782	3
58	.15586	.15779	6.3376	.98778	2
59	.15615	.15809	6.3257	.98773	1
60	.15643	.15838	6.3138	.98769	**0**
′	Cos	Cot	Tan	Sin	′

98° (278°) (261°) **81°**

9° (189°) (350°) **170°**

′	Sin	Tan	Cot	Cos	′
0	.15643	.15838	6.3138	.98769	**60**
1	.15672	.15868	6.3019	.98764	59
2	.15701	.15898	6.2901	.98760	58
3	.15730	.15928	6.2783	.98755	57
4	.15758	.15958	6.2666	.98751	56
5	.15787	.15988	6.2549	.98746	**55**
6	.15816	.16017	6.2432	.98741	54
7	.15845	.16047	6.2316	.98737	53
8	.15873	.16077	6.2200	.98732	52
9	.15902	.16107	6.2085	.98728	51
10	.15931	.16137	6.1970	.98723	**50**
11	.15959	.16167	6.1856	.98718	49
12	.15988	.16196	6.1742	.98714	48
13	.16017	.16226	6.1628	.98709	47
14	.16046	.16256	6.1515	.98704	46
15	.16074	.16286	6.1402	.98700	**45**
16	.16103	.16316	6.1290	.98695	44
17	.16132	.16346	6.1178	.98690	43
18	.16160	.16376	6.1066	.98686	42
19	.16189	.16405	6.0955	.98681	41
20	.16218	.16435	6.0844	.98676	**40**
21	.16246	.16465	6.0734	.98671	39
22	.16275	.16495	6.0624	.98667	38
23	.16304	.16525	6.0514	.98662	37
24	.16333	.16555	6.0405	.98657	36
25	.16361	.16585	6.0296	.98652	**35**
26	.16390	.16615	6.0188	.98648	34
27	.16419	.16645	6.0080	.98643	33
28	.16447	.16674	5.9972	.98638	32
29	.16476	.16704	5.9865	.98633	31
30	.16505	.16734	5.9758	.98629	**30**
31	.16533	.16764	5.9651	.98624	29
32	.16562	.16794	5.9545	.98619	28
33	.16591	.16824	5.9439	.98614	27
34	.16620	.16854	5.9333	.98609	26
35	.16648	.16884	5.9228	.98604	**25**
36	.16677	.16914	5.9124	.98600	24
37	.16706	.16944	5.9019	.98595	23
38	.16734	.16974	5.8915	.98590	22
39	.16763	.17004	5.8811	.98585	21
40	.16792	.17033	5.8708	.98580	**20**
41	.16820	.17063	5.8605	.98575	19
42	.16849	.17093	5.8502	.98570	18
43	.16878	.17123	5.8400	.98565	17
44	.16906	.17153	5.8298	.98561	16
45	.16935	.17183	5.8197	.98556	**15**
46	.16964	.17213	5.8095	.98551	14
47	.16992	.17243	5.7994	.98546	13
48	.17021	.17273	5.7894	.98541	12
49	.17050	.17303	5.7794	.98536	11
50	.17078	.17333	5.7694	.98531	**10**
51	.17107	.17363	5.7594	.98526	9
52	.17136	.17393	5.7495	.98521	8
53	.17164	.17423	5.7396	.98516	7
54	.17193	.17453	5.7297	.98511	6
55	.17222	.17483	5.7199	.98506	**5**
56	.17250	.17513	5.7101	.98501	4
57	.17279	.17543	5.7004	.98496	3
58	.17308	.17573	5.6906	.98491	2
59	.17336	.17603	5.6809	.98486	1
60	.17365	.17633	5.6713	.98481	**0**
′	Cos	Cot	Tan	Sin	′

99° (279°) (260°) **80°**

10° (190°) (349°) **169°**

′	Sin	Tan	Cot	Cos	′
0	.17365	.17633	5.6713	.98481	60
1	.17393	.17663	5.6617	.98476	59
2	.17422	.17693	5.6521	.98471	58
3	.17451	.17723	5.6425	.98466	57
4	.17479	.17753	5.6329	.98461	56
5	.17508	.17783	5.6234	.98455	55
6	.17537	.17813	5.6140	.98450	54
7	.17565	.17843	5.6045	.98445	53
8	.17594	.17873	5.5951	.98440	52
9	.17623	.17903	5.5857	.98435	51
10	.17651	.17933	5.5764	.98430	50
11	.17680	.17963	5.5671	.98425	49
12	.17708	.17993	5.5578	.98420	48
13	.17737	.18023	5.5485	.98414	47
14	.17766	.18053	5.5393	.98409	46
15	.17794	.18083	5.5301	.98404	45
16	.17823	.18113	5.5209	.98399	44
17	.17852	.18143	5.5118	.98394	43
18	.17880	.18173	5.5026	.98389	42
19	.17909	.18203	5.4936	.98383	41
20	.17937	.18233	5.4845	.98378	40
21	.17966	.18263	5.4755	.98373	39
22	.17995	.18293	5.4665	.98368	38
23	.18023	.18323	5.4575	.98362	37
24	.18052	.18353	5.4486	.98357	36
25	.18081	.18384	5.4397	.98352	35
26	.18109	.18414	5.4308	.98347	34
27	.18138	.18444	5.4219	.98341	33
28	.18166	.18474	5.4131	.98336	32
29	.18195	.18504	5.4043	.98331	31
30	.18224	.18534	5.3955	.98325	30
31	.18252	.18564	5.3868	.98320	29
32	.18281	.18594	5.3781	.98315	28
33	.18309	.18624	5.3694	.98310	27
34	.18338	.18654	5.3607	.98304	26
35	.18367	.18684	5.3521	.98299	25
36	.18395	.18714	5.3435	.98294	24
37	.18424	.18745	5.3349	.98288	23
38	.18452	.18775	5.3263	.98283	22
39	.18481	.18805	5.3178	.98277	21
40	.18509	.18835	5.3093	.98272	20
41	.18538	.18865	5.3008	.98267	19
42	.18567	.18895	5.2924	.98261	18
43	.18595	.18925	5.2839	.98256	17
44	.18624	.18955	5.2755	.98250	16
45	.18652	.18986	5.2672	.98245	15
46	.18681	.19016	5.2588	.98240	14
47	.18710	.19046	5.2505	.98234	13
48	.18738	.19076	5.2422	.98229	12
49	.18767	.19106	5.2339	.98223	11
50	.18795	.19136	5.2257	.98218	10
51	.18824	.19166	5.2174	.98212	9
52	.18852	.19197	5.2092	.98207	8
53	.18881	.19227	5.2011	.98201	7
54	.18910	.19257	5.1929	.98196	6
55	.18938	.19287	5.1848	.98190	5
56	.18967	.19317	5.1767	.98185	4
57	.18995	.19347	5.1686	.98179	3
58	.19024	.19378	5.1606	.98174	2
59	.19052	.19408	5.1526	.98168	1
60	.19081	.19438	5.1446	.98163	0
′	Cos	Cot	Tan	Sin	′

100° (280°) (259°) **79°**

11° (191°) (348°) **168°**

′	Sin	Tan	Cot	Cos	′
0	.19081	.19438	5.1446	.98163	60
1	.19109	.19468	5.1366	.98157	59
2	.19138	.19498	5.1286	.98152	58
3	.19167	.19529	5.1207	.98146	57
4	.19195	.19559	5.1128	.98140	56
5	.19224	.19589	5.1049	.98135	55
6	.19252	.19619	5.0970	.98129	54
7	.19281	.19649	5.0892	.98124	53
8	.19309	.19680	5.0814	.98118	52
9	.19338	.19710	5.0736	.98112	51
10	.19366	.19740	5.0658	.98107	50
11	.19395	.19770	5.0581	.98101	49
12	.19423	.19801	5.0504	.98096	48
13	.19452	.19831	5.0427	.98090	47
14	.19481	.19861	5.0350	.98084	46
15	.19509	.19891	5.0273	.98079	45
16	.19538	.19921	5.0197	.98073	44
17	.19566	.19952	5.0121	.98067	43
18	.19595	.19982	5.0045	.98061	42
19	.19623	.20012	4.9969	.98056	41
20	.19652	.20042	4.9894	.98050	40
21	.19680	.20073	4.9819	.98044	39
22	.19709	.20103	4.9744	.98039	38
23	.19737	.20133	4.9669	.98033	37
24	.19766	.20164	4.9594	.98027	36
25	.19794	.20194	4.9520	.98021	35
26	.19823	.20224	4.9446	.98016	34
27	.19851	.20254	4.9372	.98010	33
28	.19880	.20285	4.9298	.98004	32
29	.19908	.20315	4.9225	.97998	31
30	.19937	.20345	4.9152	.97992	30
31	.19965	.20376	4.9078	.97987	29
32	.19994	.20406	4.9006	.97981	28
33	.20022	.20436	4.8933	.97975	27
34	.20051	.20466	4.8860	.97969	26
35	.20079	.20497	4.8788	.97963	25
36	.20108	.20527	4.8716	.97958	24
37	.20136	.20557	4.8644	.97952	23
38	.20165	.20588	4.8573	.97946	22
39	.20193	.20618	4.8501	.97940	21
40	.20222	.20648	4.8430	.97934	20
41	.20250	.20679	4.8359	.97928	19
42	.20279	.20709	4.8288	.97922	18
43	.20307	.20739	4.8218	.97916	17
44	.20336	.20770	4.8147	.97910	16
45	.20364	.20800	4.8077	.97905	15
46	.20393	.20830	4.8007	.97899	14
47	.20421	.20861	4.7937	.97893	13
48	.20450	.20891	4.7867	.97887	12
49	.20478	.20921	4.7798	.97881	11
50	.20507	.20952	4.7729	.97875	10
51	.20535	.20982	4.7659	.97869	9
52	.20563	.21013	4.7591	.97863	8
53	.20592	.21043	4.7522	.97857	7
54	.20620	.21073	4.7453	.97851	6
55	.20649	.21104	4.7385	.97845	5
56	.20677	.21134	4.7317	.97839	4
57	.20706	.21164	4.7249	.97833	3
58	.20734	.21195	4.7181	.97827	2
59	.20763	.21225	4.7114	.97821	1
60	.20791	.21256	4.7046	.97815	0
′	Cos	Cot	Tan	Sin	′

101° (281°) (258°) **78°**

12° (192°) (347°) **167°**

′	Sin	Tan	Cot	Cos	′
0	.20791	.21256	4.7046	.97815	**60**
1	.20820	.21286	4.6979	.97809	59
2	.20848	.21316	4.6912	.97803	58
3	.20877	.21347	4.6845	.97797	57
4	.20905	.21377	4.6779	.97791	56
5	.20933	.21408	4.6712	.97784	**55**
6	.20962	.21438	4.6646	.97778	54
7	.20990	.21469	4.6580	.97772	53
8	.21019	.21499	4.6514	.97766	52
9	.21047	.21529	4.6448	.97760	51
10	.21076	.21560	4.6382	.97754	**50**
11	.21104	.21590	4.6317	.97748	49
12	.21132	.21621	4.6252	.97742	48
13	.21161	.21651	4.6187	.97735	47
14	.21189	.21682	4.6122	.97729	46
15	.21218	.21712	4.6057	.97723	**45**
16	.21246	.21743	4.5993	.97717	44
17	.21275	.21773	4.5928	.97711	43
18	.21303	.21804	4.5864	.97705	42
19	.21331	.21834	4.5800	.97698	41
20	.21360	.21864	4.5736	.97692	**40**
21	.21388	.21895	4.5673	.97686	39
22	.21417	.21925	4.5609	.97680	38
23	.21445	.21956	4.5546	.97673	37
24	.21474	.21986	4.5483	.97667	36
25	.21502	.22017	4.5420	.97661	**35**
26	.21530	.22047	4.5357	.97655	34
27	.21559	.22078	4.5294	.97648	33
28	.21587	.22108	4.5232	.97642	32
29	.21616	.22139	4.5169	.97636	31
30	.21644	.22169	4.5107	.97630	**30**
31	.21672	.22200	4.5045	.97623	29
32	.21701	.22231	4.4983	.97617	28
33	.21729	.22261	4.4922	.97611	27
34	.21758	.22292	4.4860	.97604	26
35	.21786	.22322	4.4799	.97598	**25**
36	.21814	.22353	4.4737	.97592	24
37	.21843	.22383	4.4676	.97585	23
38	.21871	.22414	4.4615	.97579	22
39	.21899	.22444	4.4555	.97573	21
40	.21928	.22475	4.4494	.97566	**20**
41	.21956	.22505	4.4434	.97560	19
42	.21985	.22536	4.4373	.97553	18
43	.22013	.22567	4.4313	.97547	17
44	.22041	.22597	4.4253	.97541	16
45	.22070	.22628	4.4194	.97534	**15**
46	.22098	.22658	4.4134	.97528	14
47	.22126	.22689	4.4075	.97521	13
48	.22155	.22719	4.4015	.97515	12
49	.22183	.22750	4.3956	.97508	11
50	.22212	.22781	4.3897	.97502	**10**
51	.22240	.22811	4.3838	.97496	9
52	.22268	.22842	4.3779	.97489	8
53	.22297	.22872	4.3721	.97483	7
54	.22325	.22903	4.3662	.97476	6
55	.22353	.22934	4.3604	.97470	**5**
56	.22382	.22964	4.3546	.97463	4
57	.22410	.22995	4.3488	.97457	3
58	.22438	.23026	4.3430	.97450	2
59	.22467	.23056	4.3372	.97444	1
60	.22495	.23087	4.3315	.97437	**0**
′	Cos	Cot	Tan	Sin	′

102° (282°) (257°)**77°**

13° (193°) (346°) **166°**

′	Sin	Tan	Cot	Cos	′
0	.22495	.23087	4.3315	.97437	**60**
1	.22523	.23117	4.3257	.97430	59
2	.22552	.23148	4.3200	.97424	58
3	.22580	.23179	4.3143	.97417	57
4	.22608	.23209	4.3086	.97411	56
5	.22637	.23240	4.3029	.97404	**55**
6	.22665	.23271	4.2972	.97398	54
7	.22693	.23301	4.2916	.97391	53
8	.22722	.23332	4.2859	.97384	52
9	.22750	.23363	4.2803	.97378	51
10	.22778	.23393	4.2747	.97371	**50**
11	.22807	.23424	4.2691	.97365	49
12	.22835	.23455	4.2635	.97358	48
13	.22863	.23485	4.2580	.97351	47
14	.22892	.23516	4.2524	.97345	46
15	.22920	.23547	4.2468	.97338	**45**
16	.22948	.23578	4.2413	.97331	44
17	.22977	.23608	4.2358	.97325	43
18	.23005	.23639	4.2303	.97318	42
19	.23033	.23670	4.2248	.97311	41
20	.23062	.23700	4.2193	.97304	**40**
21	.23090	.23731	4.2139	.97298	39
22	.23118	.23762	4.2084	.97291	38
23	.23146	.23793	4.2030	.97284	37
24	.23175	.23823	4.1976	.97278	36
25	.23203	.23854	4.1922	.97271	**35**
26	.23231	.23885	4.1868	.97264	34
27	.23260	.23916	4.1814	.97257	33
28	.23288	.23946	4.1760	.97251	32
29	.23316	.23977	4.1706	.97244	31
30	.23345	.24008	4.1653	.97237	**30**
31	.23373	.24039	4.1600	.97230	29
32	.23401	.24069	4.1547	.97223	28
33	.23429	.24100	4.1493	.97217	27
34	.23458	.24131	4.1441	.97210	26
35	.23486	.24162	4.1388	.97203	**25**
36	.23514	.24193	4.1335	.97196	24
37	.23542	.24223	4.1282	.97189	23
38	.23571	.24254	4.1230	.97182	22
39	.23599	.24285	4.1178	.97176	21
40	.23627	.24316	4.1126	.97169	**20**
41	.23656	.24347	4.1074	.97162	19
42	.23684	.24377	4.1022	.97155	18
43	.23712	.24408	4.0970	.97148	17
44	.23740	.24439	4.0918	.97141	16
45	.23769	.24470	4.0867	.97134	**15**
46	.23797	.24501	4.0815	.97127	14
47	.23825	.24532	4.0764	.97120	13
48	.23853	.24562	4.0713	.97113	12
49	.23882	.24593	4.0662	.97106	11
50	.23910	.24624	4.0611	.97100	**10**
51	.23938	.24655	4.0560	.97093	9
52	.23966	.24686	4.0509	.97086	8
53	.23995	.24717	4.0459	.97079	7
54	.24023	.24747	4.0408	.97072	6
55	.24051	.24778	4.0358	.97065	**5**
56	.24079	.24809	4.0308	.97058	4
57	.24108	.24840	4.0257	.97051	3
58	.24136	.24871	4.0207	.97044	2
59	.24164	.24902	4.0158	.97037	1
60	.24192	.24933	4.0108	.97030	**0**
′	Cos	Cot	Tan	Sin	′

103° (283°) (256°) **76°**

14° (194°) (345°) **165°**

′	Sin	Tan	Cot	Cos	′
0	.24192	.24933	4.0108	.97030	**60**
1	.24220	.24964	4.0058	.97023	59
2	.24249	.24995	4.0009	.97015	58
3	.24277	.25026	3.9959	.97008	57
4	.24305	.25056	3.9910	.97001	56
5	.24333	.25087	3.9861	.96994	**55**
6	.24362	.25118	3.9812	.96987	54
7	.24390	.25149	3.9763	.96980	53
8	.24418	.25180	3.9714	.96973	52
9	.24446	.25211	3.9665	.96966	51
10	.24474	.25242	3.9617	.96959	**50**
11	.24503	.25273	3.9568	.96952	49
12	.24531	.25304	3.9520	.96945	48
13	.24559	.25335	3.9471	.96937	47
14	.24587	.25366	3.9423	.96930	46
15	.24615	.25397	3.9375	.96923	**45**
16	.24644	.25428	3.9327	.96916	44
17	.24672	.25459	3.9279	.96909	43
18	.24700	.25490	3.9232	.96902	42
19	.24728	.25521	3.9184	.96894	41
20	.24756	.25552	3.9136	.96887	**40**
21	.24784	.25583	3.9089	.96880	39
22	.24813	.25614	3.9042	.96873	38
23	.24841	.25645	3.8995	.96866	37
24	.24869	.25676	3.8947	.96858	36
25	.24897	.25707	3.8900	.96851	**35**
26	.24925	.25738	3.8854	.96844	34
27	.24954	.25769	3.8807	.96837	33
28	.24982	.25800	3.8760	.96829	32
29	.25010	.25831	3.8714	.96822	31
30	.25038	.25862	3.8667	.96815	**30**
31	.25066	.25893	3.8621	.96807	29
32	.25094	.25924	3.8575	.96800	28
33	.25122	.25955	3.8528	.96793	27
34	.25151	.25986	3.8482	.96786	26
35	.25179	.26017	3.8436	.96778	**25**
36	.25207	.26048	3.8391	.96771	24
37	.25235	.26079	3.8345	.96764	23
38	.25263	.26110	3.8299	.96756	22
39	.25291	.26141	3.8254	.96749	21
40	.25320	.26172	3.8208	.96742	**20**
41	.25348	.26203	3.8163	.96734	19
42	.25376	.26235	3.8118	.96727	18
43	.25404	.26266	3.8073	.96719	17
44	.25432	.26297	3.8028	.96712	16
45	.25460	.26328	3.7983	.96705	**15**
46	.25488	.26359	3.7938	.96697	14
47	.25516	.26390	3.7893	.96690	13
48	.25545	.26421	3.7848	.96682	12
49	.25573	.26452	3.7804	.96675	11
50	.25601	.26483	3.7760	.96667	**10**
51	.25629	.26515	3.7715	.96660	9
52	.25657	.26546	3.7671	.96653	8
53	.25685	.26577	3.7627	.96645	7
54	.25713	.26608	3.7583	.96638	6
55	.25741	.26639	3.7539	.96630	**5**
56	.25769	.26670	3.7495	.96623	4
57	.25798	.26701	3.7451	.96615	3
58	.25826	.26733	3.7408	.96608	2
59	.25854	.26764	3.7364	.96600	1
60	.25882	.26795	3.7321	.96593	**0**
′	Cos	Cot	Tan	Sin	′

104° (284°) (255°) **75°**

15° (195°) (344°) **164°**

′	Sin	Tan	Cot	Cos	′
0	.25882	.26795	3.7321	.96593	**60**
1	.25910	.26826	3.7277	.96585	59
2	.25938	.26857	3.7234	.96578	58
3	.25966	.26888	3.7191	.96570	57
4	.25994	.26920	3.7148	.96562	56
5	.26022	.26951	3.7105	.96555	**55**
6	.26050	.26982	3.7062	.96547	54
7	.26079	.27013	3.7019	.96540	53
8	.26107	.27044	3.6976	.96532	52
9	.26135	.27076	3.6933	.96524	51
10	.26163	.27107	3.6891	.96517	**50**
11	.26191	.27138	3.6848	.96509	49
12	.26219	.27169	3.6806	.96502	48
13	.26247	.27201	3.6764	.96494	47
14	.26275	.27232	3.6722	.96486	46
15	.26303	.27263	3.6680	.96479	**45**
16	.26331	.27294	3.6638	.96471	44
17	.26359	.27326	3.6596	.96463	43
18	.26387	.27357	3.6554	.96456	42
19	.26415	.27388	3.6512	.96448	41
20	.26443	.27419	3.6470	.96440	**40**
21	.26471	.27451	3.6429	.96433	39
22	.26500	.27482	3.6387	.96425	38
23	.26528	.27513	3.6346	.96417	37
24	.26556	.27545	3.6305	.96410	36
25	.26584	.27576	3.6264	.96402	**35**
26	.26612	.27607	3.6222	.96394	34
27	.26640	.27638	3.6181	.96386	33
28	.26668	.27670	3.6140	.96379	32
29	.26696	.27701	3.6100	.96371	31
30	.26724	.27732	3.6059	.96363	**30**
31	.26752	.27764	3.6018	.96355	29
32	.26780	.27795	3.5978	.96347	28
33	.26808	.27826	3.5937	.96340	27
34	.26836	.27858	3.5897	.96332	26
35	.26864	.27889	3.5856	.96324	**25**
36	.26892	.27921	3.5816	.96316	24
37	.26920	.27952	3.5776	.96308	23
38	.26948	.27983	3.5736	.96301	22
39	.26976	.28015	3.5696	.96293	21
40	.27004	.28046	3.5656	.96285	**20**
41	.27032	.28077	3.5616	.96277	19
42	.27060	.28109	3.5576	.96269	18
43	.27088	.28140	3.5536	.96261	17
44	.27116	.28172	3.5497	.96253	16
45	.27144	.28203	3.5457	.96246	**15**
46	.27172	.28234	3.5418	.96238	14
47	.27200	.28266	3.5379	.96230	13
48	.27228	.28297	3.5339	.96222	12
49	.27256	.28329	3.5300	.96214	11
50	.27284	.28360	3.5261	.96206	**10**
51	.27312	.28391	3.5222	.96198	9
52	.27340	.28423	3.5183	.96190	8
53	.27368	.28454	3.5144	.96182	7
54	.27396	.28486	3.5105	.96174	6
55	.27424	.28517	3.5067	.96166	**5**
56	.27452	.28549	3.5028	.96158	4
57	.27480	.28580	3.4989	.96150	3
58	.27508	.28612	3.4951	.96142	2
59	.27536	.28643	3.4912	.96134	1
60	.27564	.28675	3.4874	.96126	**0**
′	Cos	Cot	Tan	Sin	′

105° (285°) (254°) **74°**

16° (196°) (343°) **163°**

′	Sin	Tan	Cot	Cos	′
0	.27564	.28675	3.4874	.96126	**60**
1	.27592	.28706	3.4836	.96118	59
2	.27620	.28738	3.4798	.96110	58
3	.27648	.28769	3.4760	.96102	57
4	.27676	.28801	3.4722	.96094	56
5	.27704	.28832	3.4684	.96086	**55**
6	.27731	.28864	3.4646	.96078	54
7	.27759	.28895	3.4608	.96070	53
8	.27787	.28927	3.4570	.96062	52
9	.27815	.28958	3.4533	.96054	51
10	.27843	.28990	3.4495	.96046	**50**
11	.27871	.29021	3.4458	.96037	49
12	.27899	.29053	3.4420	.96029	48
13	.27927	.29084	3.4383	.96021	47
14	.27955	.29116	3.4346	.96013	46
15	.27983	.29147	3.4308	.96005	**45**
16	.28011	.29179	3.4271	.95997	44
17	.28039	.29210	3.4234	.95989	43
18	.28067	.29242	3.4197	.95981	42
19	.28095	.29274	3.4160	.95972	41
20	.28123	.29305	3.4124	.95964	**40**
21	.28150	.29337	3.4087	.95956	39
22	.28178	.29368	3.4050	.95948	38
23	.28206	.29400	3.4014	.95940	37
24	.28234	.29432	3.3977	.95931	36
25	.28262	.29463	3.3941	.95923	**35**
26	.28290	.29495	3.3904	.95915	34
27	.28318	.29526	3.3868	.95907	33
28	.28346	.29558	3.3832	.95898	32
29	.28374	.29590	3.3796	.95890	31
30	.28402	.29621	3.3759	.95882	**30**
31	.28429	.29653	3.3723	.95874	29
32	.28457	.29685	3.3687	.95865	28
33	.28485	.29716	3.3652	.95857	27
34	.28513	.29748	3.3616	.95849	26
35	.28541	.29780	3.3580	.95841	**25**
36	.28569	.29811	3.3544	.95832	24
37	.28597	.29843	3.3509	.95824	23
38	.28625	.29875	3.3473	.95816	22
39	.28652	.29906	3.3438	.95807	21
40	.28680	.29938	3.3402	.95799	**20**
41	.28708	.29970	3.3367	.95791	19
42	.28736	.30001	3.3332	.95782	18
43	.28764	.30033	3.3297	.95774	17
44	.28792	.30065	3.3261	.95766	16
45	.28820	.30097	3.3226	.95757	**15**
46	.28847	.30128	3.3191	.95749	14
47	.28875	.30160	3.3156	.95740	13
48	.28903	.30192	3.3122	.95732	12
49	.28931	.30224	3.3087	.95724	11
50	.28959	.30255	3.3052	.95715	**10**
51	.28987	.30287	3.3017	.95707	9
52	.29015	.30319	3.2983	.95698	8
53	.29042	.30351	3.2948	.95690	7
54	.29070	.30382	3.2914	.95681	6
55	.29098	.30414	3.2879	.95673	**5**
56	.29126	.30446	3.2845	.95664	4
57	.29154	.30478	3.2811	.95656	3
58	.29182	.30509	3.2777	.95647	2
59	.29209	.30541	3.2743	.95639	1
60	.29237	.30573	3.2709	.95630	**0**
′	Cos	Cot	Tan	Sin	′

106° (286°) (253°) **73°**

17° (197°) (342°) **162°**

′	Sin	Tan	Cot	Cos	′
0	.29237	.30573	3.2709	.95630	**60**
1	.29265	.30605	3.2675	.95622	59
2	.29293	.30637	3.2641	.95613	58
3	.29321	.30669	3.2607	.95605	57
4	.29348	.30700	3.2573	.95596	56
5	.29376	.30732	3.2539	.95588	**55**
6	.29404	.30764	3.2506	.95579	54
7	.29432	.30796	3.2472	.95571	53
8	.29460	.30828	3.2438	.95562	52
9	.29487	.30860	3.2405	.95554	51
10	.29515	.30891	3.2371	.95545	**50**
11	.29543	.30923	3.2338	.95536	49
12	.29571	.30955	3.2305	.95528	48
13	.29599	.30987	3.2272	.95519	47
14	.29626	.31019	3.2238	.95511	46
15	.29654	.31051	3.2205	.95502	**45**
16	.29682	.31083	3.2172	.95493	44
17	.29710	.31115	3.2139	.95485	43
18	.29737	.31147	3.2106	.95476	42
19	.29765	.31178	3.2073	.95467	41
20	.29793	.31210	3.2041	.95459	**40**
21	.29821	.31242	3.2008	.95450	39
22	.29849	.31274	3.1975	.95441	38
23	.29876	.31306	3.1943	.95433	37
24	.29904	.31338	3.1910	.95424	36
25	.29932	.31370	3.1878	.95415	**35**
26	.29960	.31402	3.1845	.95407	34
27	.29987	.31434	3.1813	.95398	33
28	.30015	.31466	3.1780	.95389	32
29	.30043	.31498	3.1748	.95380	31
30	.30071	.31530	3.1716	.95372	**30**
31	.30098	.31562	3.1684	.95363	29
32	.30126	.31594	3.1652	.95354	28
33	.30154	.31626	3.1620	.95345	27
34	.30182	.31658	3.1588	.95337	26
35	.30209	.31690	3.1556	.95328	**25**
36	.30237	.31722	3.1524	.95319	24
37	.30265	.31754	3.1492	.95310	23
38	.30292	.31786	3.1460	.95301	22
39	.30320	.31818	3.1429	.95293	21
40	.30348	.31850	3.1397	.95284	**20**
41	.30376	.31882	3.1366	.95275	19
42	.30403	.31914	3.1334	.95266	18
43	.30431	.31946	3.1303	.95257	17
44	.30459	.31978	3.1271	.95248	16
45	.30486	.32010	3.1240	.95240	**15**
46	.30514	.32042	3.1209	.95231	14
47	.30542	.32074	3.1178	.95222	13
48	.30570	.32106	3.1146	.95213	12
49	.30597	.32139	3.1115	.95204	11
50	.30625	.32171	3.1084	.95195	**10**
51	.30653	.32203	3.1053	.95186	9
52	.30680	.32235	3.1022	.95177	8
53	.30708	.32267	3.0991	.95168	7
54	.30736	.32299	3.0961	.95159	6
55	.30763	.32331	3.0930	.95150	**5**
56	.30791	.32363	3.0899	.95142	4
57	.30819	.32396	3.0868	.95133	3
58	.30846	.32428	3.0838	.95124	2
59	.30874	.32460	3.0807	.95115	1
60	.30902	.32492	3.0777	.95106	**0**
′	Cos	Cot	Tan	Sin	′

107° (287°) (252°) **72°**

18° (198°) (341°) **161°**

′	Sin	Tan	Cot	Cos	′
0	.30902	.32492	3.0777	.95106	**60**
1	.30929	.32524	3.0746	.95097	59
2	.30957	.32556	3.0716	.95088	58
3	.30985	.32588	3.0686	.95079	57
4	.31012	.32621	3.0655	.95070	56
5	.31040	.32653	3.0625	.95061	**55**
6	.31068	.32685	3.0595	.95052	54
7	.31095	.32717	3.0565	.95043	53
8	.31123	.32749	3.0535	.95033	52
9	.31151	.32782	3.0505	.95024	51
10	.31178	.32814	3.0475	.95015	**50**
11	.31206	.32846	3.0445	.95006	49
12	.31233	.32878	3.0415	.94997	48
13	.31261	.32911	3.0385	.94988	47
14	.31289	.32943	3.0356	.94979	46
15	.31316	.32975	3.0326	.94970	**45**
16	.31344	.33007	3.0296	.94961	44
17	.31372	.33040	3.0267	.94952	43
18	.31399	.33072	3.0237	.94943	42
19	.31427	.33104	3.0208	.94933	41
20	.31454	.33136	3.0178	.94924	**40**
21	.31482	.33169	3.0149	.94915	39
22	.31510	.33201	3.0120	.94906	38
23	.31537	.33233	3.0090	.94897	37
24	.31565	.33266	3.0061	.94888	36
25	.31593	.33298	3.0032	.94878	**35**
26	.31620	.33330	3.0003	.94869	34
27	.31648	.33363	2.9974	.94860	33
28	.31675	.33395	2.9945	.94851	32
29	.31703	.33427	2.9916	.94842	31
30	.31730	.33460	2.9887	.94832	**30**
31	.31758	.33492	2.9858	.94823	29
32	.31786	.33524	2.9829	.94814	28
33	.31813	.33557	2.9800	.94805	27
34	.31841	.33589	2.9772	.94795	26
35	.31868	.33621	2.9743	.94786	**25**
36	.31896	.33654	2.9714	.94777	24
37	.31923	.33686	2.9686	.94768	23
38	.31951	.33718	2.9657	.94758	22
39	.31979	.33751	2.9629	.94749	21
40	.32006	.33783	2.9600	.94740	**20**
41	.32034	.33816	2.9572	.94730	19
42	.32061	.33848	2.9544	.94721	18
43	.32089	.33881	2.9515	.94712	17
44	.32116	.33913	2.9487	.94702	16
45	.32144	.33945	2.9459	.94693	**15**
46	.32171	.33978	2.9431	.94684	14
47	.32199	.34010	2.9403	.94674	13
48	.32227	.34043	2.9375	.94665	12
49	.32254	.34075	2.9347	.94656	11
50	.32282	.34108	2.9319	.94646	**10**
51	.32309	.34140	2.9291	.94637	9
52	.32337	.34173	2.9263	.94627	8
53	.32364	.34205	2.9235	.94618	7
54	.32392	.34238	2.9208	.94609	6
55	.32419	.34270	2.9180	.94599	**5**
56	.32447	.34303	2.9152	.94590	4
57	.32474	.34335	2.9125	.94580	3
58	.32502	.34368	2.9097	.94571	2
59	.32529	.34400	2.9070	.94561	1
60	.32557	.34433	2.9042	.94552	**0**
′	Cos	Cot	Tan	Sin	′

108° (288°) (251°) **71°**

19° (199°) (340°) **160°**

′	Sin	Tan	Cot	Cos	′
0	.32557	.34433	2.9042	.94552	**60**
1	.32584	.34465	2.9015	.94542	59
2	.32612	.34498	2.8987	.94533	58
3	.32639	.34530	2.8960	.94523	57
4	.32667	.34563	2.8933	.94514	56
5	.32694	.34596	2.8905	.94504	**55**
6	.32722	.34628	2.8878	.94495	54
7	.32749	.34661	2.8851	.94485	53
8	.32777	.34693	2.8824	.94476	52
9	.32804	.34726	2.8797	.94466	51
10	.32832	.34758	2.8770	.94457	**50**
11	.32859	.34791	2.8743	.94447	49
12	.32887	.34824	2.8716	.94438	48
13	.32914	.34856	2.8689	.94428	47
14	.32942	.34889	2.8662	.94418	46
15	.32969	.34922	2.8636	.94409	**45**
16	.32997	.34954	2.8609	.94399	44
17	.33024	.34987	2.8582	.94390	43
18	.33051	.35020	2.8556	.94380	42
19	.33079	.35052	2.8529	.94370	41
20	.33106	.35085	2.8502	.94361	**40**
21	.33134	.35118	2.8476	.94351	39
22	.33161	.35150	2.8449	.94342	38
23	.33189	.35183	2.8423	.94332	37
24	.33216	.35216	2.8397	.94322	36
25	.33244	.35248	2.8370	.94313	**35**
26	.33271	.35281	2.8344	.94303	34
27	.33298	.35314	2.8318	.94293	33
28	.33326	.35346	2.8291	.94284	32
29	.33353	.35379	2.8265	.94274	31
30	.33381	.35412	2.8239	.94264	**30**
31	.33408	.35445	2.8213	.94254	29
32	.33436	.35477	2.8187	.94245	28
33	.33463	.35510	2.8161	.94235	27
34	.33490	.35543	2.8135	.94225	26
35	.33518	.35576	2.8109	.94215	**25**
36	.33545	.35608	2.8083	.94206	24
37	.33573	.35641	2.8057	.94196	23
38	.33600	.35674	2.8032	.94186	22
39	.33627	.35707	2.8006	.94176	21
40	.33655	.35740	2.7980	.94167	**20**
41	.33682	.35772	2.7955	.94157	19
42	.33710	.35805	2.7929	.94147	18
43	.33737	.35838	2.7903	.94137	17
44	.33764	.35871	2.7878	.94127	16
45	.33792	.35904	2.7852	.94118	**15**
46	.33819	.35937	2.7827	.94108	14
47	.33846	.35969	2.7801	.94098	13
48	.33874	.36002	2.7776	.94088	12
49	.33901	.36035	2.7751	.94078	11
50	.33929	.36068	2.7725	.94068	**10**
51	.33956	.36101	2.7700	.94058	9
52	.33983	.36134	2.7675	.94049	8
53	.34011	.36167	2.7650	.94039	7
54	.34038	.36199	2.7625	.94029	6
55	.34065	.36232	2.7600	.94019	**5**
56	.34093	.36265	2.7575	.94009	4
57	.34120	.36298	2.7550	.93999	3
58	.34147	.36331	2.7525	.93989	2
59	.34175	.36364	2.7500	.93979	1
60	.34202	.36397	2.7475	.93969	**0**
′	Cos	Cot	Tan	Sin	′

109° (289°) (250°) **70°**

20° (200°) (339°) **159°**

′	Sin	Tan	Cot	Cos	′
0	.34202	.36397	2.7475	.93969	**60**
1	.34229	.36430	2.7450	.93959	59
2	.34257	.36463	2.7425	.93949	58
3	.34284	.36496	2.7400	.93939	57
4	.34311	.36529	2.7376	.93929	56
5	.34339	.36562	2.7351	.93919	**55**
6	.34366	.36595	2.7326	.93909	54
7	.34393	.36628	2.7302	.93899	53
8	.34421	.36661	2.7277	.93889	52
9	.34448	.36694	2.7253	.93879	51
10	.34475	.36727	2.7228	.93869	**50**
11	.34503	.36760	2.7204	.93859	49
12	.34530	.36793	2.7179	.93849	48
13	.34557	.36826	2.7155	.93839	47
14	.34584	.36859	2.7130	.93829	46
15	.34612	.36892	2.7106	.93819	**45**
16	.34639	.36925	2.7082	.93809	44
17	.34666	.36958	2.7058	.93799	43
18	.34694	.36991	2.7034	.93789	42
19	.34721	.37024	2.7009	.93779	41
20	.34748	.37057	2.6985	.93769	**40**
21	.34775	.37090	2.6961	.93759	39
22	.34803	.37123	2.6937	.93748	38
23	.34830	.37157	2.6913	.93738	37
24	.34857	.37190	2.6889	.93728	36
25	.34884	.37223	2.6865	.93718	**35**
26	.34912	.37256	2.6841	.93708	34
27	.34939	.37289	2.6818	.93698	33
28	.34966	.37322	2.6794	.93688	32
29	.34993	.37355	2.6770	.93677	31
30	.35021	.37388	2.6746	.93667	**30**
31	.35048	.37422	2.6723	.93657	29
32	.35075	.37455	2.6699	.93647	28
33	.35102	.37488	2.6675	.93637	27
34	.35130	.37521	2.6652	.93626	26
35	.35157	.37554	2.6628	.93616	**25**
36	.35184	.37588	2.6605	.93606	24
37	.35211	.37621	2.6581	.93596	23
38	.35239	.37654	2.6558	.93585	22
39	.35266	.37687	2.6534	.93575	21
40	.35293	.37720	2.6511	.93565	**20**
41	.35320	.37754	2.6488	.93555	19
42	.35347	.37787	2.6464	.93544	18
43	.35375	.37820	2.6441	.93534	17
44	.35402	.37853	2.6418	.93524	16
45	.35429	.37887	2.6395	.93514	**15**
46	.35456	.37920	2.6371	.93503	14
47	.35484	.37953	2.6348	.93493	13
48	.35511	.37986	2.6325	.93483	12
49	.35538	.38020	2.6302	.93472	11
50	.35565	.38053	2.6279	.93462	**10**
51	.35592	.38086	2.6256	.93452	9
52	.35619	.38120	2.6233	.93441	8
53	.35647	.38153	2.6210	.93431	7
54	.35674	.38186	2.6187	.93420	6
55	.35701	.38220	2.6165	.93410	**5**
56	.35728	.38253	2.6142	.93400	4
57	.35755	.38286	2.6119	.93389	3
58	.35782	.38320	2.6096	.93379	2
59	.35810	.38353	2.6074	.93368	1
60	.35837	.38386	2.6051	.93358	**0**
′	Cos	Cot	Tan	Sin	′

110° (290°) (249°) **69°**

21° (201°) (338°) **158°**

′	Sin	Tan	Cot	Cos	′
0	.35837	.38386	2.6051	.93358	**60**
1	.35864	.38420	2.6028	.93348	59
2	.35891	.38453	2.6006	.93337	58
3	.35918	.38487	2.5983	.93327	57
4	.35945	.38520	2.5961	.93316	56
5	.35973	.38553	2.5938	.93306	**55**
6	.36000	.38587	2.5916	.93295	54
7	.36027	.38620	2.5893	.93285	53
8	.36054	.38654	2.5871	.93274	52
9	.36081	.38687	2.5848	.93264	51
10	.36108	.38721	2.5826	.93253	**50**
11	.36135	.38754	2.5804	.93243	49
12	.36162	.38787	2.5782	.93232	48
13	.36190	.38821	2.5759	.93222	47
14	.36217	.38854	2.5737	.93211	46
15	.36244	.38888	2.5715	.93201	**45**
16	.36271	.38921	2.5693	.93190	44
17	.36298	.38955	2.5671	.93180	43
18	.36325	.38988	2.5649	.93169	42
19	.36352	.39022	2.5627	.93159	41
20	.36379	.39055	2.5605	.93148	**40**
21	.36406	.39089	2.5583	.93137	39
22	.36434	.39122	2.5561	.93127	38
23	.36461	.39156	2.5539	.93116	37
24	.36488	.39190	2.5517	.93106	36
25	.36515	.39223	2.5495	.93095	**35**
26	.36542	.39257	2.5473	.93084	34
27	.36569	.39290	2.5452	.93074	33
28	.36596	.39324	2.5430	.93063	32
29	.36623	.39357	2.5408	.93052	31
30	.36650	.39391	2.5386	.93042	**30**
31	.36677	.39425	2.5365	.93031	29
32	.36704	.39458	2.5343	.93020	28
33	.36731	.39492	2.5322	.93010	27
34	.36758	.39526	2.5300	.92999	26
35	.36785	.39559	2.5279	.92988	**25**
36	.36812	.39593	2.5257	.92978	24
37	.36839	.39626	2.5236	.92967	23
38	.36867	.39660	2.5214	.92956	22
39	.36894	.39694	2.5193	.92945	21
40	.36921	.39727	2.5172	.92935	**20**
41	.36948	.39761	2.5150	.92924	19
42	.36975	.39795	2.5129	.92913	18
43	.37002	.39829	2.5108	.92902	17
44	.37029	.39862	2.5086	.92892	16
45	.37056	.39896	2.5065	.92881	**15**
46	.37083	.39930	2.5044	.92870	14
47	.37110	.39963	2.5023	.92859	13
48	.37137	.39997	2.5002	.92849	12
49	.37164	.40031	2.4981	.92838	11
50	.37191	.40065	2.4960	.92827	**10**
51	.37218	.40098	2.4939	.92816	9
52	.37245	.40132	2.4918	.92805	8
53	.37272	.40166	2.4897	.92794	7
54	.37299	.40200	2.4876	.92784	6
55	.37326	.40234	2.4855	.92773	**5**
56	.37353	.40267	2.4834	.92762	4
57	.37380	.40301	2.4813	.92751	3
58	.37407	.40335	2.4792	.92740	2
59	.37434	.40369	2.4772	.92729	1
60	.37461	.40403	2.4751	.92718	**0**
′	Cos	Cot	Tan	Sin	′

111° (291°) (248°) **68°**

22° (202°) (337°) **157°**

′	Sin	Tan	Cot	Cos	′
0	.37461	.40403	2.4751	.92718	**60**
1	.37488	.40436	2.4730	.92707	59
2	.37515	.40470	2.4709	.92697	58
3	.37542	.40504	2.4689	.92686	57
4	.37569	.40538	2.4668	.92675	56
5	.37595	.40572	2.4648	.92664	**55**
6	.37622	.40606	2.4627	.92653	54
7	.37649	.40640	2.4606	.92642	53
8	.37676	.40674	2.4586	.92631	52
9	.37703	.40707	2.4566	.92620	51
10	.37730	.40741	2.4545	.92609	**50**
11	.37757	.40775	2.4525	.92598	49
12	.37784	.40809	2.4504	.92587	48
13	.37811	.40843	2.4484	.92576	47
14	.37838	.40877	2.4464	.92565	46
15	.37865	.40911	2.4443	.92554	**45**
16	.37892	.40945	2.4423	.92543	44
17	.37919	.40979	2.4403	.92532	43
18	.37946	.41013	2.4383	.92521	42
19	.37973	.41047	2.4362	.92510	41
20	.37999	.41081	2.4342	.92499	**40**
21	.38026	.41115	2.4322	.92488	39
22	.38053	.41149	2.4302	.92477	38
23	.38080	.41183	2.4282	.92466	37
24	.38107	.41217	2.4262	.92455	36
25	.38134	.41251	2.4242	.92444	**35**
26	.38161	.41285	2.4222	.92432	34
27	.38188	.41319	2.4202	.92421	33
28	.38215	.41353	2.4182	.92410	32
29	.38241	.41387	2.4162	.92399	31
30	.38268	.41421	2.4142	.92388	**30**
31	.38295	.41455	2.4122	.92377	29
32	.38322	.41490	2.4102	.92366	28
33	.38349	.41524	2.4083	.92355	27
34	.38376	.41558	2.4063	.92343	26
35	.38403	.41592	2.4043	.92332	**25**
36	.38430	.41626	2.4023	.92321	24
37	.38456	.41660	2.4004	.92310	23
38	.38483	.41694	2.3984	.92299	22
39	.38510	.41728	2.3964	.92287	21
40	.38537	.41763	2.3945	.92276	**20**
41	.38564	.41797	2.3925	.92265	19
42	.38591	.41831	2.3906	.92254	18
43	.38617	.41865	2.3886	.92243	17
44	.38644	.41899	2.3867	.92231	16
45	.38671	.41933	2.3847	.92220	**15**
46	.38698	.41968	2.3828	.92209	14
47	.38725	.42002	2.3808	.92198	13
48	.38752	.42036	2.3789	.92186	12
49	.38778	.42070	2.3770	.92175	11
50	.38805	.42105	2.3750	.92164	**10**
51	.38832	.42139	2.3731	.92152	9
52	.38859	.42173	2.3712	.92141	8
53	.38886	.42207	2.3693	.92130	7
54	.38912	.42242	2.3673	.92119	6
55	.38939	.42276	2.3654	.92107	**5**
56	.38966	.42310	2.3635	.92096	4
57	.38993	.42345	2.3616	.92085	3
58	.39020	.42379	2.3597	.92073	2
59	.39046	.42413	2.3578	.92062	1
60	.39073	.42447	2.3559	.92050	**0**
′	Cos	Cot	Tan	Sin	′

112° (292°) (247°) **67°**

23° (203°) (336°) **156°**

′	Sin	Tan	Cot	Cos	′
0	.39073	.42447	2.3559	.92050	**60**
1	.39100	.42482	2.3539	.92039	59
2	.39127	.42516	2.3520	.92028	58
3	.39153	.42551	2.3501	.92016	57
4	.39180	.42585	2.3483	.92005	56
5	.39207	.42619	2.3464	.91994	**55**
6	.39234	.42654	2.3445	.91982	54
7	.39260	.42688	2.3426	.91971	53
8	.39287	.42722	2.3407	.91959	52
9	.39314	.42757	2.3388	.91948	51
10	.39341	.42791	2.3369	.91936	**50**
11	.39367	.42826	2.3351	.91925	49
12	.39394	.42860	2.3332	.91914	48
13	.39421	.42894	2.3313	.91902	47
14	.39448	.42929	2.3294	.91891	46
15	.39474	.42963	2.3276	.91879	**45**
16	.39501	.42998	2.3257	.91868	44
17	.39528	.43032	2.3238	.91856	43
18	.39555	.43067	2.3220	.91845	42
19	.39581	.43101	2.3201	.91833	41
20	.39608	.43136	2.3183	.91822	**40**
21	.39635	.43170	2.3164	.91810	39
22	.39661	.43205	2.3146	.91799	38
23	.39688	.43239	2.3127	.91787	37
24	.39715	.43274	2.3109	.91775	36
25	.39741	.43308	2.3090	.91764	**35**
26	.39768	.43343	2.3072	.91752	34
27	.39795	.43378	2.3053	.91741	33
28	.39822	.43412	2.3035	.91729	32
29	.39848	.43447	2.3017	.91718	31
30	.39875	.43481	2.2998	.91706	**30**
31	.39902	.43516	2.2980	.91694	29
32	.39928	.43550	2.2962	.91683	28
33	.39955	.43585	2.2944	.91671	27
34	.39982	.43620	2.2925	.91660	26
35	.40008	.43654	2.2907	.91648	**25**
36	.40035	.43689	2.2889	.91636	24
37	.40062	.43724	2.2871	.91625	23
38	.40088	.43758	2.2853	.91613	22
39	.40115	.43793	2.2835	.91601	21
40	.40141	.43828	2.2817	.91590	**20**
41	.40168	.43862	2.2799	.91578	19
42	.40195	.43897	2.2781	.91566	18
43	.40221	.43932	2.2763	.91555	17
44	.40248	.43966	2.2745	.91543	16
45	.40275	.44001	2.2727	.91531	**15**
46	.40301	.44036	2.2709	.91519	14
47	.40328	.44071	2.2691	.91508	13
48	.40355	.44105	2.2673	.91496	12
49	.40381	.44140	2.2655	.91484	11
50	.40408	.44175	2.2637	.91472	**10**
51	.40434	.44210	2.2620	.91461	9
52	.40461	.44244	2.2602	.91449	8
53	.40488	.44279	2.2584	.91437	7
54	.40514	.44314	2.2566	.91425	6
55	.40541	.44349	2.2549	.91414	**5**
56	.40567	.44384	2.2531	.91402	4
57	.40594	.44418	2.2513	.91390	3
58	.40621	.44453	2.2496	.91378	2
59	.40647	.44488	2.2478	.91366	1
60	.40674	.44523	2.2460	.91355	**0**
′	Cos	Cot	Tan	Sin	′

113° (293°) (246°) **66°**

24° (204°) (335°) **155°**

′	Sin	Tan	Cot	Cos	′
0	.40674	.44523	2.2460	.91355	**60**
1	.40700	.44558	2.2443	.91343	59
2	.40727	.44593	2.2425	.91331	58
3	.40753	.44627	2.2408	.91319	57
4	.40780	.44662	2.2390	.91307	56
5	.40806	.44697	2.2373	.91295	**55**
6	.40833	.44732	2.2355	.91283	54
7	.40860	.44767	2.2338	.91272	53
8	.40886	.44802	2.2320	.91260	52
9	.40913	.44837	2.2303	.91248	51
10	.40939	.44872	2.2286	.91236	**50**
11	.40966	.44907	2.2268	.91224	49
12	.40992	.44942	2.2251	.91212	48
13	.41019	.44977	2.2234	.91200	47
14	.41045	.45012	2.2216	.91188	46
15	.41072	.45047	2.2199	.91176	**45**
16	.41098	.45082	2.2182	.91164	44
17	.41125	.45117	2.2165	.91152	43
18	.41151	.45152	2.2148	.91140	42
19	.41178	.45187	2.2130	.91128	41
20	.41204	.45222	2.2113	.91116	**40**
21	.41231	.45257	2.2096	.91104	39
22	.41257	.45292	2.2079	.91092	38
23	.41284	.45327	2.2062	.91080	37
24	.41310	.45362	2.2045	.91068	36
25	.41337	.45397	2.2028	.91056	**35**
26	.41363	.45432	2.2011	.91044	34
27	.41390	.45467	2.1994	.91032	33
28	.41416	.45502	2.1977	.91020	32
29	.41443	.45538	2.1960	.91008	31
30	.41469	.45573	2.1943	.90996	**30**
31	.41496	.45608	2.1926	.90984	29
32	.41522	.45643	2.1909	.90972	28
33	.41549	.45678	2.1892	.90960	27
34	.41575	.45713	2.1876	.90948	26
35	.41602	.45748	2.1859	.90936	**25**
36	.41628	.45784	2.1842	.90924	24
37	.41655	.45819	2.1825	.90911	23
38	.41681	.45854	2.1808	.90899	22
39	.41707	.45889	2.1792	.90887	21
40	.41734	.45924	2.1775	.90875	**20**
41	.41760	.45960	2.1758	.90863	19
42	.41787	.45995	2.1742	.90851	18
43	.41813	.46030	2.1725	.90839	17
44	.41840	.46065	2.1708	.90826	16
45	.41866	.46101	2.1692	.90814	**15**
46	.41892	.46136	2.1675	.90802	14
47	.41919	.46171	2.1659	.90790	13
48	.41945	.46206	2.1642	.90778	12
49	.41972	.46242	2.1625	.90766	11
50	.41998	.46277	2.1609	.90753	**10**
51	.42024	.46312	2.1592	.90741	9
52	.42051	.46348	2.1576	.90729	8
53	.42077	.46383	2.1560	.90717	7
54	.42104	.46418	2.1543	.90704	6
55	.42130	.46454	2.1527	.90692	**5**
56	.42156	.46489	2.1510	.90680	4
57	.42183	.46525	2.1494	.90668	3
58	.42209	.46560	2.1478	.90655	2
59	.42235	.46595	2.1461	.90643	1
60	.42262	.46631	2.1445	.90631	**0**
′	Cos	Cot	Tan	Sin	′

114° (294°) (245°) **65°**

25° (205°) (334°) **154°**

′	Sin	Tan	Cot	Cos	′
0	.42262	.46631	2.1445	.90631	**60**
1	.42288	.46666	2.1429	.90618	59
2	.42315	.46702	2.1413	.90606	58
3	.42341	.46737	2.1396	.90594	57
4	.42367	.46772	2.1380	.90582	56
5	.42394	.46808	2.1364	.90569	**55**
6	.42420	.46843	2.1348	.90557	54
7	.42446	.46879	2.1332	.90545	53
8	.42473	.46914	2.1315	.90532	52
9	.42499	.46950	2.1299	.90520	51
10	.42525	.46985	2.1283	.90507	**50**
11	.42552	.47021	2.1267	.90495	49
12	.42578	.47056	2.1251	.90483	48
13	.42604	.47092	2.1235	.90470	47
14	.42631	.47128	2.1219	.90458	46
15	.42657	.47163	2.1203	.90446	**45**
16	.42683	.47199	2.1187	.90433	44
17	.42709	.47234	2.1171	.90421	43
18	.42736	.47270	2.1155	.90408	42
19	.42762	.47305	2.1139	.90396	41
20	.42788	.47341	2.1123	.90383	**40**
21	.42815	.47377	2.1107	.90371	39
22	.42841	.47412	2.1092	.90358	38
23	.42867	.47448	2.1076	.90346	37
24	.42894	.47483	2.1060	.90334	36
25	.42920	.47519	2.1044	.90321	**35**
26	.42946	.47555	2.1028	.90309	34
27	.42972	.47590	2.1013	.90296	33
28	.42999	.47626	2.0997	.90284	32
29	.43025	.47662	2.0981	.90271	31
30	.43051	.47698	2.0965	.90259	**30**
31	.43077	.47733	2.0950	.90246	29
32	.43104	.47769	2.0934	.90233	28
33	.43130	.47805	2.0918	.90221	27
34	.43156	.47840	2.0903	.90208	26
35	.43182	.47876	2.0887	.90196	**25**
36	.43209	.47912	2.0872	.90183	24
37	.43235	.47948	2.0856	.90171	23
38	.43261	.47984	2.0840	.90158	22
39	.43287	.48019	2.0825	.90146	21
40	.43313	.48055	2.0809	.90133	**20**
41	.43340	.48091	2.0794	.90120	19
42	.43366	.48127	2.0778	.90108	18
43	.43392	.48163	2.0763	.90095	17
44	.43418	.48198	2.0748	.90082	16
45	.43445	.48234	2.0732	.90070	**15**
46	.43471	.48270	2.0717	.90057	14
47	.43497	.48306	2.0701	.90045	13
48	.43523	.48342	2.0686	.90032	12
49	.43549	.48378	2.0671	.90019	11
50	.43575	.48414	2.0655	.90007	**10**
51	.43602	.48450	2.0640	.89994	9
52	.43628	.48486	2.0625	.89981	8
53	.43654	.48521	2.0609	.89968	7
54	.43680	.48557	2.0594	.89956	6
55	.43706	.48593	2.0579	.89943	**5**
56	.43733	.48629	2.0564	.89930	4
57	.43759	.48665	2.0549	.89918	3
58	.43785	.48701	2.0533	.89905	2
59	.43811	.48737	2.0518	.89892	1
60	.43837	.48773	2.0503	.89879	**0**
′	Cos	Cot	Tan	Sin	′

115° (295°) (244°) **64°**

34° (214°) (325°) **145°**

′	Sin	Tan	Cot	Cos	′
0	.55919	.67451	1.4826	.82904	**60**
1	.55943	.67493	1.4816	.82887	59
2	.55968	.67536	1.4807	.82871	58
3	.55992	.67578	1.4798	.82855	57
4	.56016	.67620	1.4788	.82839	56
5	.56040	.67663	1.4779	.82822	**55**
6	.56064	.67705	1.4770	.82806	54
7	.56088	.67748	1.4761	.82790	53
8	.56112	.67790	1.4751	.82773	52
9	.56136	.67832	1.4742	.82757	51
10	.56160	.67875	1.4733	.82741	**50**
11	.56184	.67917	1.4724	.82724	49
12	.56208	.67960	1.4715	.82708	48
13	.56232	.68002	1.4705	.82692	47
14	.56256	.68045	1.4696	.82675	46
15	.56280	.68088	1.4687	.82659	**45**
16	.56305	.68130	1.4678	.82643	44
17	.56329	.68173	1.4669	.82626	43
18	.56353	.68215	1.4659	.82610	42
19	.56377	.68258	1.4650	.82593	41
20	.56401	.68301	1.4641	.82577	**40**
21	.56425	.68343	1.4632	.82561	39
22	.56449	.68386	1.4623	.82544	38
23	.56473	.68429	1.4614	.82528	37
24	.56497	.68471	1.4605	.82511	36
25	.56521	.68514	1.4596	.82495	**35**
26	.56545	.68557	1.4586	.82478	34
27	.56569	.68600	1.4577	.82462	33
28	.56593	.68642	1.4568	.82446	32
29	.56617	.68685	1.4559	.82429	31
30	.56641	.68728	1.4550	.82413	**30**
31	.56665	.68771	1.4541	.82396	29
32	.56689	.68814	1.4532	.82380	28
33	.56713	.68857	1.4523	.82363	27
34	.56736	.68900	1.4514	.82347	26
35	.56760	.68942	1.4505	.82330	**25**
36	.56784	.68985	1.4496	.82314	24
37	.56808	.69028	1.4487	.82297	23
38	.56832	.69071	1.4478	.82281	22
39	.56856	.69114	1.4469	.82264	21
40	.56880	.69157	1.4460	.82248	**20**
41	.56904	.69200	1.4451	.82231	19
42	.56928	.69243	1.4442	.82214	18
43	.56952	.69286	1.4433	.82198	17
44	.56976	.69329	1.4424	.82181	16
45	.57000	.69372	1.4415	.82165	**15**
46	.57024	.69416	1.4406	.82148	14
47	.57047	.69459	1.4397	.82132	13
48	.57071	.69502	1.4388	.82115	12
49	.57095	.69545	1.4379	.82098	11
50	.57119	.69588	1.4370	.82082	**10**
51	.57143	.69631	1.4361	.82065	9
52	.57167	.69675	1.4352	.82048	8
53	.57191	.69718	1.4344	.82032	7
54	.57215	.69761	1.4335	.82015	6
55	.57238	.69804	1.4326	.81999	**5**
56	.57262	.69847	1.4317	.81982	4
57	.57286	.69891	1.4308	.81965	3
58	.57310	.69934	1.4299	.81949	2
59	.57334	.69977	1.4290	.81932	1
60	.57358	.70021	1.4281	.81915	**0**
′	Cos	Cot	Tan	Sin	′

124° (304°) (235°) **55°**

35° (215°) (324°) **144°**

′	Sin	Tan	Cot	Cos	′
0	.57358	.70021	1.4281	.81915	**60**
1	.57381	.70064	1.4273	.81899	59
2	.57405	.70107	1.4264	.81882	58
3	.57429	.70151	1.4255	.81865	57
4	.57453	.70194	1.4246	.81848	56
5	.57477	.70238	1.4237	.81832	**55**
6	.57501	.70281	1.4229	.81815	54
7	.57524	.70325	1.4220	.81798	53
8	.57548	.70368	1.4211	.81782	52
9	.57572	.70412	1.4202	.81765	51
10	.57596	.70455	1.4193	.81748	**50**
11	.57619	.70499	1.4185	.81731	49
12	.57643	.70542	1.4176	.81714	48
13	.57667	.70586	1.4167	.81698	47
14	.57691	.70629	1.4158	.81681	46
15	.57715	.70673	1.4150	.81664	**45**
16	.57738	.70717	1.4141	.81647	44
17	.57762	.70760	1.4132	.81631	43
18	.57786	.70804	1.4124	.81614	42
19	.57810	.70848	1.4115	.81597	41
20	.57833	.70891	1.4106	.81580	**40**
21	.57857	.70935	1.4097	.81563	39
22	.57881	.70979	1.4089	.81546	38
23	.57904	.71023	1.4080	.81530	37
24	.57928	.71066	1.4071	.81513	36
25	.57952	.71110	1.4063	.81496	**35**
26	.57976	.71154	1.4054	.81479	34
27	.57999	.71198	1.4045	.81462	33
28	.58023	.71242	1.4037	.81445	32
29	.58047	.71285	1.4028	.81428	31
30	.58070	.71329	1.4019	.81412	**30**
31	.58094	.71373	1.4011	.81395	29
32	.58118	.71417	1.4002	.81378	28
33	.58141	.71461	1.3994	.81361	27
34	.58165	.71505	1.3985	.81344	26
35	.58189	.71549	1.3976	.81327	**25**
36	.58212	.71593	1.3968	.81310	24
37	.58236	.71637	1.3959	.81293	23
38	.58260	.71681	1.3951	.81276	22
39	.58283	.71725	1.3942	.81259	21
40	.58307	.71769	1.3934	.81242	**20**
41	.58330	.71813	1.3925	.81225	19
42	.58354	.71857	1.3916	.81208	18
43	.58378	.71901	1.3908	.81191	17
44	.58401	.71946	1.3899	.81174	16
45	.58425	.71990	1.3891	.81157	**15**
46	.58449	.72034	1.3882	.81140	14
47	.58472	.72078	1.3874	.81123	13
48	.58496	.72122	1.3865	.81106	12
49	.58519	.72167	1.3857	.81089	11
50	.58543	.72211	1.3848	.81072	**10**
51	.58567	.72255	1.3840	.81055	9
52	.58590	.72299	1.3831	.81038	8
53	.58614	.72344	1.3823	.81021	7
54	.58637	.72388	1.3814	.81004	6
55	.58661	.72432	1.3806	.80987	**5**
56	.58684	.72477	1.3798	.80970	4
57	.58708	.72521	1.3789	.80953	3
58	.58731	.72565	1.3781	.80936	2
59	.58755	.72610	1.3772	.80919	1
60	.58779	.72654	1.3764	.80902	**0**
′	Cos	Cot	Tan	Sin	′

125° (305°) (234°) **54°**

36° (216°) (323°) **143°**

′	Sin	Tan	Cot	Cos	′
0	.58779	.72654	1.3764	.80902	**60**
1	.58802	.72699	1.3755	.80885	59
2	.58826	.72743	1.3747	.80867	58
3	.58849	.72788	1.3739	.80850	57
4	.58873	.72832	1.3730	.80833	56
5	.58896	.72877	1.3722	.80816	**55**
6	.58920	.72921	1.3713	.80799	54
7	.58943	.72966	1.3705	.80782	53
8	.58967	.73010	1.3697	.80765	52
9	.58990	.73055	1.3688	.80748	51
10	.59014	.73100	1.3680	.80730	**50**
11	.59037	.73144	1.3672	.80713	49
12	.59061	.73189	1.3663	.80696	48
13	.59084	.73234	1.3655	.80679	47
14	.59108	.73278	1.3647	.80662	46
15	.59131	.73323	1.3638	.80644	**45**
16	.59154	.73368	1.3630	.80627	44
17	.59178	.73413	1.3622	.80610	43
18	.59201	.73457	1.3613	.80593	42
19	.59225	.73502	1.3605	.80576	41
20	.59248	.73547	1.3597	.80558	**40**
21	.59272	.73592	1.3588	.80541	39
22	.59295	.73637	1.3580	.80524	38
23	.59318	.73681	1.3572	.80507	37
24	.59342	.73726	1.3564	.80489	36
25	.59365	.73771	1.3555	.80472	**35**
26	.59389	.73816	1.3547	.80455	34
27	.59412	.73861	1.3539	.80438	33
28	.59436	.73906	1.3531	.80420	32
29	.59459	.73951	1.3522	.80403	31
30	.59482	.73996	1.3514	.80386	**30**
31	.59506	.74041	1.3506	.80368	29
32	.59529	.74086	1.3498	.80351	28
33	.59552	.74131	1.3490	.80334	27
34	.59576	.74176	1.3481	.80316	26
35	.59599	.74221	1.3473	.80299	**25**
36	.59622	.74267	1.3465	.80282	24
37	.59646	.74312	1.3457	.80264	23
38	.59669	.74357	1.3449	.80247	22
39	.59693	.74402	1.3440	.80230	21
40	.59716	.74447	1.3432	.80212	**20**
41	.59739	.74492	1.3424	.80195	19
42	.59763	.74538	1.3416	.80178	18
43	.59786	.74583	1.3408	.80160	17
44	.59809	.74628	1.3400	.80143	16
45	.59832	.74674	1.3392	.80125	**15**
46	.59856	.74719	1.3384	.80108	14
47	.59879	.74764	1.3375	.80091	13
48	.59902	.74810	1.3367	.80073	12
49	.59926	.74855	1.3359	.80056	11
50	.59949	.74900	1.3351	.80038	**10**
51	.59972	.74946	1.3343	.80021	9
52	.59995	.74991	1.3335	.80003	8
53	.60019	.75037	1.3327	.79986	7
54	.60042	.75082	1.3319	.79968	6
55	.60065	.75128	1.3311	.79951	**5**
56	.60089	.75173	1.3303	.79934	4
57	.60112	.75219	1.3295	.79916	3
58	.60135	.75264	1.3287	.79899	2
59	.60158	.75310	1.3278	.79881	1
60	.60182	.75355	1.3270	.79864	**0**
′	Cos	Cot	Tan	Sin	′

126° (306°) (233°) **53°**

37° (217°) (322°) **142°**

′	Sin	Tan	Cot	Cos	′
0	.60182	.75355	1.3270	.79864	**60**
1	.60205	.75401	1.3262	.79846	59
2	.60228	.75447	1.3254	.79829	58
3	.60251	.75492	1.3246	.79811	57
4	.60274	.75538	1.3238	.79793	56
5	.60298	.75584	1.3230	.79776	**55**
6	.60321	.75629	1.3222	.79758	54
7	.60344	.75675	1.3214	.79741	53
8	.60367	.75721	1.3206	.79723	52
9	.60390	.75767	1.3198	.79706	51
10	.60414	.75812	1.3190	.79688	**50**
11	.60437	.75858	1.3182	.79671	49
12	.60460	.75904	1.3175	.79653	48
13	.60483	.75950	1.3167	.79635	47
14	.60506	.75996	1.3159	.79618	46
15	.60529	.76042	1.3151	.79600	**45**
16	.60553	.76088	1.3143	.79583	44
17	.60576	.76134	1.3135	.79565	43
18	.60599	.76180	1.3127	.79547	42
19	.60622	.76226	1.3119	.79530	41
20	.60645	.76272	1.3111	.79512	**40**
21	.60668	.76318	1.3103	.79494	39
22	.60691	.76364	1.3095	.79477	38
23	.60714	.76410	1.3087	.79459	37
24	.60738	.76456	1.3079	.79441	36
25	.60761	.76502	1.3072	.79424	**35**
26	.60784	.76548	1.3064	.79406	34
27	.60807	.76594	1.3056	.79388	33
28	.60830	.76640	1.3048	.79371	32
29	.60853	.76686	1.3040	.79353	31
30	.60876	.76733	1.3032	.79335	**30**
31	.60899	.76779	1.3024	.79318	29
32	.60922	.76825	1.3017	.79300	28
33	.60945	.76871	1.3009	.79282	27
34	.60968	.76918	1.3001	.79264	26
35	.60991	.76964	1.2993	.79247	**25**
36	.61015	.77010	1.2985	.79229	24
37	.61038	.77057	1.2977	.79211	23
38	.61061	.77103	1.2970	.79193	22
39	.61084	.77149	1.2962	.79176	21
40	.61107	.77196	1.2954	.79158	**20**
41	.61130	.77242	1.2946	.79140	19
42	.61153	.77289	1.2938	.79122	18
43	.61176	.77335	1.2931	.79105	17
44	.61199	.77382	1.2923	.79087	16
45	.61222	.77428	1.2915	.79069	**15**
46	.61245	.77475	1.2907	.79051	14
47	.61268	.77521	1.2900	.79033	13
48	.61291	.77568	1.2892	.79016	12
49	.61314	.77615	1.2884	.78998	11
50	.61337	.77661	1.2876	.78980	**10**
51	.61360	.77708	1.2869	.78962	9
52	.61383	.77754	1.2861	.78944	8
53	.61406	.77801	1.2853	.78926	7
54	.61429	.77848	1.2846	.78908	6
55	.61451	.77895	1.2838	.78891	**5**
56	.61474	.77941	1.2830	.78873	4
57	.61497	.77988	1.2822	.78855	3
58	.61520	.78035	1.2815	.78837	2
59	.61543	.78082	1.2807	.78819	1
60	.61566	.78129	1.2799	.78801	**0**
′	Cos	Cot	Tan	Sin	′

127° (307°) (232°) **52°**

38° (218°) (321°) **141°**

′	Sin	Tan	Cot	Cos	′
0	.61566	.78129	1.2799	.78801	**60**
1	.61589	.78175	1.2792	.78783	59
2	.61612	.78222	1.2784	.78765	58
3	.61635	.78269	1.2776	.78747	57
4	.61658	.78316	1.2769	.78729	56
5	.61681	.78363	1.2761	.78711	**55**
6	.61704	.78410	1.2753	.78694	54
7	.61726	.78457	1.2746	.78676	53
8	.61749	.78504	1.2738	.78658	52
9	.61772	.78551	1.2731	.78640	51
10	.61795	.78598	1.2723	.78622	**50**
11	.61818	.78645	1.2715	.78604	49
12	.61841	.78692	1.2708	.78586	48
13	.61864	.78739	1.2700	.78568	47
14	.61887	.78786	1.2693	.78550	46
15	.61909	.78834	1.2685	.78532	**45**
16	.61932	.78881	1.2677	.78514	44
17	.61955	.78928	1.2670	.78496	43
18	.61978	.78975	1.2662	.78478	42
19	.62001	.79022	1.2655	.78460	41
20	.62024	.79070	1.2647	.78442	**40**
21	.62046	.79117	1.2640	.78424	39
22	.62069	.79164	1.2632	.78405	38
23	.62092	.79212	1.2624	.78387	37
24	.62115	.79259	1.2617	.78369	36
25	.62138	.79306	1.2609	.78351	**35**
26	.62160	.79354	1.2602	.78333	34
27	.62183	.79401	1.2594	.78315	33
28	.62206	.79449	1.2587	.78297	32
29	.62229	.79496	1.2579	.78279	31
30	.62251	.79544	1.2572	.78261	**30**
31	.62274	.79591	1.2564	.78243	29
32	.62297	.79639	1.2557	.78225	28
33	.62320	.79686	1.2549	.78206	27
34	.62342	.79734	1.2542	.78188	26
35	.62365	.79781	1.2534	.78170	**25**
36	.62388	.79829	1.2527	.78152	24
37	.62411	.79877	1.2519	.78134	23
38	.62433	.79924	1.2512	.78116	22
39	.62456	.79972	1.2504	.78098	21
40	.62479	.80020	1.2497	.78079	**20**
41	.62502	.80067	1.2489	.78061	19
42	.62524	.80115	1.2482	.78043	18
43	.62547	.80163	1.2475	.78025	17
44	.62570	.80211	1.2467	.78007	16
45	.62592	.80258	1.2460	.77988	**15**
46	.62615	.80306	1.2452	.77970	14
47	.62638	.80354	1.2445	.77952	13
48	.62660	.80402	1.2437	.77934	12
49	.62683	.80450	1.2430	.77916	11
50	.62706	.80498	1.2423	.77897	**10**
51	.62728	.80546	1.2415	.77879	9
52	.62751	.80594	1.2408	.77861	8
53	.62774	.80642	1.2401	.77843	7
54	.62796	.80690	1.2393	.77824	6
55	.62819	.80738	1.2386	.77806	**5**
56	.62842	.80786	1.2378	.77788	4
57	.62864	.80834	1.2371	.77769	3
58	.62887	.80882	1.2364	.77751	2
59	.62909	.80930	1.2356	.77733	1
60	.62932	.80978	1.2349	.77715	**0**
′	Cos	Cot	Tan	Sin	′

128° (308°) (231°) **51°**

39° (219°) (320°) **140°**

′	Sin	Tan	Cot	Cos	′
0	.62932	.80978	1.2349	.77715	**60**
1	.62955	.81027	1.2342	.77696	59
2	.62977	.81075	1.2334	.77678	58
3	.63000	.81123	1.2327	.77660	57
4	.63022	.81171	1.2320	.77641	56
5	.63045	.81220	1.2312	.77623	**55**
6	.63068	.81268	1.2305	.77605	54
7	.63090	.81316	1.2298	.77586	53
8	.63113	.81364	1.2290	.77568	52
9	.63135	.81413	1.2283	.77550	51
10	.63158	.81461	1.2276	.77531	**50**
11	.63180	.81510	1.2268	.77513	49
12	.63203	.81558	1.2261	.77494	48
13	.63225	.81606	1.2254	.77476	47
14	.63248	.81655	1.2247	.77458	46
15	.63271	.81703	1.2239	.77439	**45**
16	.63293	.81752	1.2232	.77421	44
17	.63316	.81800	1.2225	.77402	43
18	.63338	.81849	1.2218	.77384	42
19	.63361	.81898	1.2210	.77366	41
20	.63383	.81946	1.2203	.77347	**40**
21	.63406	.81995	1.2196	.77329	39
22	.63428	.82044	1.2189	.77310	38
23	.63451	.82092	1.2181	.77292	37
24	.63473	.82141	1.2174	.77273	36
25	.63496	.82190	1.2167	.77255	**35**
26	.63518	.82238	1.2160	.77236	34
27	.63540	.82287	1.2153	.77218	33
28	.63563	.82336	1.2145	.77199	32
29	.63585	.82385	1.2138	.77181	31
30	.63608	.82434	1.2131	.77162	**30**
31	.63630	.82483	1.2124	.77144	29
32	.63653	.82531	1.2117	.77125	28
33	.63675	.82580	1.2109	.77107	27
34	.63698	.82629	1.2102	.77088	26
35	.63720	.82678	1.2095	.77070	**25**
36	.63742	.82727	1.2088	.77051	24
37	.63765	.82776	1.2081	.77033	23
38	.63787	.82825	1.2074	.77014	22
39	.63810	.82874	1.2066	.76996	21
40	.63832	.82923	1.2059	.76977	**20**
41	.63854	.82972	1.2052	.76959	19
42	.63877	.83022	1.2045	.76940	18
43	.63899	.83071	1.2038	.76921	17
44	.63922	.83120	1.2031	.76903	16
45	.63944	.83169	1.2024	.76884	**15**
46	.63966	.83218	1.2017	.76866	14
47	.63989	.83268	1.2009	.76847	13
48	.64011	.83317	1.2002	.76828	12
49	.64033	.83366	1.1995	.76810	11
50	.64056	.83415	1.1988	.76791	**10**
51	.64078	.83465	1.1981	.76772	9
52	.64100	.83514	1.1974	.76754	8
53	.64123	.83564	1.1967	.76735	7
54	.64145	.83613	1.1960	.76717	6
55	.64167	.83662	1.1953	.76698	**5**
56	.64190	.83712	1.1946	.76679	4
57	.64212	.83761	1.1939	.76661	3
58	.64234	.83811	1.1932	.76642	2
59	.64256	.83860	1.1925	.76623	1
60	.64279	.83910	1.1918	.76604	**0**
′	Cos	Cot	Tan	Sin	′

129° (309°) (230°) **50°**

40° (220°) (319°) **139°**

′	Sin	Tan	Cot	Cos	′
0	.64279	.83910	1.1918	.76604	**60**
1	.64301	.83960	1.1910	.76586	59
2	.64323	.84009	1.1903	.76567	58
3	.64346	.84059	1.1896	.76548	57
4	.64368	.84108	1.1889	.76530	56
5	.64390	.84158	1.1882	.76511	**55**
6	.64412	.84208	1.1875	.76492	54
7	.64435	.84258	1.1868	.76473	53
8	.64457	.84307	1.1861	.76455	52
9	.64479	.84357	1.1854	.76436	51
10	.64501	.84407	1.1847	.76417	**50**
11	.64524	.84457	1.1840	.76398	49
12	.64546	.84507	1.1833	.76380	48
13	.64568	.84556	1.1826	.76361	47
14	.64590	.84606	1.1819	.76342	46
15	.64612	.84656	1.1812	.76323	**45**
16	.64635	.84706	1.1806	.76304	44
17	.64657	.84756	1.1799	.76286	43
18	.64679	.84806	1.1792	.76267	42
19	.64701	.84856	1.1785	.76248	41
20	.64723	.84906	1.1778	.76229	**40**
21	.64746	.84956	1.1771	.76210	39
22	.64768	.85006	1.1764	.76192	38
23	.64790	.85057	1.1757	.76173	37
24	.64812	.85107	1.1750	.76154	36
25	.64834	.85157	1.1743	.76135	**35**
26	.64856	.85207	1.1736	.76116	34
27	.64878	.85257	1.1729	.76097	33
28	.64901	.85308	1.1722	.76078	32
29	.64923	.85358	1.1715	.76059	31
30	.64945	.85408	1.1708	.76041	**30**
31	.64967	.85458	1.1702	.76022	29
32	.64989	.85509	1.1695	.76003	28
33	.65011	.85559	1.1688	.75984	27
34	.65033	.85609	1.1681	.75965	26
35	.65055	.85660	1.1674	.75946	**25**
36	.65077	.85710	1.1667	.75927	24
37	.65100	.85761	1.1660	.75908	23
38	.65122	.85811	1.1653	.75889	22
39	.65144	.85862	1.1647	.75870	21
40	.65166	.85912	1.1640	.75851	**20**
41	.65188	.85963	1.1633	.75832	19
42	.65210	.86014	1.1626	.75813	18
43	.65232	.86064	1.1619	.75794	17
44	.65254	.86115	1.1612	.75775	16
45	.65276	.86166	1.1606	.75756	**15**
46	.65298	.86216	1.1599	.75738	14
47	.65320	.86267	1.1592	.75719	13
48	.65342	.86318	1.1585	.75700	12
49	.65364	.86368	1.1578	.75680	11
50	.65386	.86419	1.1571	.75661	**10**
51	.65408	.86470	1.1565	.75642	9
52	.65430	.86521	1.1558	.75623	8
53	.65452	.86572	1.1551	.75604	7
54	.65474	.86623	1.1544	.75585	6
55	.65496	.86674	1.1538	.75566	**5**
56	.65518	.86725	1.1531	.75547	4
57	.65540	.86776	1.1524	.75528	3
58	.65562	.86827	1.1517	.75509	2
59	.65584	.86878	1.1510	.75490	1
60	.65606	.86929	1.1504	.75471	**0**
′	Cos	Cot	Tan	Sin	′

130° (310°) (229°) **49°**

41° (221°) (318°) **138°**

′	Sin	Tan	Cot	Cos	′
0	.65606	.86929	1.1504	.75471	**60**
1	.65628	.86980	1.1497	.75452	59
2	.65650	.87031	1.1490	.75433	58
3	.65672	.87082	1.1483	.75414	57
4	.65694	.87133	1.1477	.75395	56
5	.65716	.87184	1.1470	.75375	**55**
6	.65738	.87236	1.1463	.75356	54
7	.65759	.87287	1.1456	.75337	53
8	.65781	.87338	1.1450	.75318	52
9	.65803	.87389	1.1443	.75299	51
10	.65825	.87441	1.1436	.75280	**50**
11	.65847	.87492	1.1430	.75261	49
12	.65869	.87543	1.1423	.75241	48
13	.65891	.87595	1.1416	.75222	47
14	.65913	.87646	1.1410	.75203	46
15	.65935	.87698	1.1403	.75184	**45**
16	.65956	.87749	1.1396	.75165	44
17	.65978	.87801	1.1389	.75146	43
18	.66000	.87852	1.1383	.75126	42
19	.66022	.87904	1.1376	.75107	41
20	.66044	.87955	1.1369	.75088	**40**
21	.66066	.88007	1.1363	.75069	39
22	.66088	.88059	1.1356	.75050	38
23	.66109	.88110	1.1349	.75030	37
24	.66131	.88162	1.1343	.75011	36
25	.66153	.88214	1.1336	.74992	**35**
26	.66175	.88265	1.1329	.74973	34
27	.66197	.88317	1.1323	.74953	33
28	.66218	.88369	1.1316	.74934	32
29	.66240	.88421	1.1310	.74915	31
30	.66262	.88473	1.1303	.74896	**30**
31	.66284	.88524	1.1296	.74876	29
32	.66306	.88576	1.1290	.74857	28
33	.66327	.88628	1.1283	.74838	27
34	.66349	.88680	1.1276	.74818	26
35	.66371	.88732	1.1270	.74799	**25**
36	.66393	.88784	1.1263	.74780	24
37	.66414	.88836	1.1257	.74760	23
38	.66436	.88888	1.1250	.74741	22
39	.66458	.88940	1.1243	.74722	21
40	.66480	.88992	1.1237	.74703	**20**
41	.66501	.89045	1.1230	.74683	19
42	.66523	.89097	1.1224	.74664	18
43	.66545	.89149	1.1217	.74644	17
44	.66566	.89201	1.1211	.74625	16
45	.66588	.89253	1.1204	.74606	**15**
46	.66610	.89306	1.1197	.74586	14
47	.66632	.89358	1.1191	.74567	13
48	.66653	.89410	1.1184	.74548	12
49	.66675	.89463	1.1178	.74528	11
50	.66697	.89515	1.1171	.74509	**10**
51	.66718	.89567	1.1165	.74489	9
52	.66740	.89620	1.1158	.74470	8
53	.66762	.89672	1.1152	.74451	7
54	.66783	.89725	1.1145	.74431	6
55	.66805	.89777	1.1139	.74412	**5**
56	.66827	.89830	1.1132	.74392	4
57	.66848	.89883	1.1126	.74373	3
58	.66870	.89935	1.1119	.74353	2
59	.66891	.89988	1.1113	.74334	1
60	.66913	.90040	1.1106	.74314	**0**
′	Cos	Cot	Tan	Sin	′

131° (311°) (228°) **48°**

42° (222°) (317°) **137°**

′	Sin	Tan	Cot	Cos	′
0	.66913	.90040	1.1106	.74314	**60**
1	.66935	.90093	1.1100	.74295	59
2	.66956	.90146	1.1093	.74276	58
3	.66978	.90199	1.1087	.74256	57
4	.66999	.90251	1.1080	.74237	56
5	.67021	.90304	1.1074	.74217	**55**
6	.67043	.90357	1.1067	.74198	54
7	.67064	.90410	1.1061	.74178	53
8	.67086	.90463	1.1054	.74159	52
9	.67107	.90516	1.1048	.74139	51
10	.67129	.90569	1.1041	.74120	**50**
11	.67151	.90621	1.1035	.74100	49
12	.67172	.90674	1.1028	.74080	48
13	.67194	.90727	1.1022	.74061	47
14	.67215	.90781	1.1016	.74041	46
15	.67237	.90834	1.1009	.74022	**45**
16	.67258	.90887	1.1003	.74002	44
17	.67280	.90940	1.0996	.73983	43
18	.67301	.90993	1.0990	.73963	42
19	.67323	.91046	1.0983	.73944	41
20	.67344	.91099	1.0977	.73924	**40**
21	.67366	.91153	1.0971	.73904	39
22	.67387	.91206	1.0964	.73885	38
23	.67409	.91259	1.0958	.73865	37
24	.67430	.91313	1.0951	.73846	36
25	.67452	.91366	1.0945	.73826	**35**
26	.67473	.91419	1.0939	.73806	34
27	.67495	.91473	1.0932	.73787	33
28	.67516	.91526	1.0926	.73767	32
29	.67538	.91580	1.0919	.73747	31
30	.67559	.91633	1.0913	.73728	**30**
31	.67580	.91687	1.0907	.73708	29
32	.67602	.91740	1.0900	.73688	28
33	.67623	.91794	1.0894	.73669	27
34	.67645	.91847	1.0888	.73649	26
35	.67666	.91901	1.0881	.73629	**25**
36	.67688	.91955	1.0875	.73610	24
37	.67709	.92008	1.0869	.73590	23
38	.67730	.92062	1.0862	.73570	22
39	.67752	.92116	1.0856	.73551	21
40	.67773	.92170	1.0850	.73531	**20**
41	.67795	.92224	1.0843	.73511	19
42	.67816	.92277	1.0837	.73491	18
43	.67837	.92331	1.0831	.73472	17
44	.67859	.92385	1.0824	.73452	16
45	.67880	.92439	1.0818	.73432	**15**
46	.67901	.92493	1.0812	.73413	14
47	.67923	.92547	1.0805	.73393	13
48	.67944	.92601	1.0799	.73373	12
49	.67965	.92655	1.0793	.73353	11
50	.67987	.92709	1.0786	.73333	**10**
51	.68008	.92763	1.0780	.73314	9
52	.68029	.92817	1.0774	.73294	8
53	.68051	.92872	1.0768	.73274	7
54	.68072	.92926	1.0761	.73254	6
55	.68093	.92980	1.0755	.73234	**5**
56	.68115	.93034	1.0749	.73215	4
57	.68136	.93088	1.0742	.73195	3
58	.68157	.93143	1.0736	.73175	2
59	.68179	.93197	1.0730	.73155	1
60	.68200	.93252	1.0724	.73135	**0**
′	Cos	Cot	Tan	Sin	′

132° (312°) (227°) **47°**

43° (223°) (316°) **136°**

′	Sin	Tan	Cot	Cos	′
0	.68200	.93252	1.0724	.73135	**60**
1	.68221	.93306	1.0717	.73116	59
2	.68242	.93360	1.0711	.73096	58
3	.68264	.93415	1.0705	.73076	57
4	.68285	.93469	1.0699	.73056	56
5	.68306	.93524	1.0692	.73036	**55**
6	.68327	.93578	1.0686	.73016	54
7	.68349	.93633	1.0680	.72996	53
8	.68370	.93688	1.0674	.72976	52
9	.68391	.93742	1.0668	.72957	51
10	.68412	.93797	1.0661	.72937	**50**
11	.68434	.93852	1.0655	.72917	49
12	.68455	.93906	1.0649	.72897	48
13	.68476	.93961	1.0643	.72877	47
14	.68497	.94016	1.0637	.72857	46
15	.68518	.94071	1.0630	.72837	**45**
16	.68539	.94125	1.0624	.72817	44
17	.68561	.94180	1.0618	.72797	43
18	.68582	.94235	1.0612	.72777	42
19	.68603	.94290	1.0606	.72757	41
20	.68624	.94345	1.0599	.72737	**40**
21	.68645	.94400	1.0593	.72717	39
22	.68666	.94455	1.0587	.72697	38
23	.68688	.94510	1.0581	.72677	37
24	.68709	.94565	1.0575	.72657	36
25	.68730	.94620	1.0569	.72637	**35**
26	.68751	.94676	1.0562	.72617	34
27	.68772	.94731	1.0556	.72597	33
28	.68793	.94786	1.0550	.72577	32
29	.68814	.94841	1.0544	.72557	31
30	.68835	.94896	1.0538	.72537	**30**
31	.68857	.94952	1.0532	.72517	29
32	.68878	.95007	1.0526	.72497	28
33	.68899	.95062	1.0519	.72477	27
34	.68920	.95118	1.0513	.72457	26
35	.68941	.95173	1.0507	.72437	**25**
36	.68962	.95229	1.0501	.72417	24
37	.68983	.95284	1.0495	.72397	23
38	.69004	.95340	1.0489	.72377	22
39	.69025	.95395	1.0483	.72357	21
40	.69046	.95451	1.0477	.72337	**20**
41	.69067	.95506	1.0470	.72317	19
42	.69088	.95562	1.0464	.72297	18
43	.69109	.95618	1.0458	.72277	17
44	.69130	.95673	1.0452	.72257	16
45	.69151	.95729	1.0446	.72236	**15**
46	.69172	.95785	1.0440	.72216	14
47	.69193	.95841	1.0434	.72196	13
48	.69214	.95897	1.0428	.72176	12
49	.69235	.95952	1.0422	.72156	11
50	.69256	.96008	1.0416	.72136	**10**
51	.69277	.96064	1.0410	.72116	9
52	.69298	.96120	1.0404	.72095	8
53	.69319	.96176	1.0398	.72075	7
54	.69340	.96232	1.0392	.72055	6
55	.69361	.96288	1.0385	.72035	**5**
56	.69382	.96344	1.0379	.72015	4
57	.69403	.96400	1.0373	.71995	3
58	.69424	.96457	1.0367	.71974	2
59	.69445	.96513	1.0361	.71954	1
60	.69466	.96569	1.0355	.71934	**0**
′	Cos	Cot	Tan	Sin	′

133° (313°) (226°) **46°**

44° (224°) (315°) **135°**

′	Sin	Tan	Cot	Cos	′
0	.69466	.96569	1.0355	.71934	**60**
1	.69487	.96625	1.0349	.71914	59
2	.69508	.96681	1.0343	.71894	58
3	.69529	.96738	1.0337	.71873	57
4	.69549	.96794	1.0331	.71853	56
5	.69570	.96850	1.0325	.71833	**55**
6	.69591	.96907	1.0319	.71813	54
7	.69612	.96963	1.0313	.71792	53
8	.69633	.97020	1.0307	.71772	52
9	.69654	.97076	1.0301	.71752	51
10	.69675	.97133	1.0295	.71732	**50**
11	.69696	.97189	1.0289	.71711	49
12	.69717	.97246	1.0283	.71691	48
13	.69737	.97302	1.0277	.71671	47
14	.69758	.97359	1.0271	.71650	46
15	.69779	.97416	1.0265	.71630	**45**
16	.69800	.97472	1.0259	.71610	44
17	.69821	.97529	1.0253	.71590	43
18	.69842	.97586	1.0247	.71569	42
19	.69862	.97643	1.0241	.71549	41
20	.69883	.97700	1.0235	.71529	**40**
21	.69904	.97756	1.0230	.71508	39
22	.69925	.97813	1.0224	.71488	38
23	.69946	.97870	1.0218	.71468	37
24	.69966	.97927	1.0212	.71447	36
25	.69987	.97984	1.0206	.71427	**35**
26	.70008	.98041	1.0200	.71407	34
27	.70029	.98098	1.0194	.71386	33
28	.70049	.98155	1.0188	.71366	32
29	.70070	.98213	1.0182	.71345	31
30	.70091	.98270	1.0176	.71325	**30**
31	.70112	.98327	1.0170	.71305	29
32	.70132	.98384	1.0164	.71284	28
33	.70153	.98441	1.0158	.71264	27
34	.70174	.98499	1.0152	.71243	26
35	.70195	.98556	1.0147	.71223	**25**
36	.70215	.98613	1.0141	.71203	24
37	.70236	.98671	1.0135	.71182	23
38	.70257	.98728	1.0129	.71162	22
39	.70277	.98786	1.0123	.71141	21
40	.70298	.98843	1.0117	.71121	**20**
41	.70319	.98901	1.0111	.71100	19
42	.70339	.98958	1.0105	.71080	18
43	.70360	.99016	1.0099	.71059	17
44	.70381	.99073	1.0094	.71039	16
45	.70401	.99131	1.0088	.71019	**15**
46	.70422	.99189	1.0082	.70998	14
47	.70443	.99247	1.0076	.70978	13
48	.70463	.99304	1.0070	.70957	12
49	.70484	.99362	1.0064	.70937	11
50	.70505	.99420	1.0058	.70916	**10**
51	.70525	.99478	1.0052	.70896	9
52	.70546	.99536	1.0047	.70875	8
53	.70567	.99594	1.0041	.70855	7
54	.70587	.99652	1.0035	.70834	6
55	.70608	.99710	1.0029	.70813	**5**
56	.70628	.99768	1.0023	.70793	4
57	.70649	.99826	1.0017	.70772	3
58	.70670	.99884	1.0012	.70752	2
59	.70690	.99942	1.0006	.70731	1
60	.70711	1.0000	1.0000	.70711	**0**
′	Cos	Cot	Tan	Sin	′

134° (314°) (225°) **45°**

NATURAL TRIGONOMETRIC FUNCTIONS FOR DECIMAL FRACTIONS OF A DEGREE

Deg.	Sin	Cos	Tan	Cot	Deg.
0.0	0.00000	1.0000	0.00000	∞	**90.0**
.1	.00175	1.0000	.00175	573.0	.9
.2	.00349	1.0000	.00349	286.5	.8
.3	.00524	1.0000	.00524	191.0	.7
.4	.00698	1.0000	.00698	143.24	.6
.5	.00873	1.0000	.00873	114.59	.5
.6	.01047	0.9999	.01047	95.49	.4
.7	.01222	.9999	.01222	81.85	.3
.8	.01396	.9999	.01396	71.62	.2
.9	.01571	.9999	.01571	63.66	.1
1.0	0.01745	0.9998	0.01746	57.29	**89.0**
.1	.01920	.9998	.01920	52.08	.9
.2	.02094	.9998	.02095	47.74	.8
.3	.02269	.9997	.02269	44.07	.7
.4	.02443	.9997	.02444	40.92	.6
.5	.02618	.9997	.02619	38.19	.5
.6	.02792	.9996	.02793	35.80	.4
.7	.02967	.9996	.02968	33.69	.3
.8	.03141	.9995	.03143	31.82	.2
.9	.03316	.9995	.03317	30.14	.1
2.0	0.03490	0.9994	0.03492	28.64	**88.0**
.1	.03664	.9993	.03667	27.27	.9
.2	.03839	.9993	.03842	26.03	.8
.3	.04013	.9992	.04016	24.90	.7
.4	.04188	.9991	.04191	23.86	.6
.5	.04362	.9990	.04366	22.90	.5
.6	.04536	.9990	.04541	22.02	.4
.7	.04711	.9989	.04716	21.20	.3
.8	.04885	.9988	.04891	20.45	.2
.9	.05059	.9987	.05066	19.74	.1
3.0	0.05234	0.9986	0.05241	19.081	**87.0**
.1	.05408	.9985	.05416	18.464	.9
.2	.05582	.9984	.05591	17.886	.8
.3	.05756	.9983	.05766	17.343	.7
.4	.05931	.9982	.05941	16.832	.6
.5	.06105	.9981	.06116	16.350	.5
.6	.06279	.9980	.06291	15.895	.4
.7	.06453	.9979	.06467	15.464	.3
.8	.06627	.9978	.06642	15.056	.2
.9	.06802	.9977	.06817	14.669	.1
4.0	0.06976	0.9976	0.06993	14.301	**86.0**
.1	.07150	.9974	.07168	13.951	.9
.2	.07324	.9973	.07344	13.617	.8
.3	.07498	.9972	.07519	13.300	.7
.4	.07672	.9971	.07695	12.996	.6
.5	.07846	.9969	.07870	12.706	.5
.6	.08020	.9968	.08046	12.429	.4
.7	.08194	.9966	.08221	12.163	.3
.8	.08368	.9965	.08397	11.909	.2
.9	.08542	.9963	.08573	11.664	.1
5.0	0.08716	0.9962	0.08749	11.430	**85.0**
.1	.08889	.9960	.08925	11.205	.9
.2	.09063	.9959	.09101	10.988	.8
.3	.09237	.9957	.09277	10.780	.7
.4	.09411	.9956	.09453	10.579	.6
.5	.09585	.9954	.09629	10.385	.5
.6	.09758	.9952	.09805	10.199	.4
.7	.09932	.9951	.09981	10.019	.3
.8	.10106	.9949	.10158	9.845	.2
.9	.10279	.9947	.10334	9.677	.1
6.0	0.10453	0.9945	0.10510	9.514	**84.0**
Deg.	Cos	Sin	Cot	Tan	Deg.

Deg.	Sin	Cos	Tan	Cot	Deg.
6.0	0.10453	0.9945	0.10510	9.514	**84.0**
.1	.10626	.9943	.10687	9.357	.9
.2	.10800	.9942	.10863	9.205	.8
.3	.10973	.9940	.11040	9.058	.7
.4	.11147	.9938	.11217	8.915	.6
.5	.11320	.9936	.11394	8.777	.5
.6	.11494	.9934	.11570	8.643	.4
.7	.11667	.9932	.11747	8.513	.3
.8	.11840	.9930	.11924	8.386	.2
.9	.12014	.9928	.12101	8.264	.1
7.0	0.12187	0.9925	0.12278	8.144	**83.0**
.1	.12360	.9923	.12456	8.028	.9
.2	.12533	.9921	.12633	7.916	.8
.3	.12706	.9919	.12810	7.806	.7
.4	.12880	.9917	.12988	7.700	.6
.5	.13053	.9914	.13165	7.596	.5
.6	.13226	.9912	.13343	7.495	.4
.7	.13399	.9910	.13521	7.396	.3
.8	.13572	.9907	.13698	7.300	.2
.9	.13744	.9905	.13876	7.207	.1
8.0	0.13917	0.9903	0.14054	7.115	**82.0**
.1	.14090	.9900	.14232	7.026	.9
.2	.14263	.9898	.14410	6.940	.8
.3	.14436	.9895	.14588	6.855	.7
.4	.14608	.9893	.14767	6.772	.6
.5	.14781	.9890	.14945	6.691	.5
.6	.14954	.9888	.15124	6.612	.4
.7	.15126	.9885	.15302	6.535	.3
.8	.15299	.9882	.15481	6.460	.2
.9	.15471	.9880	.15660	6.386	.1
9.0	0.15643	0.9877	0.15838	6.314	**81.0**
.1	.15816	.9874	.16017	6.243	.9
.2	.15988	.9871	.16196	6.174	.8
.3	.16160	.9869	.16376	6.107	.7
.4	.16333	.9866	.16555	6.041	.6
.5	.16505	.9863	.16734	5.976	.5
.6	.16677	.9860	.16914	5.912	.4
.7	.16849	.9857	.17093	5.850	.3
.8	.17021	.9854	.17273	5.789	.2
.9	.17193	.9851	.17453	5.730	.1
10.0	0.1736	0.9848	0.1763	5.671	**80.0**
.1	.1754	.9845	.1781	5.614	.9
.2	.1771	.9842	.1799	5.558	.8
.3	.1788	.9839	.1817	5.503	.7
.4	.1805	.9836	.1835	5.449	.6
.5	.1822	.9833	.1853	5.396	.5
.6	.1840	.9829	.1871	5.343	.4
.7	.1857	.9826	.1890	5.292	.3
.8	.1874	.9823	.1908	5.242	.2
.9	.1891	.9820	.1926	5.193	.1
11.0	0.1908	0.9816	0.1944	5.145	**79.0**
.1	.1925	.9813	.1962	5.097	.9
.2	.1942	.9810	.1980	5.050	.8
.3	.1959	.9806	.1998	5.005	.7
.4	.1977	.9803	.2016	4.959	.6
.5	.1994	.9799	.2035	4.915	.5
.6	.2011	.9796	.2053	4.872	.4
.7	.2028	.9792	.2071	4.829	.3
.8	.2045	.9789	.2089	4.787	.2
.9	.2062	.9785	.2107	4.745	.1
12.0	0.2079	0.9781	0.2126	4.705	**78.0**
Deg.	Cos	Sin	Cot	Tan	Deg.

NATURAL TRIGONOMETRIC FUNCTIONS FOR DECIMAL FRACTIONS OF A DEGREE

Deg.	Sin	Cos	Tan	Cot	Deg.
12.0	0.2079	0.9781	0.2126	4.705	**78.0**
.1	.2096	.9778	.2144	4.665	.9
.2	.2113	.9774	.2162	4.625	.8
.3	.2130	.9770	.2180	4.586	.7
.4	.2147	.9767	.2199	4.548	.6
.5	.2164	.9763	.2217	4.511	.5
.6	.2181	.9759	.2235	4.474	.4
.7	.2198	.9755	.2254	4.437	.3
.8	.2215	.9751	.2272	4.402	.2
.9	.2233	.9748	.2290	4.366	.1
13.0	0.2250	0.9744	0.2309	4.331	**77.0**
.1	.2267	.9740	.2327	4.297	.9
.2	.2284	.9736	.2345	4.264	.8
.3	.2300	.9732	.2364	4.230	.7
.4	.2317	.9728	.2382	4.198	.6
.5	.2334	.9724	.2401	4.165	.5
.6	.2351	.9720	.2419	4.134	.4
.7	.2368	.9715	.2438	4.102	.3
.8	.2385	.9711	.2456	4.071	.2
.9	.2402	.9707	.2475	4.041	.1
14.0	0.2419	0.9703	0.2493	4.011	**76.0**
.1	.2436	.9699	.2512	3.981	.9
.2	.2453	.9694	.2530	3.952	.8
.3	.2470	.9690	.2549	3.923	.7
.4	.2487	.9686	.2568	3.895	.6
.5	.2504	.9681	.2586	3.867	.5
.6	.2521	.9677	.2605	3.839	.4
.7	.2538	.9673	.2623	3.812	.3
.8	.2554	.9668	.2642	3.785	.2
.9	.2571	.9664	.2661	3.758	.1
15.0	0.2588	0.9659	0.2679	3.732	**75.0**
.1	.2605	.9655	.2698	3.706	.9
.2	.2622	.9650	.2717	3.681	.8
.3	.2639	.9646	.2736	3.655	.7
.4	.2656	.9641	.2754	3.630	.6
.5	.2672	.9636	.2773	3.606	.5
.6	.2689	.9632	.2792	3.582	.4
.7	.2706	.9627	.2811	3.558	.3
.8	.2723	.9622	.2830	3.534	.2
.9	.2740	.9617	.2849	3.511	.1
16.0	0.2756	0.9613	0.2867	3.487	**74.0**
.1	.2773	.9608	.2886	3.465	.9
.2	.2790	.9603	.2905	3.442	.8
.3	.2807	.9598	.2924	3.420	.7
.4	.2823	.9593	.2943	3.398	.6
.5	.2840	.9588	.2962	3.376	.5
.6	.2857	.9583	.2981	3.354	.4
.7	.2874	.9578	.3000	3.333	.3
.8	.2890	.9573	.3019	3.312	.2
.9	.2907	.9568	.3038	3.291	.1
17.0	0.2924	0.9563	0.3057	3.271	**73.0**
.1	.2940	.9558	.3076	3.251	.9
.2	.2957	.9553	.3096	3.230	.8
.3	.2974	.9548	.3115	3.211	.7
.4	.2990	.9542	.3134	3.191	.6
.5	.3007	.9537	.3153	3.172	.5
.6	.3024	.9532	.3172	3.152	.4
.7	.3040	.9527	.3191	3.133	.3
.8	.3057	.9521	.3211	3.115	.2
.9	.3074	.9516	.3230	3.096	.1
18.0	0.3090	0.9511	0.3249	3.078	**72.0**
Deg.	Cos	Sin	Cot	Tan	Deg.

Deg.	Sin	Cos	Tan	Cot	Deg
18.0	0.3090	0.9511	0.3249	3.078	**72.0**
.1	.3107	.9505	.3269	3.060	.9
.2	.3123	.9500	.3288	3.042	.8
.3	.3140	.9494	.3307	3.024	.7
.4	.3156	.9489	.3327	3.006	.6
.5	.3173	.9483	.3346	2.989	.5
.6	.3190	.9478	.3365	2.971	.4
.7	.3206	.9472	.3385	2.954	.3
.8	.3223	.9466	.3404	2.937	.2
.9	.3239	.9461	.3424	2.921	.1
19.0	0.3256	0.9455	0.3443	2.904	**71.0**
.1	.3272	.9449	.3463	2.888	.9
.2	.3289	.9444	.3482	2.872	.8
.3	.3305	.9438	.3502	2.856	.7
.4	.3322	.9432	.3522	2.840	.6
.5	.3338	.9426	.3541	2.824	.5
.6	.3355	.9421	.3561	2.808	.4
.7	.3371	.9415	.3581	2.793	.3
.8	.3387	.9409	.3600	2.778	.2
.9	.3404	.9403	.3620	2.762	.1
20.0	0.3420	0.9397	0.3640	2.747	**70.0**
.1	.3437	.9391	.3659	2.733	.9
.2	.3453	.9385	.3679	2.718	.8
.3	.3469	.9379	.3699	2.703	.7
.4	.3486	.9373	.3719	2.689	.6
.5	.3502	.9367	.3739	2.675	.5
.6	.3518	.9361	.3759	2.660	.4
.7	.3535	.9354	.3779	2.646	.3
.8	.3551	.9348	.3799	2.633	.2
.9	.3567	.9342	.3819	2.619	.1
21.0	0.3584	0.9336	0.3839	2.605	**69.0**
.1	.3600	.9330	.3859	2.592	.9
.2	.3616	.9323	.3879	2.578	.8
.3	.3633	.9317	.3899	2.565	.7
.4	.3649	.9311	.3919	2.552	.6
.5	.3665	.9304	.3939	2.539	.5
.6	.3681	.9298	.3959	2.526	.4
.7	.3697	.9291	.3979	2.513	.3
.8	.3714	.9285	.4000	2.500	.2
.9	.3730	.9278	.4020	2.488	.1
22.0	0.3746	0.9272	0.4040	2.475	**68.0**
.1	.3762	.9265	.4061	2.463	.9
.2	.3778	.9259	.4081	2.450	.8
.3	.3795	.9252	.4101	2.438	.7
.4	.3811	.9245	.4122	2.426	.6
.5	.3827	.9239	.4142	2.414	.5
.6	.3843	.9232	.4163	2.402	.4
.7	.3859	.9225	.4183	2.391	.3
.8	.3875	.9219	.4204	2.379	.2
.9	.3891	.9212	.4224	2.367	.1
23.0	0.3907	0.9205	0.4245	2.356	**67.0**
.1	.3923	.9198	.4265	2.344	.9
.2	.3939	.9191	.4286	2.333	.8
.3	.3955	.9184	.4307	2.322	.7
.4	.3971	.9178	.4327	2.311	.6
.5	.3987	.9171	.4348	2.300	.5
.6	.4003	.9164	.4369	2.289	.4
.7	.4019	.9157	.4390	2.278	.3
.8	.4035	.9150	.4411	2.267	.2
.9	.4051	.9143	.4431	2.257	.1
24.0	0.4067	0.9135	0.4452	2.246	**66.0**
Deg.	Cos	Sin	Cot	Tan	Deg.

NATURAL TRIGONOMETRIC FUNCTIONS FOR DECIMAL FRACTIONS OF A DEGREE

Deg.	Sin	Cos	Tan	Cot	Deg.
24.0	0.4067	0.9135	0.4452	2.246	**66.0**
.1	.4083	.9128	.4473	2.236	.9
.2	.4099	.9121	.4494	2.225	.8
.3	.4115	.9114	.4515	2.215	.7
.4	.4131	.9107	.4536	2.204	.6
.5	.4147	.9100	.4557	2.194	.5
.6	.4163	.9092	.4578	2.184	.4
.7	.4179	.9085	.4599	2.174	.3
.8	.4195	.9078	.4621	2.164	.2
.9	.4210	.9070	.4642	2.154	.1
25.0	0.4226	0.9063	0.4663	2.145	**65.0**
.1	.4242	.9056	.4684	2.135	.9
.2	.4258	.9048	.4706	2.125	.8
.3	.4274	.9041	.4727	2.116	.7
.4	.4289	.9033	.4748	2.106	.6
.5	.4305	.9026	.4770	2.097	.5
.6	.4321	.9018	.4791	2.087	.4
.7	.4337	.9011	.4813	2.078	.3
.8	.4352	.9003	.4834	2.069	.2
.9	.4368	.8996	.4856	2.059	.1
26.0	0.4384	0.8988	0.4877	2.050	**64.0**
.1	.4399	.8980	.4899	2.041	.9
.2	.4415	.8973	.4921	2.032	.8
.3	.4431	.8965	.4942	2.023	.7
.4	.4446	.8957	.4964	2.014	.6
.5	.4462	.8949	.4986	2.006	.5
.6	.4478	.8942	.5008	1.997	.4
.7	.4493	.8934	.5029	1.988	.3
.8	.4509	.8926	.5051	1.980	.2
.9	.4524	.8918	.5073	1.971	.1
27.0	0.4540	0.8910	0.5095	1.963	**63.0**
.1	.4555	.8902	.5117	1.954	.9
.2	.4571	.8894	.5139	1.946	.8
.3	.4586	.8886	.5161	1.937	.7
.4	.4602	.8878	.5184	1.929	.6
.5	.4617	.8870	.5206	1.921	.5
.6	.4633	.8862	.5228	1.913	.4
.7	.4648	.8854	.5250	1.905	.3
.8	.4664	.8846	.5272	1.897	.2
.9	.4679	.8838	.5295	1.889	.1
28.0	0.4695	0.8829	0.5317	1.881	**62.0**
.1	.4710	.8821	.5340	1.873	.9
.2	.4726	.8813	.5362	1.865	.8
.3	.4741	.8805	.5384	1.857	.7
.4	.4756	.8796	.5407	1.849	.6
.5	.4772	.8788	.5430	1.842	.5
.6	.4787	.8780	.5452	1.834	.4
.7	.4802	.8771	.5475	1.827	.3
.8	.4818	.8763	.5498	1.819	.2
.9	.4833	.8755	.5520	1.811	.1
29.0	0.4848	0.8746	0.5543	1.804	**61.0**
.1	.4863	.8738	.5566	1.797	.9
.2	.4879	.8729	.5589	1.789	.8
.3	.4894	.8721	.5612	1.782	.7
.4	.4909	.8712	.5635	1.775	.6
.5	.4924	.8704	.5658	1.767	.5
.6	.4939	.8695	.5681	1.760	.4
.7	.4955	.8686	.5704	1.753	.3
.8	.4970	.8678	.5727	1.746	.2
.9	.4985	.8669	.5750	1.739	.1
30.0	0.5000	0.8660	0.5774	1.732	**60.0**
Deg.	Cos	Sin	Cot	Tan	Deg.

Deg.	Sin	Cos	Tan	Cot	Deg.
30.0	0.5000	0.8660	0.5774	1.7321	**60.0**
.1	.5015	.8652	.5797	1.7251	.9
.2	.5030	.8643	.5820	1.7182	.8
.3	.5045	.8634	.5844	1.7113	.7
.4	.5060	.8625	.5867	1.7045	.6
.5	.5075	.8616	.5890	1.6977	.5
.6	.5090	.8607	.5914	1.6909	.4
.7	.5105	.8599	.5938	1.6842	.3
.8	.5120	.8590	.5961	1.6775	.2
.9	.5135	.8581	.5985	1.6709	.1
31.0	0.5150	0.8572	0.6009	1.6643	**59.0**
.1	.5165	.8563	.6032	1.6577	.9
.2	.5180	.8554	.6056	1.6512	.8
.3	.5195	.8545	.6080	1.6447	.7
.4	.5210	.8536	.6104	1.6383	.6
.5	.5225	.8526	.6128	1.6319	.5
.6	.5240	.8517	.6152	1.6255	.4
.7	.5255	.8508	.6176	1.6191	.3
.8	.5270	.8499	.6200	1.6128	.2
.9	.5284	.8490	.6224	1.6066	.1
32.0	0.5299	0.8480	0.6249	1.6003	**58.0**
.1	.5314	.8471	.6273	1.5941	.9
.2	.5329	.8462	.6297	1.5880	.8
.3	.5344	.8453	.6322	1.5818	.7
.4	.5358	.8443	.6346	1.5757	.6
.5	.5373	.8434	.6371	1.5697	.5
.6	.5388	.8425	.6395	1.5637	.4
.7	.5402	.8415	.6420	1.5577	.3
.8	.5417	.8406	.6445	1.5517	.2
.9	.5432	.8396	.6469	1.5458	.1
33.0	0.5446	0.8387	0.6494	1.5399	**57.0**
.1	.5461	.8377	.6519	1.5340	.9
.2	.5476	.8368	.6544	1.5282	.8
.3	.5490	.8358	.6569	1.5224	.7
.4	.5505	.8348	.6594	1.5166	.6
.5	.5519	.8339	.6619	1.5108	.5
.6	.5534	.8329	.6644	1.5051	.4
.7	.5548	.8320	.6669	1.4994	.3
.8	.5563	.8310	.6694	1.4938	.2
.9	.5577	.8300	.6720	1.4882	.1
34.0	0.5592	0.8290	0.6745	1.4826	**56.0**
.1	.5606	.8281	.6771	1.4770	.9
.2	.5621	.8271	.6796	1.4715	.8
.3	.5635	.8261	.6822	1.4659	.7
.4	.5650	.8251	.6847	1.4605	.6
.5	.5664	.8241	.6873	1.4550	.5
.6	.5678	.8231	.6899	1.4496	.4
.7	.5693	.8221	.6924	1.4442	.3
.8	.5707	.8211	.6950	1.4388	.2
.9	.5721	.8202	.6976	1.4335	.1
35.0	0.5736	0.8192	0.7002	1.4281	**55.0**
.1	.5750	.8181	.7028	1.4229	.9
.2	.5764	.8171	.7054	1.4176	.8
.3	.5779	.8161	.7080	1.4124	.7
.4	.5793	.8151	.7107	1.4071	.6
.5	.5807	.8141	.7133	1.4019	.5
.6	.5821	.8131	.7159	1.3968	.4
.7	.5835	.8121	.7186	1.3916	.3
.8	.5850	.8111	.7212	1.3865	.2
.9	.5864	.8100	.7239	1.3814	.1
36.0	0.5878	0.8090	0.7265	1.3764	**54.0**
Deg.	Cos	Sin	Cot	Tan	Deg.

NATURAL TRIGONOMETRIC FUNCTIONS FOR DECIMAL FRACTIONS OF A DEGREE

Deg.	Sin	Cos	Tan	Cot	Deg.
36.0	0.5878	0.8090	0.7265	1.3764	**54.0**
.1	.5892	.8080	.7292	1.3713	.9
.2	.5906	.8070	.7319	1.3663	.8
.3	.5920	.8059	.7346	1.3613	.7
.4	.5934	.8049	.7373	1.3564	.6
.5	.5948	.8039	.7400	1.3514	.5
.6	.5962	.8028	.7427	1.3465	.4
.7	.5976	.8018	.7454	1.3416	.3
.8	.5990	.8007	.7481	1.3367	.2
.9	.6004	.7997	.7508	1.3319	.1
37.0	0.6018	0.7986	0.7536	1.3270	**53.0**
.1	.6032	.7976	.7563	1.3222	.9
.2	.6046	.7965	.7590	1.3175	.8
.3	.6060	.7955	.7618	1.3127	.7
.4	.6074	.7944	.7646	1.3079	.6
.5	.6088	.7934	.7673	1.3032	.5
.6	.6101	.7923	.7701	1.2985	.4
.7	.6115	.7912	.7729	1.2938	.3
.8	.6129	.7902	.7757	1.2892	.2
.9	.6143	.7891	.7785	1.2846	.1
38.0	0.6157	0.7880	0.7813	1.2799	**52.0**
.1	.6170	.7869	.7841	1.2753	.9
.2	.6184	.7859	.7869	1.2708	.8
.3	.6198	.7848	.7898	1.2662	.7
.4	.6211	.7837	.7926	1.2617	.6
.5	.6225	.7826	.7954	1.2572	.5
.6	.6239	.7815	.7983	1.2527	.4
.7	.6252	.7804	.8012	1.2482	.3
.8	.6266	.7793	.8040	1.2437	.2
.9	.6280	.7782	.8069	1.2393	.1
39.0	0.6293	0.7771	0.8098	1.2349	**51.0**
.1	.6307	.7760	.8127	1.2305	.9
.2	.6320	.7749	.8156	1.2261	.8
.3	.6334	.7738	.8185	1.2218	.7
.4	.6347	.7727	.8214	1.2174	.6
.5	.6361	.7716	.8243	1.2131	.5
.6	.6374	.7705	.8273	1.2088	.4
.7	.6388	.7694	.8302	1.2045	.3
.8	.6401	.7683	.8332	1.2002	.2
.9	.6414	.7672	.8361	1.1960	.1
40.0	0.6428	0.7660	0.8391	1.1918	**50.0**
.1	.6441	.7649	.8421	1.1875	.9
.2	.6455	.7638	.8451	1.1833	.8
.3	.6468	.7627	.8481	1.1792	.7
.4	.6481	.7615	.8511	1.1750	.6
40.5	0.6494	0.7604	0.8541	1.1708	**49.5**
Deg.	Cos	Sin	Cot	Tan	Deg.

Deg.	Sin	Cos	Tan	Cot	Deg.
40.5	0.6494	0.7604	0.8541	1.1708	**49.5**
.6	.6508	.7593	.8571	1.1667	.4
.7	.6521	.7581	.8601	1.1626	.3
.8	.6534	.7570	.8632	1.1585	.2
.9	.6547	.7559	.8662	1.1544	.1
41.0	0.6561	0.7547	0.8693	1.1504	**49.0**
.1	.6574	.7536	.8724	1.1463	.9
.2	.6587	.7524	.8754	1.1423	.8
.3	.6600	.7513	.8785	1.1383	.7
.4	.6613	.7501	.8816	1.1343	.6
.5	.6626	.7490	.8847	1.1303	.5
.6	.6639	.7478	.8878	1.1263	.4
.7	.6652	.7466	.8910	1.1224	.3
.8	.6665	.7455	.8941	1.1184	.2
.9	.6678	.7443	.8972	1.1145	.1
42.0	0.6691	0.7431	0.9004	1.1106	**48.0**
.1	.6704	.7420	.9036	1.1067	.9
.2	.6717	.7408	.9067	1.1028	.8
.3	.6730	.7396	.9099	1.0990	.7
.4	.6743	.7385	.9131	1.0951	.6
.5	.6756	.7373	.9163	1.0913	.5
.6	.6769	.7361	.9195	1.0875	.4
.7	.6782	.7349	.9228	1.0837	.3
.8	.6794	.7337	.9260	1.0799	.2
.9	.6807	.7325	.9293	1.0761	.1
43.0	0.6820	0.7314	0.9325	1.0724	**47.0**
.1	.6833	.7302	.9358	1.0686	.9
.2	.6845	.7290	.9391	1.0649	.8
.3	.6858	.7278	.9424	1.0612	.7
.4	.6871	.7266	.9457	1.0575	.6
.5	.6884	.7254	.9490	1.0538	.5
.6	.6896	.7242	.9523	1.0501	.4
.7	.6909	.7230	.9556	1.0464	.3
.8	.6921	.7218	.9590	1.0428	.2
.9	.6934	.7206	.9623	1.0392	.1
44.0	0.6947	0.7193	0.9657	1.0355	**46.0**
.1	.6959	.7181	.9691	1.0319	.9
.2	.6972	.7169	.9725	1.0283	.8
.3	.6984	.7157	.9759	1.0247	.7
.4	.6997	.7145	.9793	1.0212	.6
.5	.7009	.7133	.9827	1.0176	.5
.6	.7022	.7120	.9861	1.0141	.4
.7	.7034	.7108	.9896	1.0105	.3
.8	.7046	.7096	.9930	1.0070	.2
.9	.7059	.7083	.9965	1.0035	.1
45.0	0.7071	0.7071	1.0000	1.0000	**45.0**
Deg.	Cos	Sin	Cot	Tan	Deg.